N+R
5+5
360

readings in statistics

readings in statistics

Audrey Haber
Richard P. Runyon
C. W. Post College of Long Island University

Pietro Badia
Bowling Green State University

Addison-Wesley Publishing Company
Reading, Massachusetts
Menlo Park, California · London · Don Mills, Ontario

preface

We have long been dissatisfied with the fact that most courses in statistics present the student with only secondary and tertiary sources. *Readings in Statistics* is intended to bring the student into direct contact with some of the most significant original articles in the field. A major compelling reason for assembling the readings under one cover is to allow professors (and librarians) to avoid the incredible problems and burdens associated with library assignments. We need only note and not elaborate on them: pilfering and replacement; tearing out articles, hiding journals, inadequate holdings, reserve room limitation, reading problems with microfilm, etc.

We have attempted to select articles which represent contemporary statistical thinking. Although the articles have been organized into three separate blocks, they need not be read in any fixed order. The instructor may find that he can achieve maximum enrichment by assigning articles so that they correlate with his own organization of the course.

The primary intent of the first block is to acquaint the student with some of the problems in measurement. Included in this first block are articles dealing with scales of measurement and statistical treatment of numbers.

The second block of articles concerns itself with hypothesis testing. Included in this section are discussions of such vital issues as degrees of freedom, statistical power, and the use of A as a substitute for t. No set of readings on hypothesis testing would be complete without the forerunner, Student's "On the probable error of the mean."

The final block presents a number of significant and varied articles concerned with the use of nonparametric statistical techniques.

We are most grateful to the many authors and publishers who permitted us to use their articles. A special note of thanks to Ruth DeMarco for her assistance in compiling the material for this book.

March 1970

A. H.
R. P. R.
P. B.

contents

block 1

1. Stevens, S. S. On the theory of scales of measurement. *Science,* 1946, **103,** 677–680.

2. Baker, B. O., C. D. Hardyck, and L. F. Petrinovich. Weak measurements vs. strong statistics: an empirical critique of S. S. Stevens' proscriptions on statistics. *Educational and Psychological Measurement,* 1966, **26, No. 2,** 291–309.

3. Lord, F. M. On the statistical treatment of football numbers. *Amer. Psychol.,* 1953, **8,** 750–751.

4. Burke, C. J. Additive scales and statistics. *Psychol. Rev.,* 1953, **60,** 73–75.

5. Boneau, C. A. A note on measurement scales and statistical tests. *Amer. Psychol.,* 1961, **16,** 260–261.

6. Stevens, S. S. Measurement, statistics, and the schemapiric view. *Science,* 1968, **161,** 849–856.

Every science, at some point in its history, must delineate the variables which are its province, and decide upon the methods to investigate these variables. Implicit in this problem is the selection of appropriate units of measurement and their relation to the various statistical models which will serve as the basis for drawing inferences.

During a seven-year period a distinguished committee of British scientists undertook to explore the possibility of "quantitative estimates of sensory events." This group was unable to arrive at a consensus and, in the words of a member of the group, they "came out by that same door as they went in."

S. S. Stevens, in his controversial 1946 article entitled "On the Theory of Scales of Measurement," concluded that consensus was not achieved because it was not recognized that the key issue was semantic, i.e., the *meaning* of measurement. Stevens proceeded to classify the scales of measurement and related statistical analysis to scales.

Following Stevens' 1946 article, two conflicting schools of thought have emerged. Advocates of Stevens, referred to as the "weak measurement" school, have maintained that the scale of measurement places certain restrictions upon the choice of statistical tests. On the other hand, the "strong statistics" school asserts that the formal properties of scales of measurement should *not* influence the choice of statistical tests.

The articles critical of the "weak measurement" school are introduced by the Baker, Hardyck, and Petrinovich paper. These authors demonstrate empirically that "strong statistics such as the *t* test are more than adequate to cope with weak measurements."

In a lighter vein, Lord presents arguments in favor of the "strong statistics" school. Specifically, he demonstrates that it is perfectly legitimate to calculate means, standard deviations, and estimates of error from *any* grouping of numbers regardless of the underlying scale of measurement.

Burke presents the most widely cited and definitive argument in favor of the "strong statistics" school.

Decrying the continued influence of Stevens' position in two recent texts, Boneau presents additional arguments in support of Burke's position.

The final article in this block presents Stevens' most recent statement of his position.

1

on the theory of scales
of measurement

S. S. Stevens

For seven years a committee of the British Association for the Advancement of Science debated the problem of measurement. Appointed in 1932 to represent Section A (Mathematical and Physical Sciences) and Section J (Psychology), the committee was instructed to consider and report upon the possibility of "quantitative estimates of sensory events"—meaning simply: Is it possible to measure human sensation? Deliberation led only to disagreement, mainly about what is meant by the term measurement. An interim report in 1938 found one member complaining that his colleagues "came out by that same door as they went in," and in order to have another try at agreement, the committee begged to be continued for another year.

For its final report (1940) the committee chose a common bone for its contentions, directing its arguments at a concrete example of a sensory scale. This was the Sone scale of loudness (S. S. Stevens and H. Davis, *Hearing.* New York: Wiley, 1938), which purports to measure the subjective magnitude of an auditory sensation against a scale having the formal properties of other basic scales, such as those

Reprinted from *Science* **103**, 677–680 (June 1946), by permission of S. S. Stevens and the American Association for the Advancement of Science.

used to measure length and weight. Again the 19 members of the committee came out by the routes they entered, and their views ranged widely between two extremes. One member submitted "that any law purporting to express a quantitative relation between sensation intensity and stimulus intensity is not merely false but is in fact meaningless unless and until a meaning can be given to the concept of addition as applied to sensation" (Final Report, p. 245).

It is plain from this and from other statements by the committee that the real issue is the meaning of measurement. This, to be sure, is a semantic issue, but one susceptible of orderly discussion. Perhaps agreement can better be achieved if we recognize that measurement exists in a variety of forms and that scales of measurement fall into certain definite classes. These classes are determined both by the empirical operations invoked in the process of "measuring" and by the formal (mathematical) properties of the scales. Furthermore—and this is of great concern to several of the sciences—the statistical manipulations that can legitimately be applied to empirical data depend upon the type of scale against which the data are ordered.

**A classification of
scales of measurement**

Paraphrasing N. R. Campbell (Final Report, p. 340), we may say that measurement, in the broadest sense, is defined as the assignment of numerals to objects or events according to rules. The fact that numerals can be assigned under different rules leads to different kinds of scales and different kinds of measurement. The problem then becomes that of making explicit (a) the various rules for the assignment of numerals, (b) the mathematical properties (or group structure) of the resulting scales, and (c) the statistical operations applicable to measurements made with each type of scale.

Scales are possible in the first place only because there is a certain isomorphism between what we can do with the aspects of objects and the properties of the numeral series. In dealing with the aspects of objects we invoke empirical operations for determining equality (classifying), for rank-ordering, and for determining when differences and when ratios between the aspects of objects are equal. The conventional series of numerals yields to analogous operations: We can identify the members of a numeral series and classify them. We know their order as given by convention. We can determine equal differences, as $8 - 6 = 4 - 2$, and equal ratios, as $8/4 = 6/3$. The isomorphism between these properties of the numeral series and certain empirical operations which we perform with objects permits the use of the series as a *model* to represent aspects of the empirical world.

Table 1

Scale	Basic Empirical Operations	Mathematical Group Structure	Permissible Statistics (*invariantive*)
Nominal	Determination of equality	*Permutation group* $x' = f(x)$ $f(x)$ means any one-to-one substitution	Number of cases Mode Contingency correlation
Ordinal	Determination of greater or less	*Isotonic group* $x' = f(x)$ $f(x)$ means any monotonic increasing function	Median Percentiles
Interval	Determination of equality of intervals or differences	*General linear group* $x' = ax + b$	Mean Standard deviation Rank-order correlation Product-moment correlation
Ratio	Determination of equality of ratios	*Similarity group* $x' = ax$	Coefficient of variation

The type of scale achieved depends upon the character of the basic empirical operations performed. These operations are limited ordinarily by the nature of the thing being scaled and by our choice of procedures, but, once selected, the operations determine that there will eventuate one or another of the scales listed in Table 1.[1]

The decision to discard the scale names commonly encountered in writings on measurement is based on the ambiguity of such terms as "intensive" and "extensive." Both ordinal and interval scales have at times been called intensive, and both interval and ratio scales have sometimes been labeled extensive.

It will be noted that the column listing the basic operations needed to create each type of scale is cumulative: to an operation listed opposite a particular scale must be added all those operations preceding it. Thus, an interval scale can be erected only provided we have an operation for determining equality of intervals, for determining greater or less, and for determining equality (not greater and not less). To these

1. A classification essentially equivalent to that contained in this table was presented before the International Congress for the Unity of Science, September 1941. The writer is indebted to the late Prof. G. D. Birkoff for a stimulating discussion which led to the completion of the table in essentially its present form.

operations must be added a method for ascertaining equality of ratios if a ratio scale is to be achieved.

In the column which records the group structure of each scale are listed the mathematical transformations which leave the scale-form invariant. Thus, any numeral, x, on a scale can be replaced by another numeral, x', where x' is the function of x listed in this column. Each mathematical group in the column is contained in the group immediately above it.

The last column presents examples of the type of statistical operations appropriate to each scale. This column is cumulative in that *all* statistics listed are admissible for data scaled against a ratio scale. The criterion for the appropriateness of a statistic is *invariance* under the transformations in Column 3. Thus, the case that stands at the median (mid-point) of a distribution maintains its position under all transformations which preserve order (isotonic group), but an item located at the mean remains at the mean only under transformations as restricted as those of the linear group. The ratio expressed by the coefficient of variation remains invariant only under the similarity transformation (multiplication by a constant). (The rank-order correlation coefficient is usually deemed appropriate to an ordinal scale, but actually this statistic assumes equal intervals between successive ranks and therefore calls for an interval scale.)

Let us now consider each scale in turn.

Nominal scale

The *nominal scale* represents the most unrestricted assignment of numerals. The numerals are used only as labels or type numbers, and words or letters would serve as well. Two types of nominal assignments are sometimes distinguished, as illustrated (a) by the "numbering" of football players for the identification of the individuals, and (b) by the "numbering" of types or classes, where each member of a class is assigned the same numeral. Actually, the first is a special case of the second, for when we label our football players we are dealing with unit classes of one member each. Since the purpose is just as well served when any two designating numerals are interchanged, this scale form remains invariant under the general substitution or permutation group (sometimes called the symmetric group of transformations). The only statistic relevant to nominal scales of Type A is the number of cases, e.g., the number of players assigned numerals. But once classes containing several individuals have been formed (Type B), we can determine the most numerous class (the mode), and under certain conditions we can test, by the contingency methods, hypotheses regarding the distribution of cases among the classes.

The nominal scale is a primitive form, and quite naturally there are many who will urge that it is absurd to attribute to this process of assigning numerals the dignity implied by the term measurement. Certainly there can be no quarrel with this objection, for the naming of things is an arbitrary business. However we christen it, the use of numerals as names for classes is an example of the "assignment of numerals according to rule." The rule is: Do not assign the same numeral to different classes or different numerals to the same class. Beyond that, anything goes with the nominal scale.

Ordinal scale

The *ordinal scale* arises from the operation of rank-ordering. Since any "order-preserving" transformation will leave the scale form invariant, this scale has the structure of what may be called the isotonic or order-preserving group. A classic example of an ordinal scale is the scale of hardness of minerals. Other instances are found among scales of intelligence, personality traits, grade or quality of leather, etc.

As a matter of fact, most of the scales used widely and effectively by psychologists are ordinal scales. In the strictest propriety the ordinary statistics involving means and standard deviations ought not to be used with these scales, for these statistics imply a knowledge of something more than the relative rank-order of data. On the other hand, for this "illegal" statisticizing there can be invoked a kind of pragmatic sanction: In numerous instances it leads to fruitful results. While the outlawing of this procedure would probably serve no good purpose, it is proper to point out that means and standard deviations computed on an ordinal scale are in error to the extent that the successive intervals on the scale are unequal in size. When only the rank-order of data is known, we should proceed cautiously with our statistics, and especially with the conclusions we draw from them.

Even in applying those statistics that are normally appropriate for ordinal scales, we sometimes find rigor compromised. Thus, although it is indicated in Table 1 that percentile measures may be applied to rank-ordered data, it should be pointed out that the customary procedure of assigning a value to a percentile by interpolating linearly within a class interval is, in all strictness, wholly out of bounds. Likewise, it is not strictly proper to determine the mid-point of a class interval by linear interpolation, because the linearity of an ordinal scale is precisely the property which is open to question.

Interval scale

With the *interval scale* we come to a form that is "quantitative" in the ordinary sense of the word. Almost all the usual statistical measures are applicable here, unless they are the kinds that imply a knowledge of a "true" zero point. The zero point on an interval scale is a matter of convention or convenience, as is shown by the fact that the scale form remains invariant when a constant is added.

This point is illustrated by our two scales of temperature, Centigrade and Fahrenheit. Equal intervals of temperature are scaled off by noting equal volumes of expansion; an arbitrary zero is agreed upon for each scale; and a numerical value on one of the scales is transformed into a value on the other by means of an equation of the form $x' = ax + b$. Our scales of time offer a similar example. Dates on one calendar are transformed to those on another by way of this same equation. On these scales, of course, it is meaningless to say that one value is twice or some other proportion greater than another.

Periods of time, however, can be measured on ratio scales and one period may be correctly defined as double another. The same is probably true of temperature measured on the so-called Absolute Scale.

Most psychological measurement aspires to create interval scales, and it sometimes succeeds. The problem usually is to devise operations for equalizing the units of the scales—a problem not always easy of solution but one for which there are several possible modes of attack. Only occasionally is there concern for the location of a "true" zero point, because the human attributes measured by psychologists usually exist in a positive degree that is large compared with the range of its variation. In this respect these attributes are analogous to temperature as it is encountered in everyday life. Intelligence, for example, is usefully assessed on ordinal scales which try to approximate interval scales, and it is not necessary to define what zero intelligence would mean.

Ratio scale

Ratio scales are those most commonly encountered in physics and are possible only when there exist operations for determining all four relations: equality, rank-order, equality of intervals, and equality of ratios. Once such a scale is erected, its numerical values can be transformed (as from inches to feet) only by multiplying each value by a constant. An absolute zero is always implied, even though the zero value on some scales (e.g., Absolute Temperature) may never be produced. All types of statistical measures are applicable to ratio scales, and only with these scales may we properly indulge in logarithmic transformations such as are involved in the use of decibels.

Foremost among the ratio scales is the scale of number itself—cardinal number—the scale we use when we count such things as eggs, pennies, and apples. This scale of the numerosity of aggregates is so basic and so common that it is ordinarily not even mentioned in discussions of measurement.

It is conventional in physics to distinguish between two types of ratio scales: *fundamental* and *derived*. Fundamental scales are represented by length, weight, and electrical resistance, whereas derived scales are represented by density, force, and elasticity.

These latter are *derived* magnitudes in the sense that they are mathematical functions of certain fundamental magnitudes. They are actually more numerous in physics than are the fundamental magnitudes, which are commonly held to be basic because they satisfy the criterion of *additivity*. Weights, lengths, and resistances can be added in the physical sense, but this important empirical fact is generally accorded more prominence in the theory of measurement than it deserves. The so-called fundamental scales are important instances of ratio scales, but they are only instances. As a matter of fact, it can be demonstrated that the fundamental scales could be set up even if the physical operation of addition were ruled out as impossible of performance. Given three balances, for example, each having the proper construction, a set of standard weights could be manufactured without it ever being necessary to place two weights in the same scale pan at the same time. The procedure is too long to describe in these pages, but its feasibility is mentioned here simply to suggest that physical addition, even though it is sometimes possible, is not necessarily the basis of all measurement. Too much measuring goes on where resort can never be had to the process of laying things end-to-end or of piling them up in a heap.

Ratio scales of psychological magnitudes are rare but not entirely unknown. The Sone scale discussed by the British committee is an example founded on a deliberate attempt to have human observers judge the loudness ratios of pairs of tones. The judgment of equal intervals had long been established as a legitimate method, and with the work on sensory ratios, started independently in several laboratories, the final step was taken to assign numerals to sensations of loudness in such a way that relations among the sensations are reflected by the ordinary arithmetical relations in the numerical series. As in all measurement, there are limits imposed by error and variability, but within these limits the Sone scale ought properly to be classed as a ratio scale.

To the British committee, then, we may venture to suggest by way of conclusion that the most liberal and useful definition of measurement is, as one of its members advised, "the assignment of numerals to things so as to represent facts and conventions about them." The problem as to what is and is not measurement then reduces to the simple question: What are the rules, if any, under which numerals are assigned? If we can point to a consistent set of rules, we are obviously concerned with measurement of some sort, and we can then proceed to the more interesting question as to the kind of measurement it is. In most cases a formulation of the rules of assignment discloses directly the kind of measurement and hence the kind of scale involved. If there remains any ambiguity, we may seek the final and definitive answer in the mathematical group-structure of the scale form: In what ways can we transform its values and still have it serve all the functions previously fulfilled? We know that the values of all scales can be multiplied by a constant, which changes the size of the unit. If, in addition, a constant can be added (or a new zero point chosen), it is proof positive that we are not concerned with a ratio scale. Then, if the purpose of the scale is still served when its values are squared or cubed, it is not even an interval scale. And finally, if any two values may be interchanged at will, the ordinal scale is ruled out and the nominal scale is the sole remaining possibility.

This proposed solution to the semantic problem is not meant to imply that all scales belonging to the same mathematical group are equally precise or accurate or useful or "fundamental." Measurement is never better than the empirical operations by which it is carried out, and operations range from bad to good. Any particular scale, sensory or physical, may be objected to on the grounds of bias, low precision, restricted generality, and other factors, but the objector should remember that these are relative and practical matters and that no scale used by mortals is perfectly free of their taint.

2

weak measurements vs. strong statistics: an empirical critique of S. S. Stevens' proscriptions on statistics

Bela O. Baker,
Curtis D. Hardyck,
Lewis F. Petrinovich

The disagreement between those who belong to what Lubin (1962) called the "school of 'weak measurement' theorists" and those who belong to what might be called the school of "strong statistics" has persisted for a number of years with little apparent change of attitude on either side. Stevens, as the leading spokesman for the weak measurement school, has asserted (1951) and reasserted (1959, 1960) the view that measurement scales are models of object relationships and, for the most part, rather poor models which can lead one far astray from the truth if the scores they yield are added when they should only be

Reprinted from *Educational and Psychological Measurement* **26,** No. 2, 291–309 (1966), by permission of the authors and the publisher.

This research was supported by research grants from the National Institutes of Health, U.S. Public Health Service (MH 07310) and the Research Committee, University of California Medical Center. Preliminary work was accomplished by a grant of free computer time by the Computer Center, University of California, Berkeley.

We are grateful to Professor Jack Block, Professor Quinn McNemar, and Miss Mary Epling for their many helpful suggestions throughout this study. We are also indebted to Mrs. Eleanor Krasnow who developed and tested the computer programs used in this study.

counted. At least two current statistics texts intended for psychologists (Senders, 1958; Siegel, 1956) present this view as gospel.

Opposing this view, an assortment of statistically minded psychologists—e.g., Lord (1953), Burke (1953), Anderson (1961), McNemar (1962), and Hays (1963) have argued that statistics apply to numbers rather than to things and that the formal properties of measurement scales, as such, should have no influence on the choice of statistics. Savage (1957), a statistician, has supported this point of view, stating: "I know of no reason to limit statistical procedures to those involving arithmetic operations consistent with the scale properties of the observed quantities." In other words, a statistical test answers the question it is designed to answer whether measurement is weak or strong.

In his widely cited discussion of measurement, Stevens (1951) distinguished four classes of scales: Nominal, ordinal, interval, and ratio, and specified the arithmetic operations (and hence the statistics) which are permissible for each scale. Nominal scales consist simply of class names and can be treated only by counting operations and frequency statistics. Ordinal scales are developed by demonstrating that some objects have more of a particular quality than do other objects and representing numerically this order among objects. Lacking units, the numbers of an ordinal scale cannot be added, subtracted, multiplied, or divided, but they can be treated by order statistics such as the median or the rank-order correlation. Interval scales represent equal increments in the magnitudes of an object property by equal numerical increments. An increase of one unit in any region of an interval scale represents the same increment in the object property as does an increase of one unit in any other region of the scale. Scores from interval scales can be added and subtracted and hence such statistics as the mean, the standard deviation, and the product-moment correlation can be used. Ratio scales add a true zero point to equal intervals and can be multiplied, divided, and treated by subtle statistics which are of little concern to most psychologists.

Although Stevens develops his rationale for relating measurements and statistics almost exclusively in terms of descriptive statistics, he introduces the issue of hypothesis testing somewhat obliquely in his discussions of invariance of results under scale transformations (1951, 1959). He says, "The basic principle is this: Having measured a set of items by making numerical assignments in accordance with a set of rules, we are free to change the assignments by whatever group of transformations will preserve the empirical information in the scale. These transformations, depending on which group they belong to, will upset some statistical measures and leave others unaffected" (1959, p. 30).

If parametric significance tests, such as t or F are used, the permissible transformations are linear. Only then will invariant results be found in comparing groups. An implication of this point of view, which is not made explicit by Stevens, is that if a scale is viewed as a model of object relationships, then any scale transformation is a transformation of those relationships. Hence the problem of invariance of results under scale transformations raises the following question: Can we make correct decisions about the nature of reality if we disregard the nature of the measurement scale when we apply statistical tests?

This aspect of Stevens' position has apparently been ignored by many of his critics. Anderson (1961) dismisses out of hand any restriction on the uses of t arising from the nature of the measurements to which it is applied but discusses the question of invariance of results under scale transformations seriously and at length before concluding that: "The practical problems of invariance or generality of results far transcend measurement scale typology" (p. 316).

The aspects of the problem as related to descriptive and inferential statistics are as follows: The problem for descriptive statistics as presented by Stevens (1951, 1959, 1960) concerns the relationship of the value of a particular statistic computed on obtained measurements to the value of the same statistic computed under conditions of perfect measurement. The argument is that the farther the measurement model departs from the underlying properties of the objects being measured, the less accurate the statistics. In other words, this aspect is concerned with precision of measurement.

In making statistical inferences, however, the issue is whether one will arrive at the same probability estimates from different types of measurement scales. Given the condition that a measurement scale may be a very poor model indeed of the properties of the objects under study, the question of the effect of the scale on the sampling distribution of a statistic remains unanswered. Where hypothesis testing is the issue, the appropriate question is: Do statistics computed on measures which are inaccurate descriptions of reality distribute differently than the same statistics computed under conditions of perfect measurement? If not, then a research worker who has nothing better than an ordinal scale to work with may have to face the problem of more precise measurement for descriptive purposes, but at least the probability decisions he may make from his ordinal measurements will not be inappropriate for parametric statistical models.

In view of the importance of the issue raised by Stevens for users of statistics, it is surprising, as Lubin (1962) notes, that so few detailed discussions of the problem are available. If Stevens is correct, then psychologists should be disturbed about the state of their research literature. Since it can be safely asserted that most measurements in psychology yield scales which are somewhere between ordinal and interval scales, many psychologists may have been propagating fiction when they have made statistical inferences based on significance tests inappropriate to anything less than interval measurements. If Stevens' position is correct, it should be emphasized more intensively; if it is incorrect, something should be done to alleviate the lingering feelings of guilt that plague research workers who deliberately use statistics such as *t* on weak measurements.

A test of the issue would seem to require a comparison of the sampling distribution of a statistic computed under conditions of "perfect" measurement with the sampling distribution of the same statistic based on imperfect measurements. Since it is not possible to obtain such "perfect" measurements, this comparison is manifestly impossible. As noted above, however, Stevens has suggested that the main issue is that of invariance of results when measurement scales are transformed. Cast in these terms, the problem can be examined empirically. All that is required is that the sampling distribution of a statistic based on one set of scores be compared with the sampling distribution of the same statistic based on scores which are not "permissible" transformations of the first set. If Stevens is right, these sampling distributions should differ in some important way. If they do not, then the nature of the measurement scale is, within potentially determinable limits, an irrelevant consideration when one chooses an hypothesis testing statistic.

Method

The statistic selected for study was Student's *t*. Not only is this one of the most commonly used statistics in psychology but it also has the advantage of having been demonstrated empirically to be relatively robust in the face of violations of the assumptions of normality and equality of variances (Norton, 1953; Boneau, 1960).

The first set of scores used—which will be referred to as criterion (unit-interval) scores—comprised the cardinal numbers from 1 to 30. Three populations of 1000 scores each were constructed by assigned frequencies to the unit-interval scores to approximate as closely as possible the expected frequencies for

1) a normal distribution,
2) a rectangular distribution, and
3) an exponential distribution ($f = 1 + 275^{(e - .25x)}$).

According to Stevens (1951), when one uses the mean or standard deviation the permissible score transformations are linear. And so, to evaluate this proscription, 35 nonlinear transformations of the unit-interval scores were constructed. These fell into three subsets, each designed to simulate a common measurement problem in psychology. The rationale for this approach is that an investigator can almost always develop a measuring device that looks as if it yields scores with equal intervals. However, relations among the objects represented by these numbers may not be equal—this is, of course, Stevens' main concern—and consequently by producing nonlinear transformations of cardinal numbers, a class of situations is produced directly analogous to the situation that obtains when a measurement scale correctly represents the order among objects but incorrectly represents the magnitude of differences between objects. A statistic such as *t*, it is argued, cannot be used with such a measuring device, since the operations of addition, subtraction, multiplication, and division are inappropriate—a condition which rather limits the investigator seeking statistical support for his conclusions.

The first set of transformations (1 through 15) was constructed to simulate the situation in which an ordinal scale is achieved but interval sizes vary randomly. This may often be the case when the sum of responses in a keyed direction on a personality inventory is used as a trait measure. The first score of each transformation was the number 1, to which was added a number selected at random within pre-set limits to produce the second score. Another random number was then added to the second score to produce the third number, continuing until 30 scores had been developed. With this technique, the intervals between successive scores could vary randomly from 1 to a preselected maximum. In order to examine the effects of the magnitude of interval variations, three different maximum interval sizes were used in the first 15 transformations. Transformations 1 through 5 were constructed with a maximum of 2, allowing the largest interval to be twice as large as the smallest. Transformations 6 through 10 were constructed with a maximum of 10, and transformations 11 through 15 were constructed with a maximum of 25. Therefore, in transformations 11 through 15 one interval potentially could be 25 times as large as another. Figure 1 illustrates the relationship between the scores of transformation 7 and the unit-interval criterion scores. Each preselected maximum value was used to develop five transformations—a precaution which served to cancel out artifacts of sampling for a particular transformation.

The second set of transformations (16 through 25) was devised to simulate the situation which may often occur in the measurement of achievement and ability in which the magnitudes of trait differences

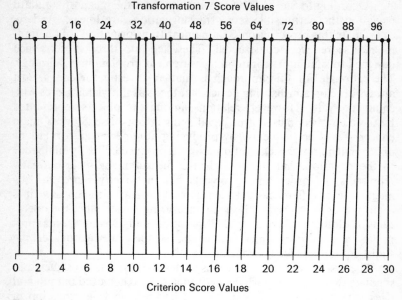

Fig. 1
Relationship between the intervals of transformation 7 and the unit intervals of the criterion scores.

represented by intervals at the extremes of a scale may be greater than those represented by equal appearing intervals in the middle of the scale. Each transformation was produced by choosing a number from 1 to a relatively large maximum for the first interval, a number from 1 to a somewhat smaller maximum for the second interval, and so forth, progressively reducing the maximum until the center of the score array was reached, then increasing the maximum at the same rate to the end of the score array. For transformations 16 through 20, the series of maximum values decreased by one unit steps from a possible maximum of 15 at the beginning of the array to 1 at the center of the array, increasing again by one unit steps to a possible maximum of 15 again at the other end of the array. For transformations 21 through 25, the maximum was decreased by 3 unit steps from 45 to 3 at the center of the array and back to 45. The type of transformation produced by this procedure is illustrated in Figure 2.

For the third set of transformations (26 through 35), unit intervals were retained for scores ranging from 1 to 15, the remaining 15 intervals being varied randomly. This procedure crudely imitates a problem

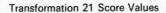

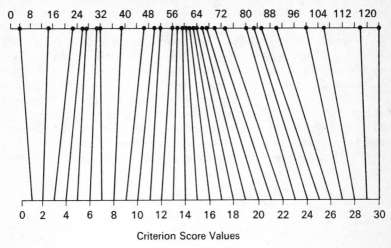

Fig. 2
Relationship between the intervals of transformation 21 *and the unit intervals of the criterion scores.*

which may be present sometimes in social distance scales or in the Thurstone type scaling of attitude items. For transformations 26 through 30, the maximum interval size above the center of the score array was 10. For transformations 31 through 35, the maximum was 25. Figure 3 illustrates this type of transformation.

For each of the populations, the unit-interval scores and the transformations were stored in the memory of an IBM 7090 digital computer as 36 scores for each of 1,000 cases, which were identified by the numbers 1 through 1,000. Random samples of cases were selected by means of a multiplying random number generator, with some additional features to insure complete randomness and to guard against cycling. The generator sequence was initiated by obtaining a 35 binary digit (bit) number from the clock of the computer. This number was forced to be odd by the insertion of a low-order bit. A tape containing the one million random digits produced by the RAND Corporation (Rand, 1955) was then referenced and a word of ten decimal digits read from this tape. The first half of the 10 digit word, R, was then transformed by the value $8R + 3$. This value served as the initial multiplier for the number obtained from the computer clock. This multiplication produced a 70 bit number, the right 35 bits of which were extracted from the random number. The left bits of the latter were used to obtain an integer in the range 1–1,000. This value determined the "case" to be selected from the population. The 35 bit random number was retained and multiplied by 8R + 3 to obtain the next value from the population.

The second half of the ten-digit number first read from the RAND tape was divided by the quantity (NA + NB)/2, where NA and NB are the respective sizes of the pairs of samples drawn. The remainder occurring from this division determined the number of times the value 8R + 3 was used as a multiplier in generating a random sequence. When the number of values generated equaled the value of the remainder, another ten-digit record was read from the RAND tape and the sequence of generation repeated. When samples of size NA and NB had been drawn, t was computed using a standard computing formula.

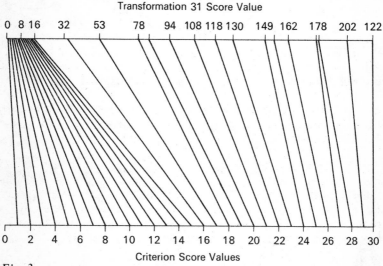

Fig. 3
Relationship between the intervals of transformation 31 and the unit intervals of the criterion scores.

A total of 36 t values were computed for each pair of samples drawn: One value for the unit-interval or criterion scores and one for each of the 35 transformations of the criterion. This is analogous to sampling from a pool of 1,000 subjects with scores on 36 variables, the first variable representing a set of measurements with equal intervals and the remaining 35 variables representing measurement scales standing in varying nonlinear relationships to the first set.

The following notation will be used throughout the paper:

N,R,E	The type of distribution used: Normal, Rectangular, or Exponential
5,5; 15,15; 5,15	Size of first and second samples
C	The criterion set of values
T_n	The nth transformation
T_{j-k}	Transformations j through k.

The sequence of the notation is as follows: $N,15,15,T_{6-10}$; a normal distribution with sample sizes of 15 and 15 for transformations 6 through 10.

The computations were summarized in three forms:

1. Contingency tables showing the relationship of the criterion t value to each transformation t value for the .01 and .05 significance levels were tabulated. These tables allow the determination of the difference in the percentage of t's reaching given significance levels for a particular transformation and for the criterion scores.

2. Frequency distributions of all sets of t values were tabulated. Figure 4 shows the frequency distributions of t for $N,5,5,C$; $N,5,5,T_5$; $N,5,5,T_{20}$; and $N,5,5,T_{35}$.

3. Pearson correlation coefficients between the criterion t values and each of the transformation t values were calculated over the total number of sample pairs drawn for a given condition. The standard error of estimate was also computed. These statistics provide estimates of the degree to which t's based on transformed scores varied from t's based on unit-interval scores for the same pairs of samples.

Parts (1) and (2) of the computation summaries are directly relevant to the question of the effect of the measurement model on the sampling distribution of t. Part (3) is an attempt to represent the deviation of the various types of "inappropriate" measurement models from a true value (represented by the criterion).

As has been mentioned earlier, three types of distributions—normal, rectangular, and exponential, were used. Three variations in sample size were studied—NA = NB = 5; NA = NB = 15; and NA = 5, NB = 15. These combinations are identical with those used by Boneau (1960) and permit the present results to be compared directly with his.

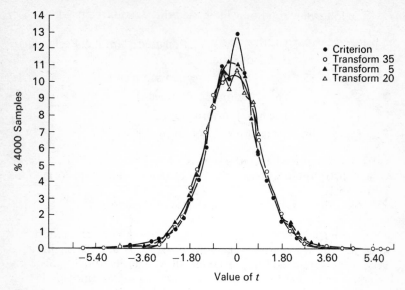

Fig. 4
Empirical sampling distributions of t *for 4,000 pairs of samples with
NA = NB = 5, from a normal distribution for the criterion and trans-
formations 5, 20, and 35.*

Results

As a first step, the distributions of *t* on the criterion measurements for
all conditions were compared with the theoretical distributions for the
appropriate degrees of freedom. Table 1 contains the percentage of
t values falling in the 5 percent and 1 percent regions of the distribution
for the criterion scores.

The deviations of the empirical distributions from the expected
theoretical values for the normal curve are quite small. The results
are very similar to those reported by Boneau (1960), including the
underestimates for the exponential distribution. Somewhat surprisingly, the deviations are reduced only slightly from those reported
by Boneau, despite the fact that the present results are based on 4,000 *t*'s
as compared to Boneau's 1,000.

The results for the first set of transformations, which were constructed to simulate a situation where intervals vary randomly throughout
the range of the measuring instrument, are given in Table 2. Since the
tabulation of results for individual transformations within and across

Table 1
*Percent of t's based on criterion unit interval scores falling in the 5%
and 1% regions of rejection for 4,000 random sampling runs*

Population Distribution	Sample Sizes					
	NA = NB = 5		NA = NB = 15		NA = 5, NB = 15	
	5% Level	1% Level	5% Level	1% Level	5% Level	1% Level
Normal	4.8	.8	5.4	1.0	5.3	1.1
Rectangular	5.4	1.6	4.6	.9	5.1	.8
Exponential	3.9	.9	5.1	1.0	4.2	.9

sets T_{1-5}, T_{6-10}, and T_{11-15} revealed little variation, only mean values for all transformations are given in Table 2.[1] The mean value tabled for each transformation is based on 60,000 t's.

Examination of Table 2 indicates that random variations tend to have little effect on the number of t's falling in the 5 percent and 1 percent regions of rejection. Columns (1) and (3) contain the total percentages for the 5 percent and 1 percent levels of the t distribution for all distributions and sample sizes. For the first group of transformations, the total percentages in the critical regions are very close to the theoretical expectation for a normal distribution. The largest discrepancy present is for E,5,5—a discrepancy of only 1.1 percent. Columns (2) and (4), which contain the percentage in the larger tail, show similar minimal variations. If one allows for the effects of sampling and takes the deviations of each transformation from the obtained percentages of the C distribution, the discrepancies become almost nonexistent. The largest deviation is .3 percent for N,5,15. It is evident that random variations in interval sizes, regardless of the magnitude of those variations, have virtually no effect on the percentage of t's reaching conventional significance levels.

One condition reported in Table 2 (E,5,15) did result in an asymmetrical t distribution. However, as can be seen by examining the tabled values for E,5,15, the C distribution is equally asymmetrical. For E,5,15, the majority of the t values reaching the 5 percent level and all of the t's at the 1 percent level are in one tail of the distribution. The direction of the skewing is negative, indicating that where large differences between sample means occurred, the higher mean tended to be the mean of the smaller sample. On the basis of this finding, an experimenter would be ill-advised to use a one-tailed test when he is

1. Complete tables are available on request from the authors.

Table 2
Percent of t's falling in the 5% and 1% regions of rejection when interval sizes vary randomly (4,000 samples per condition)

		5% Level		1% Level	
		Total %	% in Larger Tail	Total %	% in Larger Tail
N,5,5:	C	4.8	2.4	.8	.4
	T_{1-15}	4.8	2.4	.8	.4
N,15,15:	C	5.4	3.0	1.0	.5
	T_{1-15}	5.3	2.9	.9	.5
N,5,15:	C	5.3	2.7	1.1	.6
	T_{1-15}	5.0	2.6	1.1	.6
R,5,5:	C	5.4	3.0	1.6	.9
	T_{1-15}	5.3	3.0	1.6	.9
R,15,15:	C	4.6	2.6	.9	.5
	T_{1-15}	4.6	2.5	.9	.5
R,5,15:	C	5.1	2.7	.8	.7
	T_{1-15}	5.0	2.6	.9	.7
E,5,5:	C	3.9	2.0	.9	.5
	T_{1-15}	3.9	2.0	.8	.4
E,15,15:	C	5.1	2.6	1.0	.6
	T_{1-15}	5.2	2.6	1.0	.6
E,5,15:	C	4.2	3.8	.9	.9
	T_{1-15}	4.2	3.8	1.0	1.0

using samples of unequal sizes (at least if the sizes are of the magnitudes used in this study). However, it makes little difference whether there is an interval scale of measurement or not.

The results for the more irregular and extreme transformations (16 through 35) are presented in Table 3. Again, since there was little variation within sets only mean values for transformations 16 through 25 and transformations 26 through 35 are presented.

Table 3
Percent of t's falling in the 5% and 1% regions of rejection when interval sizes vary more in some regions of the scale than in others (4,000 samples per condition)

		5% Level		1% Level	
		Total %	% in Larger Tail	Total %	% in Larger Tail
N,5,5:	C	4.8	2.4	.8	.4
	T_{16-25}	3.4	1.8	.4	.3
	T_{26-35}	4.2	2.2	.8	.4
N,15,15:	C	5.4	3.0	1.0	.5
	T_{16-25}	4.6	2.6	.6	.4
	T_{26-35}	5.1	2.8	.9	.5
N,5,15:	C	5.3	2.7	1.1	.6
	T_{16-25}	5.0	2.7	1.0	.6
	T_{26-35}	4.7	3.6	1.0	.9
R,5,5:	C	5.4	3.0	1.6	.9
	T_{16-25}	4.9	2.7	1.0	.6
	T_{26-35}	4.4	2.6	.8	.5
R,15,15:	C	4.6	2.6	.9	.5
	T_{16-25}	4.6	2.4	.8	.4
	T_{26-35}	4.9	2.8	.8	.4
R,5,15:	C	5.1	2.7	.8	.7
	T_{16-25}	4.9	2.6	.8	.6
	T_{26-35}	4.3	3.1	1.1	1.1
E,5,5:	C	3.9	2.0	.9	.5
	T_{16-25}	5.2	2.8	1.4	.7
	T_{26-35}	3.3	1.6	.7	.4
E,15,15:	C	5.1	2.6	1.0	.6
	T_{16-25}	5.4	2.7	1.2	.6
	T_{26-35}	2.8	1.4	.4	.3
E,5,15:	C	4.2	3.8	.9	.9
	T_{16-25}	4.6	3.4	.8	.7
	T_{26-35}	3.8	3.6	.6	.6

An inspection of Table 3 also permits the conclusion that the magnitude of variations in interval sizes has little effect on the t distribution. At the same time, it is apparent that t is affected more by these types of transformations than was the situation for simple random variation. However, the discrepancies are still far from extreme. In columns (1) and (3) the largest obtained discrepancy is 2.3 percent for $E,15,15,T_{26-35}$ at the 5 percent level. In columns (2) and (4), the largest discrepancy is again at the 5 percent level for $E,15,15,T_{26-35}$, a value of 1.1 percent.

When compared to the 5.1 percent of t's falling in the 5 percent region for the $E,15,15,C$ distribution, this discrepancy of 2.3 percent seems rather large. However, it seems slight compared to the discrepancies obtained when more serious violations of the assumptions for the use of t are made. For example, Boneau (1960) reported 16 percent of obtained t's at the 5 percent level for samples of 5 and 15 drawn from normally distributed populations with unequal variances.

When Table 3 is examined for asymmetry, it is evident that the transformations in which the intervals in one half of a scale stand for substantially smaller variations in the objects being measured than do intervals in the other half of the scale—T_{26-35}—yield seriously skewed distributions of t for all conditions where unequal sample sizes are used. For E distributions, skewing is present for most of the transformations. These transformations provide the only situation where the nature of the scale transformation affected the sampling distribution of t to a more serious degree than could be attributable to the use of unequal sample sizes drawn from an exponential distribution. Even for this condition the effect is quite small. For any real-life situation in which the possibility of such a measurement scale exists, an experimenter should be chary of using t to make a one-tailed test between means based on unequal sample N's. Fortunately, this problem occurs only rarely and when it does occur the use of equal sample sizes will minimize the distortion.

In reviewing the results presented so far, the following generalizations seem warranted:

1.   The percentage of t's reaching the theoretical 5 percent and 1 percent levels of significance is not seriously affected by the use of nonequal interval measurements.[2]

---

2.   It is possible that the effects of the scale transformations used in this study are actually due to changes in the shape of the distributions which the different transformations produced. However, if this is the case, the arguments presented regarding the insignificant effects of the nature of measurement scales on probability statements are strengthened even more.

2.   To the extent that there is any influence of the scale transformation on the percentage of t's reaching theoretical significance levels, the influence is more marked when intervals in one broad region of a scale are larger than intervals in another region of the scale than it is when interval sizes vary randomly.

3.   If an investigator has a measuring instrument which produces either an interval scale or an ordinal scale with randomly varied interval sizes, he can safely use t for statistical decisions under all circumstances examined in this study. The single exception is that t should not be used to do a one-tailed test when samples of unequal size have been drawn from a badly skewed population.

4.   If a measurement scale deviates from reality in such a fashion that the magnitude of trait differences represented by intervals at the extremes of the scale may be greater than those represented by equal-appearing intervals in the middle of the scale (T_{16-25}), it seems reasonably safe to use t. Unequal sample sizes can even be used if the population is symmetrical, but the proscriptions against using one-tailed tests for unequal sample sizes from exponential populations still apply.

5.   If the scale is of the kind represented by the relationship between C and T_{26-35} (in which inequality of units is present in one-half of the distribution only), it is still safe to use t, with a somewhat stricter limitation on the use of one-tailed tests. This arises from the finding that for all population distributions these transformations yielded skewed distributions of t when unequal sample sizes were used.

6.   As a maximally conservative empirical set of rules for using t, the following restrictions would seem to be sufficient to compensate for almost any violation of assumptions investigated up to this time:

a.   Have equal sample sizes.

b.   Use a two-tailed test.

7.   Returning to the question as originally formulated: Do statistics computed on a measurement scale which is at best a poor fit to reality distribute differently than the same statistics computed under conditions of perfect measurement? The answer is a firm "no," provided that the conditions of equal sample sizes and two-tailed tests are met. The research worker who has nothing better than an ordinal scale to work with may have an extremely poor fit to reality, but at least he will not be led into making incorrect probability estimates if he observes a few simple precautions.

As a final step, a different sort of analysis will be cited. The previous results and discussion related to one aspect of the measurement problem as posed by Stevens (1951); a second aspect remains. This concerns the accuracy of the descriptive statistics when the measurement model is a poor fit. Stevens has presented his point of view almost exclusively in terms of descriptive statistics and has tended to use illustrations from descriptive statistics to support his arguments. In the last analysis, this would seem to raise an epistemological question, since it is concerned with the relationship of measurement to a true value which cannot be known. However, evidence as to the correctness or incorrectness of the point of view can be examined from the data of the present study, even though the results are of no help in solving the problems faced by an experimenter who is wondering how to evaluate the validity and the precision of his measuring instrument.

The question of the accuracy of representation can be evaluated by defining the unit interval criterion t values as true measures and the values calculated on the various transformations as those obtained on a measurement model which misrepresents reality. Then the degree of relationship between the values of t calculated on specific samples for C and the values calculated on T_{1-35} can be obtained. This is a correlational question and the results are reported in Table 4.

Columns (1), (3), and (5) contain for each of the distributions the correlations between values of t for each set of transformations and the corresponding values of t for the criterion. The correlations are impressively high. However, because of the broad range of values in the t distribution, the standard errors of estimate in columns (2), (4), and (6) are more informative statistics.

Several points can be noted in connection with Table 4: There is a regular progression in the size of the standard errors of estimate across the sets of transformations used, such that they are smallest for T_{1-15}, and largest for T_{26-35}. These standard errors also become larger as the magnitude of variations in interval size increases, but this is less striking than the differences among types of transformations. Variations in sample sizes and in the shape of the population distribution do not seem to have much influence on the standard errors of estimate; consequently these results seem to show a specific influence of scale transformations on the values of t. The correspondence between values of t based on the criterion unit interval scores and values of t based on transformations decreases regularly and dramatically— from standard errors of estimate on the order of .08 to standard errors of estimate on the order of .45—as the departure from linear transformations becomes more extreme. Here, then, is a finding consistent with

Table 4
Mean[a] correlation coefficients and standard errors of estimate for the prediction of t's based on transformed scores from t's based on criterion unit-interval scores

Population Distribution	NA = NB = 5		NA = NB = 15		NA = 5, NB = 15	
	Mean r (1)	Mean $s_{y \cdot x}$ (2)	Mean r (3)	Mean $s_{y \cdot x}$ (4)	Mean r (5)	Mean $s_{y \cdot x}$ (6)
N: T_{1-5}	.997	.089	.997	.082	.997	.084
T_{6-10}	.996	.111	.995	.100	.995	.104
T_{11-15}	.992	.146	.991	.138	.991	.142
T_{16-20}	.975	.244	.966	.265	.970	.260
T_{21-25}	.968	.271	.964	.274	.966	.278
T_{26-30}	.935	.401	.933	.380	.933	.386
T_{31-35}	.914	.462	.911	.434	.912	.439
R: T_{1-5}	.999	.056	.988	.048	.999	.033
T_{6-10}	.996	.094	.996	.081	.996	.084
T_{11-15}	.994	.117	.994	.088	.988	.104
T_{16-20}	.973	.256	.973	.231	.973	.233
T_{21-25}	.973	.258	.975	.227	.976	.225
T_{26-30}	.948	.368	.943	.339	.944	.348
T_{31-35}	.927	.430	.922	.394	.924	.404
E: T_{1-5}	.994	.121	.993	.113	.992	.117
T_{6-10}	.992	.138	.992	.126	.992	.129
T_{11-15}	.984	.199	.985	.181	.983	.189
T_{16-20}	.970	.283	.946	.342	.951	.324
T_{21-25}	.963	.313	.953	.314	.954	.309
T_{26-30}	.981	.218	.930	.382	.940	.325
T_{31-35}	.966	.288	.885	.483	.922	.405

[a] Median values do not differ until the third decimal place for the majority of transformations.

Stevens' expectations: The value of t determined for a comparison of samples of noninterval scores does tend to be different from the value of t based on interval scores for the same samples and the discrepancy tends to become greater as the departure from equal intervals is more marked.

In conclusion, the views presented by Stevens (1951, 1959, 1960) and by advocates of his position such as Senders (1958), Siegel (1956), and Stake (1960) state that, when one used t, the measurement model should have equal intervals representing linear transformations of the magnitudes of the characteristics being measured, or the statistic will be "upset." This view may be correct if one considers single specific determinations of a statistic in a descriptive sense—this seems to be the significance of the standard errors of estimate reported in Table 4—but it is incorrect when applied to the problem of statistical inference.

The present findings indicate that strong statistics such as the t test are more than adequate to cope with weak measurements—and, with some minor reservations, probabilities estimated from the t distribution are little affected by the kind of measurement scale used.

References

Anderson, N. H. Scales and statistics: parametric and nonparametric. *Psychol. Bull.*, 1961, **58,** 305–316.

Boneau, C. A. The effects of violations of assumptions underlying the t test. *Psychol. Bull.*, 1960, **57,** 49–64.

Burke, C. J. Additive scales and statistics. *Psychol. Rev.*, 1953, **60,** 73–75.

Hays, W. L. *Statistics for Psychologists.* New York: Holt, Rinehart and Winston, 1963.

Lord, F. M. On the statistical treatment of football numbers. *Amer. Psychol.*, 1953, **8,** 750–751.

Lubin, A. Statistics. In *Annual Review of Psychology.* Palo Alto, Calif.: Stanford University Press, 1962.

McNemar, Q. *Psychological Statistics,* 3rd ed. New York: Wiley, 1962.

Norton, D. W. An empirical investigation of some effects of nonnormality and heterogeneity on the F-distribution. Unpublished Doctoral Dissertation, State University of Iowa, 1952. Cited in E. F. Lindquist, *Design and Analysis of Experiments in Psychology and Education.* Boston: Houghton-Mifflin, 1953.

RAND Corporation. *A Million Random Digits.* New York: The Free Press of Glencoe, 1955.

Savage, I. R. Nonparametric statistics. *J. Amer. Stat. Assoc.,* 1957, **52,** 331–344.

Senders, V. L. *Measurement and Statistics.* London: Oxford University Press, 1958.

Siegel, S. *Nonparametric Statistics.* New York: McGraw-Hill, 1956.

Stake, R. E. Review of *Elementary Statistics* by P. G. Hoel. *Educational and Psychological Measurement*, 1960, **20**, 871–873.

Stevens, S. S. Mathematics, measurement and psychophysics. In S. S. Stevens (Ed.), *Handbook of Experimental Psychology*. New York: Wiley, 1951.

Stevens, S. S. Measurement, psychophysics and utility. In G. W. Churchman and P. Ratoosh (Eds.), *Measurement: Definitions and Theories*. New York: Wiley, 1959.

Stevens, S. S. Review of *Statistical Theory* by Lancelot Hogben. *Contemp. Psychol.*, 1960, **5**, 273–276.

3

on the statistical treatment of football numbers

Frederic M. Lord

Professor X sold "football numbers." The television audience had to have some way to tell which player it was who caught the forward pass. So each player had to wear a number on his football uniform. It didn't matter what number, just so long as it wasn't more than a two-digit number.

Professor X loved numbers. Before retiring from teaching, Professor X had been chairman of the Department of Psychometrics. He would administer tests to all his students at every possible opportunity. He could hardly wait until the tests were scored. He would quickly stuff the scores in his pockets and hurry back to his office where he would lock the door, take the scores out again, add them up, and then calculate means and standard deviations for hours on end.

Professor X locked his door so that none of his students would catch him in his folly. He taught his students very carefully: "Test scores are ordinal numbers, not cardinal numbers. Ordinal numbers cannot be added. *A fortiori*, test scores cannot be multiplied or squared."

From: F. M. Lord, "On the statistical treatment of football numbers," *American Psychologist* **8**, 1953, 750–751. Copyright © 1953 by the American Psychological Association, and reproduced by permission.

The professor required his students to read the most up-to-date references on the theory of measurement (e.g., 1, 2, 3). Even the poorest student would quickly explain that it was wrong to compute means or standard deviations of test scores.

When the continual reproaches of conscience finally brought about a nervous breakdown, Professor X retired. In appreciation of his careful teaching, the university gave him the "football numbers" concession, together with a large supply of cloth numbers and a vending machine to sell them.

The first thing the professor did was to make a list of all the numbers given to him. The University had been generous and he found that he had exactly 100,000,000,000,000,000 two-digit cloth numbers to start out with. When he had listed them all on sheets of tabulating paper, he shuffled the pieces of cloth for two whole weeks. Then he put them in the vending machine.

If the numbers had been ordinal numbers, the Professor would have been sorely tempted to add them up, to square them, and to compute means and standard deviations. But these were not even serial numbers; they were only "football numbers"—they might as well have been letters of the alphabet. For instance, there were 2,681,793,401,686,191 pieces of cloth bearing the number "69," but there were only six pieces of cloth bearing the number "68," etc., etc. The numbers were for designation purposes only; there was no sense to them.

The first week, while the sophomore team bought its numbers, everything went fine. The second week the freshman team bought its numbers. By the end of the week there was trouble. Information secretly reached the professor that the numbers in the machine had been tampered with in some unspecified fashion.

The professor had barely had time to decide to investigate when the freshman team appeared in a body to complain. They said they had bought 1,600 numbers from the machine, and they complained that the numbers were too low. The sophomore team was laughing at them because they had such low numbers. The freshmen were all for routing the sophomores out of their beds one by one and throwing them in the river.

Alarmed at this possibility, the professor temporized and persuaded the freshmen to wait while he consulted the statistician who lived across the street. Perhaps, after all, the freshmen had gotten low numbers just by chance. Hastily he put on his bowler hat, took his tabulating sheets, and knocked on the door of the statistician.

Now the statistician knew the story of the poor professor's resignation from his teaching. So, when the problem had been explained to him, the statistician chose not to use the elegant nonparametric methods of modern statistical analysis. Instead he took the professor's list of the 100 quadrillion "football numbers" that had been put into the machine. He added them all together and divided by 100 quadrillion.

"The population mean," he said, "is 54.3."

"But these numbers are not cardinal numbers," the professor expostulated. "You can't add them."

"Oh, can't I?" said the statistician. "I just did. Furthermore, after squaring each number, adding the squares, and proceeding in the usual fashion, I find the population standard deviation to be exactly 16.0."

"But you can't multiply 'football numbers,'" the professor wailed. "Why, they aren't even ordinal numbers, like test scores."

"The numbers don't know that," said the statistician. "Since the numbers don't remember where they came from, they always behave just the same way, regardless."

The professor gasped.

"Now the 1,600 'football numbers' the freshmen bought have a mean of 50.3," the statistician continued. "When I divide the difference between population and sample means by the population standard deviation . . . ."

"Divide!" moaned the professor.

". . . And then multiply by $\sqrt{1,600}$, I find a critical ratio of 10," the statistician went on, ignoring the interruption. "Now if your population of 'football numbers' had happened to have a normal frequency distribution, I would be able rigorously to assure you that the sample of 1,600 obtained by the freshmen could have arisen from random sampling only once in 65,618,050,000,000,000,000,000 times; for in this case these numbers obviously would obey all the rules that apply to sampling from any normal population."

"You cannot . . ." began the professor.

"Since the population is obviously not normal, it will in this case suffice to use Tchebycheff's inequality." [1] the statistician continued calmly. "The probability of obtaining a value of 10 for such a critical ratio in random sampling from any population whatsoever is always less than .01. It is therefore highly implausible that the numbers obtained by the freshmen were actually a random sample of all numbers put into the machine."

---

1. Tchebycheff's inequality, in a convenient variant, states that in random sampling the probability that a critical ratio of the type calculated here will exceed any chosen constant, c, is always less than $1/c^2$, irrespective of the shape of the population distribution. It is impossible to devise a set of numbers for which this inequality will not hold.

"You cannot add and multiply any numbers except cardinal numbers," said the professor.

"If you doubt my conclusions," the statistician said coldly as he showed the professor to the door, "I suggest you try and see how often you can get a sample of 1,600 numbers from your machine with a mean below 50.3 or above 58.3. Good night."

To date, after reshuffling the numbers, the professor has drawn (with replacement) a little over 1,000,000,000 samples of 1,600 from his machine. Of these, only two samples have had means below 50.3 or above 58.3. He is continuing his sampling, since he enjoys the computations. But he has put a lock on his machine so that the sophomores cannot tamper with the numbers again. He is happy because, when he has added together a sample of 1,600 "football numbers," he finds that the resulting sum obeys the same laws of sampling as they would if they were real honest-to-God cardinal numbers.

Next year, he thinks, he will arrange things so that the population distribution of his "football numbers" is approximately normal. Then the means and standard deviations that he calculates from these numbers will obey the usual mathematical relations that have been proven to be applicable to random samples from any normal population.

The following year, recovering from his nervous breakdown, Professor X will give up the "football numbers" concession and resume his teaching. He will no longer lock his door when he computes the means and standard deviations of test scores.

References

1. Coombs, C. H. Mathematical models in psychological scaling. *J. Amer. stat. Ass.*, 1951, **46,** 480–489.

2. Stevens, S. S. Mathematics, measurement, and psychophysics. In S. S. Stevens (Ed.), *Handbook of experimental psychology.* New York: Wiley, 1951. Pp. 1–49.

3. Weitzenhoffer, A. M. Mathematical structures and psychological measurements. *Psychometrika*, 1951, **16,** 387–406.

4

additive scales and statistics

C. J. Burke

Psychological measurements do not possess the simple properties of the scales obtained for those basic dimensions of physics which have been designated as "fundamental magnitudes." The implications of this statement for quantitative psychology have been extensively studied and discussed with varying evaluations and recommendations. Frequently the recommendations have been such as to alter statistical practices, had they been followed.

Certain writers, notably Boring [2] and Stevens [6], have maintained that such statistical concepts as the sample mean and standard deviation presuppose, at the very least, a scale of equivalent units of some kind, thus casting doubt on the theoretical validity of extensive reliance on the t test, analysis of variance, and other statistical techniques widely used with psychological data. The resulting distrust of such widely used procedures has prompted Comrey [4] to seek their justification outside the strict limits of the traditional logic of measurement.

From: D. J. Burke, "Additive scales and statistics," *Psychological Review* **60,** 1953, 73–75. Copyright © 1953 by the American Psychological Association, and reproduced by permission.

It is the purpose of the present paper to analyze this issue and to show that the use of the sample mean and standard deviation does no violence upon the data, whatever the properties of the measurement scale. Thus, the use of the usual statistical tests is limited only by the well-known statistical restrictions.

The argument to be given can be conducted from the axioms of probability and the axiomatic basis of measurement, but such detailed treatment would be merely pretentious, since the results which are necessary to establish the basic point are familiar to almost all psychologists.

The nature of measurement scales

(The term "object" as used below should not be restricted to its usual meaning of "physical object"; rather it is to be interpreted with sufficient breadth to give the statements throughout this section meaning for psychological as well as physical measurement provided that the axioms can be satisfied.)

Objects which can be ordered on the basis of a pair of (physical, psychological, or other) relations are said to define a "dimension." For such objects there are two relations, objectual equality and objectual less-than-ness and the objects and relations satisfy the axioms of order reproduced by Comrey [4]. Each object can be tagged with a number so that the numbers will satisfy a corresponding set of axioms. Thus there is a correspondence between the two systems:

A. [Objects, objectual equality, objectual less-than-ness.]

B. [Numbers, numerical equality, numerical less-than-ness.]

For some objects and relations, a further step is possible. An operation for combining the objects, "objectual addition," can be found such that the system

C. [Objects, objectual equality, objectual less-than-ness, objectual addition]

satisfies four additional axioms of combination (Comrey [4]). When this is the case the objects can be tagged with numbers so that the system

D. [Numbers, numerical equality, numerical less-than-ness, numerical addition]

satisfies four corresponding additional axioms of combination. Thus, in this case, there is a correspondence between (C) and (D).

When the systems (C) and (D) exist and correspond, we say that the objects define an "extensive dimension" and the numbers an "additive scale." In this case, of course, the systems (A) and (B) also exist and correspond.

When the systems (A) and (B) exist and correspond, but the systems (C) and (D) do not, we say that the objects define an "intensive dimension" and the numbers a "rank-order scale."

These matters are discussed in great detail by Campbell [3] and, more adequately for psychologists, by Bergmann and Spence [1]. Pertinent information is presented in papers by Comrey [4] and Gulliksen [5]. For our purposes, it is important to note only that the classification of a scale as additive depends upon the presence or absence of a certain correspondence, expressed in sets of axioms, between the numbers of the scale and the objects to which they refer—with, of course, appropriate ordering relations and combinative operations for each.

The nature of statistics

Statistical methods serve two major functions for psychologists.

a.   They are used to summarize the salient features of individual sets of data.

b.   They are used to test for differences between different experimental groups.

We shall discuss the second function in some detail, restricting our discussion to the simple case in which two groups are compared. In the typical psychological experiment the operations performed by the experimenter yield two or more sets of numbers. (In fact, unless the data exist in numerical form, means and standard deviations cannot be computed and the data are irrelevant for the present discussion.) It is obvious that two experimental groups will be judged alike or different in a given respect according as the collections of numbers classifying them in this respect are judged to be alike or different. It should be emphasized that we are here comparing the two sets of numbers *as numbers* and nothing else about them matters until after the statistical test has been made. The application of statistical techniques reflects merely our recognition of the unreliability of the small sets of numbers we have obtained and our unwillingness to perform the experiment again and again to determine whether the direction of the difference between our groups is reliable. We conceptualize a larger set of numbers, the statistical population, from which the sets of numbers we have obtained are two small samples, and inquire into the likelihood of two samples as disparate as we have observed arising from the given population. In answering this question, we often use the sample means and standard deviations as indices of important aspects of our collections of numbers. No interpretation other than this indicial one is intended. Means and standard deviations are used because they can always be computed, since numbers can always be added, subtracted, multiplied, and divided, and because means and standard deviations, conceived of merely as the results of operations with numbers, behave in certain lawful statistical ways.

In summary, the statistical technique begins and ends with the numbers and with statements about them. The psychological interpretation given to the experiment does take cognizance of the origin of the numbers but this is irrelevant for the statistical test as such.

Obviously, the same argument applies directly to the first function of statistics as well. The statement "The mean of these scores is 121" conveys in general the same kind of information as the statement "The median of these scores is 122."

The objection that a well-established unit is necessary before the mean and standard deviation can be computed since their value is altered by a change in the absolute value of the scores (Comrey [4]) loses cogency when one notices that the mean and median will be affected in precisely the same way by adding a given number to each number in the sample and that the standard deviation and the inter-quartile range will be changed in the same way by multiplying each number in the sample by a given number.

An example

To establish the point in another way, we consider an example of a statistical test based on an additive measure. Suppose that we are presented with two sticks, A and B, of apparently equal lengths, fixed on opposite sides of a room, and asked which is longer. We measure them and obtain a larger number for A. The two numbers, however, are nearly the same and we decide to repeat the measurement "just to make sure." On this occasion, we obtain a larger value for B. We proceed until we have 100 measurements on each stick and wish to answer the question without taking further measurements.

There are two collections of 100 numbers each, one for stick A and one for stick B. We test the hypothesis that they differ only through the unreliability of the measurements. A moment's reflection will show that we are not at all concerned with the additive nature of the scale for length. In adding the 100 numbers to obtain a mean for the measurements on stick A, we treat them as numbers and as nothing else. We make no interpretations whatever about adding 100 sticks together—there are only two sticks. Moreover, our interpretation by means of the *t* test is unaffected by the choice of length units we have made, provided that the units are the same for the two sticks.

It is seen that the comparison of the sets of measurements on the two sticks differs in no essential way from the comparison of two sets of IQ's.

Summary and conclusions

We have noted that:

a. The properties of a scale of measurement involve correspondences between sets of axioms about objects and numbers, with appropriate relations and operations.

b. Statistical methods begin and end with numbers.

From (a) and (b), we have deduced that the properties of a set of numbers as a measurement scale should have no effect upon the choice of statistical techniques for representing and interpreting the numbers.

References

1. Bergmann, G. and K. W. Spence. Logic of psychophysical measurement. *Psychol. Rev.*, 1944, **51**, 1–24.

2. Boring, E. G. The logic of the normal law of error in mental measurement. *Amer. J. Psychol.*, 1920, **31**, 1–33.

3. Campbell, N. R. *Physics, the elements.* London: Cambridge University Press, 1920.

4. Comrey, A. L. An operational approach to some problems in psychological measurement. *Psychol. Rev.*, 1950, **57**, 217–228.

5. Gulliksen, H. Paired comparisons and the logic of measurement. *Psychol. Rev.*, 1946, **53**, 199–213.

6. Stevens, S. S. On the theory of scales of measurement. *Science*, 1946, **103**, 677–680.

5

a note on measurement scales and statistical tests

C. *Alan Boneau*

In the past several months, the author, having once risen to the defense of parametric tests (Boneau, 1960), has been challenged on more than one occasion to justify the use of the *t* test in many typical psychological situations where there are measurement considerations. Research involving the concept of intelligence is often given as an instance, the point being that intelligence is actually measured by an ordinal scale, that equal differences between scores (on, say, a test) represent different magnitudes at different places on the underlying continuum. This is seen as somehow invalidating the use of the *t* test with such scores or as producing queasy feelings in those individuals who bravely resort to it in the face of uncertainty.

Burke (1953) has presented an argument which should have ended further discussion, but, in view of the present concern, a restatement of the argument and the addition of a few comments would seem indicated. The present concern seems to have been stimulated by the publication by psychologists of two recent texts in the field of statistics (Senders, 1958; Siegel, 1956) both of which are organized

From: C. A. Boneau, "A note on measurement scales and statistical tests," *American Psychologist* **16**, 1961, 260–261. Copyright © 1961 by the American Psychological Association, and reproduced by permission.

around Stevens' (1951) system of classifying measurement scales. Siegel and Senders belabor the point that parametric statistics, specifically the *t* and *F* tests should be avoided when the measurement scales are no stronger than ordinal, a state of affairs purportedly typical in psychology. To quote Siegel (1956):

Probability statements derived from the application of parametric statistical tests to ordinal data are in error to the extent that the structure of the method of collecting data is not isomorphic to arithmetic. Inasmuch as most of the measurements made by behavioral scientists culminate in ordinal scales (this seems to be the case except in the field of psychophysics, and possibly in the use of a few carefully standardized tests), this point deserves strong emphasis (p. 26).[1]

If one were to take Siegel seriously on this point one would hesitate to use parametric tests with practically any attitude measure in social psychology, with practically any performance measure in experimental psychology, and with practically any rating method or personality scale in clinical psychology.

A more realistic attitude is that parametric tests are useful whenever a measurement operation exists such that one of several possible numbers (scores) can be assigned unambiguously to an item of behavior without considering the relation of that item of behavior to other similar items, i.e., without ranking. This is typically the case with attitude scales, performance measures, and rating methods. If such numbers can be assigned, then conceptually there exists a population of these numbers having a specific distribution function, mean, and variance.

When we perform a test of a hypothesis we draw samples of numbers from two or more such populations each of which we can conceive of as being the totality of all possible measurements under the specific appropriate conditions. From the samples we can make estimates of the population parameters. Typically, we are interested in deciding whether or not the samples could have arisen from populations having the same parameters. Quite frequently we are concerned with statements about the means of the populations, but sometimes with variances.

In rejecting the null hypothesis, if we may do so, we are implying that the probability is high that if we draw further samples from the

---

1. By permission from *Nonparametric Statistics for the Behavioral Sciences,* by Sidney Siegel. Copyright, 1956. McGraw-Hill Book Company, Inc.

same populations (i.e., under the same conditions and using the same measuring instrument), we will get significant differences on each occasion. In other words we are asserting that a difference exists between the means (or variances, etc.) of the populations of assigned numbers or scores.

Note that we make absolutely no assumptions about any under-lying dimension and we deal only with the numbers assigned by the measurement operation. We, and statistical tests, are concerned only with this operationally defined manifestation of the underlying dimension. The statistical test cares not whether a Social Desirability scale measures social desirability, or number of trials to extinction is an indicator of habit strength. It does not even care whether the measuring scale is monotonically related (or unrelated) to the underlying dimen-sion. Given unending piles of numbers from which to draw small samples, the t test and the F test will methodically decide for us whether the means of the piles are different. If the distributions of the numbers in the piles are normal and have equal variances we can make exact statements as to the probability that the t or F test is mistaken. Even if this is not so, the probability statements are generally not greatly in error (see Boneau, 1960, for a discussion of this point). A further point: when the measurement operation is used to generate scores rather than ranks, inferences based upon nonparametric tests will be inferences about the populations of scores, the same sorts of inferences which we make when we use parametric methods. The nonparametric methods in a sense get closer to reality or peer at the underlying continuum through the screen of numbers which we have constructed to measure it although some would have us think that these methods have such a magical property. Since parametric as well as nonpara-metric methods are called upon in most instances in psychological research to make decisions about differences in population parameters the issue of relative sensitivity to such differences must be faced. Present evidence seems to point to the superiority of the parametric methods specifically the t and F tests in a large number of instances, even though the assumptions underlying these tests are rather drastically violated.

Certainly one cannot ignore the problem of measurement. It would seem to make a difference to psychology whether or not (and in what sense) the numbers we assign by means of an intelligence test are related to the underlying concept, but the problem is a measurement problem not a statistical one. No matter how one assigns these numbers (even at random), however, he can expect to get the same objective, impartial, and neutral judgment whenever he resorts to the use of the parametric or nonparametric tests of significance.

References

Boneau, C. A. The effects of violations of assumptions underlying the *t* test. *Psychol. Bull.,* 1960, **57,** 49–64.

Burke, C. J. Additive scales and statistics. *Psychol. Rev.,* 1953, **60,** 73–75.

Senders, V. L. *Measurement and statistics.* New York: Oxford University Press, 1958.

Siegel, S. *Nonparametric statistics for the behavioral sciences.* New York: McGraw-Hill, 1956.

Stevens, S. S. Mathematics, measurement, and psychophysics. In S. S. Stevens (Ed.), *Handbook of experimental psychology.* New York: Wiley, 1951, pp. 1–49.

6

measurement, statistics, and the schemapiric view

S. S. Stevens

Like the faces of Janus, science looks
two ways—toward schematics and empirics.

A curious antagonism has sometimes infected the relations between measurement and statistics. What ought to proceed as a pact of mutual assistance has seemed to some authors to justify a feud that centers on the degree of independence of the two domains. Thus Humphreys [1] dispenses praise to a textbook because its authors "do not follow the Stevens dictum concerning the precise relationships between scales of measurement and permissible statistical operations." Since that dictum, so-called, lurks as the *bête noire* behind many recurrent complaints, there is need to reexamine its burden and to ask how measurement and statistics shape up in the scientific process—the schemapiric endeavor in which we invent schematic models to map empirical domains.

In those disciplines where measurement is noisy, uncertain, and difficult, it is only natural that statistics should flourish. Of course, if there were no measurement at all, there would be no statistics. At the other extreme, if accurate measurement were achieved in every

Reprinted from *Science* **161**, 849–856 (1968), by permission of S. S. Stevens and the American Association for the Advancement of Science. Copyright © 1968 by the American Association for the Advancement of Science.

inquiry, many of the needs for statistics would vanish. Somewhere between the two extremes of no measurement and perfect measurement, perhaps near the psychosocial-behavioral center of gravity, the ratio of statisticizing to measuring reaches its maximum. And that is where we find an acute sensitivity to the suggestion that the type of measurement achieved in an experiment may set bounds on the kinds of statistics that will prove appropriate.

After reviewing the issues Anderson [2] concluded that "the statistical test can hardly be cognizant of the empirical meaning of the numbers with which it deals. Consequently," he continued, "the validity of the statistical inference cannot depend on the type of measuring scale used." This sequitur, if we may call it that, demands scrutiny, for it compresses large issues into a few phrases. Here let me observe merely that, however much we may agree that the statistical test cannot be cognizant of the empirical meaning of the numbers, the same privilege of ignorance can scarcely be extended to experimenters.

Speaking as a statistician, Savage [3] said, "I know of no reason to limit statistical procedures to those involving arithmetic operations consistent with the scale properties of the observed quantities." A statistician, like a computer, may perhaps feign indifference to the origin of the numbers that enter into a statistical computation, but that indifference is not likely to be shared by the scientist. The man in the laboratory may rather suspect that, if something empirically useful is to emerge in the printout, something empirically meaningful must be programmed for the input.

Baker, Hardyck, and Petrinovich [4] summed up the distress: "If Stevens' position is correct, it should be emphasized more intensively; if it is incorrect, something should be done to alleviate the lingering feelings of guilt that plague research workers who deliberately use statistics such as *t* on weak measurements." If it is true that guilt must come before repentance, perhaps the age of statistical indifference to the demands of measurement may be drawing to a close. Whatever the outcome, the foregoing samples of opinion suggest that the relation between statistics and measurement is not a settled issue. Nor is it a simple issue, for it exhibits both theoretical and practical aspects. Moreover, peace is not likely to be restored until both the principles and the pragmatics have been resolved.

The schemapiric principle

Although measurement began in the empirical mode, with the accent on the counting of moons and paces and warriors, it was destined in modern times to find itself debated in the formal, schematic, syntactical mode, where models can be made to bristle with symbols. Mathematics, which like logic constitutes a formal endeavor, was not always regarded as an arbitrary construction devoid of substantive content, an adventure of postulate and theorem. In early ages mathematics and empirical measurement were as warp and woof, interpenetrating each other so closely that our ancestors thought it proper to prove arithmetic theorems by resort to counting or to some other act of measurement. The divorce took place only in recent times. And mathematics now enjoys full freedom to "play upon symbols," as Gauss phrased it, with no constraints imposed by the demands of empirical measurement.

So also with other formal or schematic systems. The propositions of a formal logic express tautologies that say nothing about the world of tangible stuff. They are analytic statements, so-called, and they stand apart from the synthetic statements that express facts and relations among empirical objects. There is a useful distinction to be made between the analytic, formal, syntactical propositions of logic and the synthetic, empirical statements of substantive discourse.

Sometimes the line may be hard to draw. Quine [5] the logician denies, in fact, that any sharp demarcation can be certified, and debate on the issue between him and Carnap has reached classic if unresolved proportions. For the scientist, meanwhile, the usefulness of the formal-empirical distinction need not be imperiled by the difficulty of making rigorous decisions in borderline cases. It is useful to distinguish between day and night despite the penumbral passage through twilight. So also is it useful to tune ourselves to distinguish between the formally schematic and the empirically substantive.

Probability exhibits the same double aspect, the same schemapiric nature. Mathematical theories of probability inhabit the formal realm as analytic, tautologous, schematic systems, and they say nothing at all about dice, roulette, or lotteries. On the empirical level, however, we count and tabulate events at the gaming table or in the laboratory and note their relative frequencies. Sometimes the relative frequencies stand in isomorphic relation to some property of a mathematical model of probability; at other times the observed frequencies exhibit scant accord with "expectations."

Those features of statistics that invoke a probabilistic schema provide a further instance of a formal-empirical dichotomy: the distinction between the probability model and the statistical data. E. B. Wilson [6], mathematician and statistician, made the point "that one must distinguish critically between probability as a purely mathematical subject of one sort or another, and statistics which cannot be so regarded." Statistics, of course, is a young discipline—one whose voice changes depending on who speaks for it. Many spokesmen would want to broaden the meaning of statistics to include a formal, mathematical segment.

In another context N. R. Hanson [7] pressed a similar distinction when he said, "Mathematics and physics on this account seem *logically* different disciplines, such that the former can only occasionally solve the latter's problems." Indeed, as Hanson later exclaimed, "Physicists have in unison pronounced, 'Let no man join what nature hath sundered, namely, the *formal creation* of spaces and the physical *description* of bodies.'" Yet it is precisely by way of the proper and judicious joining of the schematic with the empirical that we achieve our beneficial and effective mappings of the universe—the schemapiric mappings known as science. The chronic danger lies in our failure to note the distinction between the map and the terrain, between the simulation and the simulated. The map is an analogue, a schema, a model, a theory. Each of those words has a separate flavor, but they all share a common core of meaning. "Contrary to general belief," wrote Simon and Newell [8], "there is no fundamental, 'in principle,' difference between theories and analogies. All theories are analogies, and all analogies are theories." Indeed, the same can be said for all the other terms that designate the associative binding of schematics to empirics—what I have called the schemapiric bond.

Scales and invariance

Although it could be otherwise if our choice dictated, most measurement involves the assignment of numbers to aspects of objects or events according to one or another rule or convention. The variety of rules invented thus far for the assignment of numbers has already grown enormous, and novel means of measuring continue to emerge. It has proved possible, however, to formulate an invariance criterion for the classification of scales of measurement [9]. The resulting systematization of scale types has found uses in contexts ranging from physics [10] to the social sciences [11], but the conception has not enjoyed immunity from criticism [12].

Let me sketch the theory. It can be done very briefly, because details are given in other places [13]. The theory proposes that a scale type is defined by the group of transformations under which the scale form remains invariant, as follows.

A *nominal scale* admits any one-to-one substitution of the assigned numbers. Example of a nominal scale: the numbering of football players.

An *ordinal scale* can be transformed by any increasing monotonic function. Example of an ordinal scale: the hardness scale determined by the ability of one mineral to scratch another.

An *interval scale* can be subjected to a linear transformation. Examples of interval scales: temperature Fahrenheit and Celsius, calendar time, potential energy.

A *ratio scale* admits only multiplication by a constant. Examples of ratio scales: length, weight, density, temperature Kelvin, time intervals, loudness in sones.

The foregoing scales represent the four types in common use. Other types are possible. The permissible transformations defining a scale type are those that keep intact the empirical information depicted by the scale. If the empirical information has been preserved, the scale form is said to remain invariant. The critical isomorphism is maintained. That indeed is the principle of invariance that lies at the heart of the conception. More formal presentations of the foregoing theory have been undertaken by other authors, a recent one, for example, by Lea [14].

Unfortunately, those who demand an abstract tidiness that is completely aseptic may demur at the thought that the decision whether a particular scale enjoys the privilege of a particular transformation group depends on something so ill defined as the preservation of empirical information. For one thing, an empirical operation is always attended by error. Thus Lebesgue [15], who strove so well to perfect the concept of mathematical measure, took explicit note that, in the assignment of number to a physical magnitude, precision can be pushed, as he said, "in actuality only up to a certain error. It never enables us," he continued, "to discriminate between one number and all the numbers that are extremely close to it."

A second disconcerting feature of the invariance criterion lies in the difficulty of specifying the empirical information that is to be preserved. What can it be other than the information that we think we have captured by creating the scale in the first place? We may, for example, perform operations that allow us simply to identify or discriminate a particular property of an object. Sometimes we want to preserve nothing more than that simple outcome, the identification or nominal classification of the items of interest. Or we may go further, provided our empirical operations permit, and determine rank orders, equal intervals, or equal ratios. If we want our number assignments to reflect one or another accrual in information, we are free to transform the scale numbers only in a way that does not lose or distort the desired information. The choice remains ours.

Although some writers have found it possible to read an element of prescription—even proscription—into the invariance principle, as a systematizing device the principle contains no normative force. It can be read more as a description of the obvious than as a directive. It says that, once an isomorphism has been mapped out between aspects of objects or events, on the one hand, and some one or more features of the number system, on the other hand, the isomorphism can be upset by whatever transformations fail to preserve it. Precisely what is preserved or not preserved in a particular circumstance depends upon the empirical operations. Since actual day-to-day measurements range from muddled to meticulous, our ability to classify them in terms of scale type must range from hopelessly uncertain to relatively secure.

The group invariance that defines a scale type serves in turn to delimit the statistical procedures that can be said to be appropriate to a given measurement scale [16]. Examples of appropriate statistics are tabulated in Table 1. Under the permissible transformations of a measurement scale, some appropriate statistics remain invariant in value (example: the correlation coefficient r keeps its value under

Table 1
Examples of statistical measures appropriate to measurements made on various types of scales. The scale type is defined by the manner in which scale numbers can be transformed without the loss of empirical informa-tion. The statistical measures listed are those that remain invariant, as regards either value or reference, under the transformations allowed by the scale type.

Scale Type	Measures of Location	Dispersion	Association or Correlation	Significance Tests
Nominal	Mode	Information H	Information transmitted T	Chi square Fisher's exact test
Ordinal	Median	Percentiles	Rank correlation	Sign test Run test
Interval	Arithmetic mean	Standard deviation Average deviation	Product-moment correlation Correlation ratio	t test F test
Ratio	Geometric mean Harmonic mean	Percent variation Decilog dispersion		

linear transformations). Other statistics change value but refer to the same item or location (example: the median changes its value but continues to refer to mid-distribution under ordinal transformations).

Reconciliation and new problems

Two developments may serve to ease the apprehension among those who may have felt threatened by a theory of measurement that seems to place bounds on our freedom to calculate. One is a clearer understanding of the bipartite, schemapiric nature of the scientific enterprise. When the issue concerns only the schema—when, for example, critical ratios are calculated for an assumed binomial distribution—then indeed it is purely a matter of relations within a mathematical model. Natural facts stand silent. Empirical considerations impose no constraints. When, however, the text asserts a relation among such things as measured differences or variabilities, we have a right and an obligation to inquire about the operations that underlie the measurements. Those operations determine, in turn, the type of scale achieved.

The two-part schemapiric view was expressed by Hays [17] in a much-praised book: "If the statistical method involves the procedures of arithmetic used on numerical scores, then the numerical answer is formally correct. ... The difficulty comes with the interpretation of these numbers back into statements about the real world. If nonsense is put into the mathematical system, nonsense is sure to come out."

At the level of the formal model, then, statistical computations may proceed as freely as in any other syntactical exercise, unimpeded by any material outcome of empirical measurement. Nor does measurement have a presumptive voice in the creation of the statistical models themselves. As Hogben [18] said in his forthright dissection of statistical theory, "It is entirely defensible to formulate an axiomatic approach to the theory of probability as an internally consistent set of propositions, if one is content to leave to those in closer contact with reality the last word on the usefulness of the outcome." Both Hays and Hogben insist that the user of statistics, the man in the laboratory, the maker of measurements, must decide the meaning of the numbers and their capacity to advance empirical inquiry.

The second road to reconciliation winds through a region only partly explored, a region wherein lies the pragmatic problem of appraising the wages of transgression. What is the degree of risk entailed when use is made of statistics that may be inappropriate in the strict sense that they fail the test of invariance under permissible scale transformations? Specifically, let us assume that a set of items can be set in rank order, but, by the operations thus far invented, distances between the items cannot be determined. We have an ordinal but not an interval scale. What happens then if interval-scale statistics are applied to the ordinally scaled items? Therein lies a question of first-rate substance and one that should be amenable to unemotional investigation. It promises well that a few answers have already been forthcoming.

First there is the oft-heeded counsel of common sense. In the averaging of test scores, says Mosteller [19], "It seems sensible to use the statistics appropriate to the type of scale I think I am near. In taking such action we may find the justification vague and fuzzy. One reason for this vagueness is that we have not yet studied enough about classes of scales, classes appropriate to real life measurement, with perhaps real life bias and error variance."

How some of the vagueness of which Mosteller spoke can perhaps be removed is illustrated by the study of Abelson and Tukey [20] who showed how bounds may be determined for the risk involved when an interval-scale statistic is used with an ordinal scale. Specifically, they explored the effect on r^2 of a game against nature in which nature does its best (or worst!) to minimize the value of r^2. In this game of regression analysis, many interesting cases were explored, but, as the authors said, their methods need extension to other cases. They noted that we often know more about ordinal data than mere rank order. We may have reason to believe, they said, "that the scale is no worse than mildly curvilinear, that Nature behaves smoothly in some sense." Indeed the continued use of parametric statistics with ordinal data rests on that belief, a belief sustained in large measure by the pragmatic usefulness of the results achieved.

In a more synthetic study than the foregoing analysis, Baker *et al.* [4] imposed sets of monotonic transformations on an assumed set of data, and calculated the effect on the t distribution. The purpose was to compare distributions of t for data drawn from an equal-interval scale with distributions of t for several types of assumed distortions of the equal intervals. By and large, the effects on the computed t distributions were not large, and the authors concluded "that strong statistics such as the t test are more than adequate to cope with weak [ordinal] measurements . . . ." It should be noted, however, that the values of t were affected by the nonlinear transformations. As the authors said, "The correspondence between values of t based on the criterion unit interval scores and values of t based on [nonlinear] transformations decreases regularly and dramatically . . . as the departure from linear transformations becomes more extreme."

Whatever the substantive outcome of such investigations may prove to be, they point the way to reconciliation through orderly inquiry. Debate gives way to calculation. The question is thereby made to turn, not on whether the measurement scale determines the choice of a statistical procedure, but on how and to what degree an inappropriate statistic may lead to a deviant conclusion. The solution of such problems may help to refurbish the complexion of measurement theory, which has been accused of proscribing those statistics that do not remain invariant under the transformations appropriate to a given scale. By spelling out the costs, we may convert the issue from a seeming proscription to a calculated risk.

The type of measurement achieved is not, of course, the only consideration affecting the applicability of parametric statistics. Bradley is one of many scholars who have sifted the consequences of violating the assumptions that underlie some of the common parametric tests [21]. As one outcome of his studies, Bradley concluded, "The contention that, when its assumptions are violated, a parametric test is still to be preferred to a distribution-free test because it is 'more efficient' is therefore a monumental *non sequitur*. The point is not at all academic . . . violations in a test's assumptions may be attended by profound changes in its power." That conclusion is not without relevance to scales of measurement, for when ordinal data are forced into the equal-interval mold, parametric assumptions are apt to be violated. It is then that a so-called distribution-free statistic may prove more efficient than its parametric counterpart.

Although better accommodation among certain of the contending statistical usages may be brought about by computer-aided studies, there remain many statistics that find their use only with specific kinds of scales. A single example may suffice. In a classic textbook, written with a captivating clarity, Peters and Van Voorhis [22] got hung up on a minor point concerning the procedure to be used in comparing variabilities. They noted that Karl Pearson had proposed a measure called the coefficient of variation, which expresses the standard deviation as a percentage of the mean. The authors expressed doubts about its value, however, because it tells "more about the extent to which the scores are padded by a dislocation of the zero point than it does about comparable variabilities." The examples and arguments given by the authors make it plain that the coefficient of variation has little business being used with what I have called interval scales. But since their book antedated my publication in 1946 of the defining invariances for interval and ratio scales, Peters and Van Voorhis did not have a convenient way to state the relationship made explicit in Table 1, namely, that the coefficient of variation, being itself a ratio, calls for a ratio scale.

Complexities and pitfalls

Concepts like relative variability have the virtue of being uncomplicated and easy for the scientist to grasp. They fit his idiom. But in the current statistics explosion, which showers the investigator with a dense fallout of new statistical models, the scientist is likely to lose the thread on many issues. It is then that the theory of measurement, with an anchor hooked fast in empirical reality, may serve as a sanctuary against the turbulence of specialized abstraction.

"As a mathematical discipline travels far from its empirical source," said von Neumann [23], "there is grave danger that the subject will develop along the line of least resistance, that the stream, so far from its source, will separate into a multitude of insignificant branches, and that the discipline will become a disorganized mass of details and complexities." He went on to say that, "After much 'abstract' in-breeding, a mathematical subject is in danger of degeneration. At the inception the style is usually classical; when it shows signs of becoming baroque, then the danger signal is up."

There is a sense, one suspects, in which statistics needs measurement more than measurement needs statistics. R. A. Fisher alluded to that need in his discourse on the nature of probability [24]. "I am quite sure," he said, "it is only personal contact with the business of the improvement of natural knowledge in the natural sciences that is capable to keep straight the thought of mathematically-minded people who have to grope their way through the complex entanglements of error . . . ."

And lest the physical sciences should seem immune to what Schwartz [25] called "the pernicious influence of mathematics," consider his diagnosis: "Thus, in its relations with science, mathematics depends on an intellectual effort outside of mathematics for the crucial specification of the approximation which mathematics is to take literally. Give a mathematician a situation which is the least bit ill-defined—he will first of all make it well defined. Perhaps appropriately, but perhaps also inappropriately . . . . That form of wisdom which is the opposite of singlemindedness, the ability to keep many threads in hand, to draw for an argument from many disparate sources, is quite foreign to mathematics . . . . Quite typically, science leaps ahead and mathematics plods behind."

Progress in statistics often follows a similar road from practice to prescription—from field trials to the formalization of principles.

As Kruskal [26] said, "Theoretical study of a statistical procedure often comes after its intuitive proposal and use." Unfortunately for the empirical concerns of the practitioners, however, there is, as Kruskal added, "almost no end to the possible theoretical study of even the simplest procedure." So the discipline wanders far from its empirical source, and form loses sight of substance.

Not only do the forward thrusts of science often precede the mopping-up campaigns of the mathematical schema builders, but measurement itself may often find implementation only after some basic conception has been voiced. Textbooks, those distilled artifices of science, like to picture scientific conceptions as built on measurement, but the working scientist is more apt to devise his measurements to suit his conceptions. As Kuhn [27] said, "The route from theory or law to measurement can almost never be traveled backwards. Numbers gathered without some knowledge of the regularity to be expected almost never speak for themselves. Almost certainly they remain just numbers." Yet who would deny that some ears, more tuned to numbers, may hear them speak in fresh and revealing ways?

The intent here is not, of course, to affront the qualities of a discipline as useful as mathematics. Its virtues and power are too great to need extolling, but in power lies a certain danger. For mathematics, like a computer, obeys commands and asks no questions. It will process any input, however devoid of scientific sense, and it will bedeck in formulas both the meaningful and the absurd. In the behavioral sciences, where the discernment for nonsense is perhaps less sharply honed than in the physical sciences, the vigil must remain especially alert against the intrusion of a defective theory merely because it carries a mathematical visa. An absurdity in full formularized attire may be more seductive than an absurdity undressed.

Distributions and decisions

The scientist often scales items, counts them, and plots their frequency distributions. He is sometimes interested in the form of such distributions. If his data have been obtained from measurements made on interval or ratio scales, the shape of the distribution stays put (up to a scale factor) under those transformations that are permissible, namely, those that preserve the empirical information contained in the measurements. The principle seems straightforward. But what happens when the state of the art can produce no more than a rank ordering, and hence nothing better than an ordinal scale? The abscissa of the frequency distribution then loses its metric meaning and becomes like a rubber band, capable of all sorts of monotonic stretchings. With each nonlinear transformation of the scale, the form of the distribution changes. Thereupon the distribution loses structure, and we find it futile to ask whether the shape approximates a particular form, whether normal, rectangular, or whatever.

Working on the formal level, the statistician may contrive a schematic model by first assuming a frequency function, or a distribution function, of one kind or another. At the abstract level of mathematical creation, there can, of course, be no quarrel with the statistician's approach to his task. The caution light turns on, however, as soon as the model is asked to mirror an empirical domain. We must then invoke a set of semantic rules—coordinating definitions—in order to identify correspondences between model and reality. What shall we say about the frequency function $f(x)$ when the problem before us allows only an ordinal scale? Shall x be subject to a nonlinear transformation after $f(x)$ has been specified? If so, what does the transformation do to the model and to the predictions it forecasts?

The scientist has reason to feel that a statistical model that specifies the form of a canonical distribution becomes uninterpretable when the empirical domain concerns only ordinal data. Yet many consumers of statistics seem to disregard what to others is a rather obvious and critical problem. Thus Burke [28] proposed to draw "two random samples from populations known to be normal" and then "to test the hypothesis that the two populations have the same mean . . . under the assumption that the scale is ordinal at best." How, we must ask, can normality be known when only order can be certified?

The assumption of normality is repeated so blithely and so often that it becomes a kind of incantation. If enough of us sin, perhaps transgression becomes a virtue. But in the instance before us, where the numbers to be fed into the statistical mill result from operations that allow only a rank ordering, maybe we have gone too far. Consider a permissible transformation. Let us cube all the numbers. The rank order would stand as before. But what do we then say about normality? If we can know nothing about the intervals on the scale of a variable, the postulation that a distribution has a particular form would appear to proclaim a hope, not a circumstance.

The assertion that a variable is normally distributed when the variable is amenable only to ordinal measurement may loom as an acute contradiction, but it qualifies as neither the worst nor the most frequent infraction by some of the practitioners of hypothesis testing. Scientific decision by statistical calculation has become the common mode in many behavioral disciplines. In six psychological journals [29], for example, the proportion of articles that employed one or another kind of inferential statistic rose steadily from 56 percent in 1948 to 91 percent in 1962. In the *Journal of Educational Psychology* the proportion rose from 36 to 100 percent.

What does it mean? Can no one recognize a decisive result without a significance test? How much can the burgeoning of computation be blamed on fad? How often does inferential computation serve as a premature excuse for going to press? Whether the scholar has discovered something or not, he can sometimes subject his data to an analysis of variance, a *t* test, or some other device that will produce a so-called objective measure of "significance." The illusion of objectivity seems to preserve itself despite the admitted necessity for the investigator to make improbable assumptions, and to pluck off the top of his head a figure for the level of probability that he will consider significant. His argument that convention has already chosen the level that he will use does not quite absolve him.

Lubin [30] has a name for those who censure the computational and applaud the experimental in the search for scientific certainty. He calls them stochastophobes. An apt title, if applied to those whose eagerness to lay hold on the natural fact may generate impatience at the gratuitous processing of data. The extreme stochastophobe is likely to ask: What scientific discoveries owe their existence to the techniques of statistical analysis or inference? If exercises in statistical inference have occasioned few instances of a scientific breakthrough, the stochastophobe may want to ask by what magical view the stochastophile perceives glamour in statistics. The charm may stem in part from the prestige that mathematics, however inapposite, confers on those who display the dexterity of calculation. For some stochastophiles the appeal may have no deeper roots than a preference for the prudent posture at a desk as opposed to the harsher, more venturesome stance in the field or the laboratory.

The aspersions voiced by stochastophobes fall mainly on those scientists who seem, by the surfeit of their statistical chants, to turn data treatment into hierurgy. These are not the statisticians themselves, for they see statistics for what it is, a straightforward discipline designed to amplify the power of common sense in the discernment of order amid complexity. By showing how to amend the mismatch in the impedance between question and evidence, the statistician improves the probability that our experiments will speak with greater clarity. And by weighing the entailments of relevant assumptions, he shows us how to milk the most from some of those fortuitous experiments that nature performs once and may never perform again. The stochastophobe should find no quarrel here. Rather he should turn his dispair into a hope that the problem of the relevance of this or that statistical model may lead the research man toward thoughtful inquiry, not to a reflex decision based on a burst of computation.

Measurement

If the vehemence of the debate that centers on the nature and conditions of statistical inference has hinted at the vulnerability of the conception, what can be said about the other partner in the enterprise? Is the theory of measurement a settled matter? Apparently not, for it remains a topic of trenchant inquiry, not yet ready to rest its case. And debate continues.

The typical scientist pays little attention to the theory of measurement, and with good reason, for the laboratory procedures for most measurements have been well worked out, and the scientist knows how to read his dials. Most of his variables are measured on well-defined, well-instrumented ratio scales.

Among those whose interests center on variables that are not reducible to meter readings, however, the concern with measurement stays acute. How, for example, shall we measure subjective value (what the economist calls utility), or perceived brightness, or the seriousness of crimes? Those are some of the substantive problems that have forced a revision in our approach to measurement. They have entailed a loosening of the restricted view bequeathed us by the tradition of Helmholtz and Campbell—the view that the axioms of additivity must govern what we call measurement [31]. As a related development, new axiomatic systems have appeared, including axioms by Luce and Tukey [32] for a novel "conjoint" approach to fundamental measurement. But the purpose here is not to survey the formal, schematic models that have flowered in the various sciences, for the practice and conception of measurement has as yet been little influenced by them.

As with many syntactical developments, measurement models sometimes drift off into the vacuum of abstraction and become decoupled from their concrete reference. Even those authors who freely admit the empirical features as partners in the formulation of measurement may find themselves seeming to downgrade the empirical in favor of the formal. Thus we find Suppes and Zinnes [33] saying, "Some writers . . . appear to define scales in terms of the existence of certain empirical operations . . . . In the present formulation of scale type, no mention is made of the kinds of 'direct' observations or empirical relations that exist . . . . Precisely what empirical operations are involved in the empirical system is of no consequence."

How then do we distinguish different types of scales? How, in particular, do we know whether a given scale belongs among the interval scales? Suppes and Zinnes gave what I think is a proper answer: "We ask if all the admissible numerical assignments are related by a linear transformation." That, however, is not a complete answer. There remains a further question: What is it that makes a class of numerical assignments admissible? A full theory of measurement cannot detach itself from the empirical substrate that gives it meaning. But the theorist grows impatient with the empirical lumps that ruffle the fine laminar flow within his models just as the laboratory fellow may distain the arid swirls of hieroglyphics that pose as paradigms of his measurements.

Although a congenial conciliation between those two polar temperaments, the modeler and the measurer, may lie beyond reasonable expectations, a tempering détente may prove viable. The two components of schemapirics must both be accredited, each in its own imperative role. To the understanding of the world about us, neither the formal model nor the concrete measure is dispensable.

Matching and mapping

Instead of starting with origins, many accounts of measurement begin with one or another advanced state of the measuring process, a state in which units and metrics can be taken for granted. At that level, the topic already has the crust of convention upon it, obscuring the deeper problems related to its nature.

If we try to push the problem of measurement back closer to its primordial operations, we find, I think, that the basic operation is always a process of matching. That statement may sound innocent enough, but it contains a useful prescription. It suggests, for example, that if you would understand the essence of a given measuring procedure, you should ask what was matched to what. If the query leads to a pointer reading, do not stop there; ask the same question about the calibration procedure that was applied to the instruments anterior to the pointer: What was matched to what? Diligent pursuit of that question along the chain of measuring operations leads to some of the elemental operations of science.

Or we may start nearer the primordium. The sketchiness of the record forces us to conjecture the earliest history, but quite probably our forefather kept score on the numerosity of his possessions with the aid of piles of pebbles [Latin: *calculi*] or by means of some other tallying device. He paired off items against pebbles by means of a primitive matching operation, and he thereby measured his hoard.

Let us pause at this point to consider the preceding clause. Can the ancestor in question be said to have measured his possessions if he had no number system? Not if we insist on taking literally the definition often given, namely, that measurement is the assignment of numbers to objects or events according to rule. This definition serves a good purpose in many contexts, but it presumes a stage of development beyond the one that we are now seeking to probe. In an elemental sense, the matching or assigning of numbers is a sufficient but not a necessary condition for measurement, for other kinds of matching may give measures.

Numbers presumably arose after our ancestor invented names for the collection of pebbles, or perhaps for the more convenient collections, the fingers. He could then match name to collection, and collection to possessions. That gave him a method of counting, for, by pairing off each item against a finger name in an order decided upon, the name of the collection of items, and hence the numerosity of the items, was specified.

The matching principle leads to the concept of cardinality. Two sets have the same cardinal number if they can be paired off in one-to-one relation to each other. By itself, this cardinal pairing off says nothing about order. (Dictionaries often disagree with the mathematicians on the definition of cardinality, but the mathematical usage recommends itself here.) We find the cardinal principle embodied in the symbols used for the numerals in many forms of writing. Thus the Roman numeral VI pictures a hand V and a finger I.

Let us return again to our central question. In the early cardinal procedure of matching item to item, fingers to items, or names to items, at what point shall we say that measurement began? Perhaps we had best not seek a line of demarcation between measurement and matching. It may be better to go all the way and propose an unstinted definition as follows: Measurement is the matching of an aspect of one domain to an aspect of another.

The operation of matching eventuates, of course, in one domain's being mapped into another, as regards one or more attributes of the two domains. In the larger sense, then, whenever a feature of one domain is mapped isomorphically in some relation with a feature of another domain, measurement is achieved. The relation is potentially symmetrical. Our hypothetical forefather could measure his collection of fish by means of his pile of pebbles, or his pile of pebbles by means of his collection of fish.

Our contemporary concern lies not, of course, with pebbles and fish, but with a principle. We need to break the hull that confines the custom of our thought about these matters. The concern is more than merely academic, however, especially in the field of psychophysics. One justification for the enlarged view of measurement lies in a development in sensory measurement known as cross-modality matching [34]. In a suitable laboratory setup, the subject is asked, for example, to adjust the loudness of a sound applied to his ears in order to make it seem equal to the perceived strength of a vibration applied to his finger. The amplitude of the vibration is then changed and the matching process is repeated. An equal sensation function is thereby mapped out, as illustrated in Fig. 1. Loudness has been matched in that manner to ranges of values on some ten other perceptual continua, always with the result that the matching function approximates a power function [35]. In other words, in order to produce equal apparent intensity, the amplitude of the sound p must be a power function of the amplitude of the vibration a, or $p = a^b$, where b is the exponent. Or, more simply, the logarithms of the stimuli are linearly related, which means that ratios of stimuli are proportional.

Experiments suggest that the power function obtains between all pairs of intensive perceptual continua, and that the matchings exhibit a strong degree of transitivity in the sense that the exponents form an interconnected net. If two matching functions have one continuum

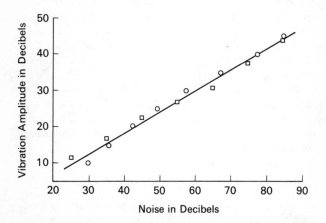

Fig. 1
Equal-sensation function for cross-modality matching between loudness and vibration. The squares indicate that the observers adjusted the intensity of vibration on the fingertip to match the loudness of a noise delivered by earphones. The circles indicate that the observers adjusted the loudness to match the vibration. Each point is the decibel average of 20 matches, two by each of ten observers. Since the coordinates are logarithmic, the straight line indicates a power function.

in common, we can predict fairly well the exponent of the matching function between the other two continua.

Now, once we have mapped out the matching function between loudness and vibration, we can, if we choose, measure the subjective strength of the vibration in terms of its equivalent loudness. Or, more generally, if all pairs of continua have been matched, we can select any one continuum to serve as the reference continuum in terms of which we then measure the subjective magnitude on each of the other continua.

In the description of a measurement system that rests on cross-modality matching, no mention has been made of numbers. If we are willing to start from scratch in a measurement of this kind, numbers can in principle be dispensed with. They would, to be sure, have practical uses in the conduct of the experiments, but by using other signs or tokens to identify the stimuli we could presumably eliminate numbers completely. It would be a tour de force, no doubt, but an instructive one.

Instead of dispensing with numbers, the practice in many psychophysical studies has been to treat numbers as one of the perceptual continua in the cross-modality matching experiment. Thus in what has come to be known as the method of magnitude estimation, numbers are matched to loudness, say. In the reverse procedure, called magnitude production, the subject adjusts the loudness to match a series of numbers given by the experimenter [36]. And as might be expected, despite all the other kinds of cross-modality matches that have been made, it is the number continuum that most authors select as the reference continuum (exponent = 1.0) in terms of which the exponent values for the other perceptual continua are stated. But the point deserves to be stressed: the choice of number as the reference continuum is wholly arbitrary, albeit eminently convenient.

Summary

Back in the days when measurement meant mainly counting, and statistics meant mainly the inventory of the state, the simple descriptive procedures of enumeration and averaging occasioned minimum conflict between measurement and statistics. But as measurement pushed on into novel behavioral domains, and statistics turned to the formalizing of stochastic models, the one-time intimate relation between the two activities dissolved into occasional misunderstanding. Measurement and statistics must live in peace, however, for both must participate in the schemapiric enterprise by which the schematic model is made to map the empirical observation.

Science presents itself as a two-faced, bipartite endeavor looking at once toward the formal, analytic, schematic features of model-building, and toward the concrete, empirical, experimental observations by which we test the usefulness of a particular representation. Schematics and empirics are both essential to science, and full understanding demands that we know which is which.

Measurement provides the numbers that enter the statistical table. But the numbers that issue from measurements have strings attached, for they carry the imprint of the operations by which they were obtained. Some transformations on the numbers will leave intact the information gained by the measurements; other transformations will destroy the desired isomorphism between the measurement scale and the property assessed. Scales of measurement therefore find a useful classification on the basis of a principle of invariance: each of the common scale types (nominal, ordinal, interval, and ratio) is defined by a group of transformations that leaves a particular isomorphism unimpaired.

Since the transformations allowed by a given scale type will alter the numbers that enter into a statistical procedure, the procedure ought properly to be one that can withstand that particular kind of number alteration. Therein lies the primacy of measurement: it sets bounds on the appropriateness of statistical operations. The widespread use on ordinal scales of statistics appropriate only to interval or ratio scales can be said to violate a technical canon, but in many instances the outcome has demonstrable utility. A few workers have begun to assess the degree of risk entailed by the use of statistics that do not remain invariant under the permissible scale transformations.

The view is proposed that measurement can be most liberally construed as the process of matching elements of one domain to those of another domain. In most kinds of measurement we match numbers to objects or events, but other matchings have been found to serve a useful purpose. The cross-modality matching of one sensory continuum to another has shown that sensory intensity increases as the stimulus intensity raised to a power. The generality of that finding supports a psychophysical law expressible as a simple invariance: equal stimulus ratios produce equal sensation ratios.

References and notes

1. L. Humphreys, *Contemp. Psychol.*, **9**, 76 (1964).
2. N. H. Anderson, *Psychol. Bull.*, **58**, 305 (1961).
3. I. R. Savage, *J. Amer. Statist. Ass.*, **52**, 331 (1957).

4. B. O. Baker, C. D. Hardyck, L. F. Petrinovich, *Educ. Psychol. Meas.*, **26,** 291 (1966).

5. W. V. O. Quine, *The Ways of Paradox and Other Essays.* Random House, New York, 1966. Pp. 126–134.

6. E. B. Wilson, *Proc. Natl. Acad. Sci. U.S.*, **51,** 539 (1964).

7. N. R. Hanson, *Philos. Sci.*, **30,** 107 (1963).

8. H. A. Simon and A. Newell. In *The State of the Social Sciences*, L. D. White, Ed. Univ. of Chicago Press, Chicago, 1956. Pp. 66–83.

9. S. S. Stevens, *Science*, **103,** 677 (1946).

10. F. B. Silsbee, *J. Wash. Acad. Sci.*, **41,** 213 (1951).

11. B. F. Green. In *Handbook of Social Psychology*, G. Lindzey, Ed. Addison-Wesley, Reading, Mass., 1954. Pp. 335–369.

12. Among those who have commented are B. Ellis, *Basic Concepts of Measurement.* University Press, Cambridge, England, 1966; B. Grunstra, "On Distinguishing Types of Measurement." *Boston Studies Phil. Sci.*, **4,** (Humanities Press, in press); S. Ross, *Logical Foundations of Psychological Measurement.* Scandinavian University Books, Munksgaard, Copenhagen, 1964; W. W. Rozeboom, *Synthese*, **16,** 170–233 (1966); W. S. Torgerson, *Theory and Methods of Scaling.* Wiley, New York, 1958.

13. S. S. Stevens. In *Handbook of Experimental Psychology*, S. S. Stevens, Ed. Wiley, New York, 1951. Pp. 1–49; S. S. Stevens. In *Measurement: Definitions and Theories*, C. W. Churchman and P. Ratoosh, Eds. Wiley, New York, 1959. Pp. 18–64.

14. W. A. Lea, "A Formalization of Measurement Scale Forms." Technical Memo. KCT-024, Computer Research Lab., NASA Electronics Res. Ctr., Cambridge, Mass., June 1967.

15. H. Lebesgue, *Measure and the Integral*, K. O. May, Ed. Holden-Day, San Francisco, 1966.

16. Other summarizing tables are presented by V. Senders, *Measurement and Statistics.* Oxford Univ. Press, New York, 1958. A further analysis of appropriate statistics has been presented by E. W. Adams, R. F. Fagot, R. E. Robinson, *Psychometrika*, **30,** 99 (1965).

17. W. L. Hays, *Statistics for Psychologists.* Holt, Rinehart & Winston, New York, 1963.

18. L. Hogben, *Statistical Theory.* Norton, New York, 1958.

19. F. Mosteller, *Psychometrika*, **23,** 279 (1958).

20. R. P. Abelson and J. W. Tukey, *Efficient Conversion of Non-Metric Information into Metric Information.* Amer. Statist. Ass., Social Statist. Sec.,

December 1959. Pp. 226–230; see also R. P. Abelson and J. W. Tukey, *Ann. Math. Stat.* **34,** 1347 (1963).

21. J. V. Bradley, "Studies in Research Methodology: II. Consequences of Violating Parametric Assumptions—Facts and Fallacy." WADC Tech. Rep. 58-574 [II], Aerospace Med. Lab., Wright-Patterson AFB, Ohio, September 1959.

22. C. C. Peters and W. R. Van Voorhis, *Statistical Procedures and Their Mathematical Bases.* McGraw-Hill, New York, 1940.

23. J. von Neumann. In *The Works of the Mind*, R. B. Heywood, Ed. Univ. of Chicago Press, Chicago, 1947. Pp. 180–196.

24. R. A. Fisher, *Smoking, the Cancer Controversy.* Oliver and Boyd, Edinburgh, 1959.

25. J. Schwartz. In *Logic, Methodology and Philosophy of Science*, E. Nagel *et al.,* Eds. Stanford Univ. Press, Stanford, Calif., 1962. Pp. 356–360.

26. W. R. Kruskal. In *International Encyclopedia of the Social Sciences.* Macmillan and Free Press, New York, 1968. Vol. 15, pp. 206–224.

27. T. S. Kuhn. In *Quantification*, H. Woolf, Ed. Bobbs-Merrill, Indianapolis, Ind., 1961. Pp. 31–63.

28. C. J. Burke. In *Theories in Contemporary Psychology*, M. H. Marx, Ed. Macmillan, New York, 1963. Pp. 147–159.

29. The journals were tabulated by E. S. Edgington, *Amer. Psychologist*, **19,** 202 (1964); also personal communication.

30. A. Lubin. In *Annual Review of Psychology*. Annual Reviews, Palo Alto, Calif., 1962. Vol. 13, pp. 345–370.

31. H. v. Helmholtz, "Zählen und Messen." In *Philosophische Aufsätze*. Fues's Verlag, Leipzig, 1887. Pp. 17–52; N. R. Campbell, *Physics: the Elements* [1920] (reissued as *The Philosophy of Theory and Experiment* by Dover, New York, 1957); N. R. Campbell, *Symposium: Measurement and Its Importance for Philosophy.* Aristotelian Soc., suppl., vol. 17. Harrison and Sons, London, 1938.

32. R. D. Luce and J. W. Tukey, *J. Math. Psychol.,* **1,** 1 (1964).

33. P. Suppes and J. L. Zinnes. In *Handbook of Mathematical Psychology*, R. D. Luce *et al.,* Eds. Wiley, New York, 1963. Pp. 1–76.

34. S. S. Stevens, *J. Exp. Psychol.,* **57,** 201 (1959); *Amer. Sci.,* **54,** 385 (1966).

35. S. S. Stevens, *Percept. Psychophys.,* **1,** 5 (1966).

36. S. S. Stevens and H. B. Greenbaum, *ibid.,* p. 439.

37. This article (Laboratory of Psychophysics Rept. PPR-336-118) was prepared with support from NIII grant NB-02974 and NSF grant GB-3211.

block 2

7. "Student." The probable error of a mean. *Biometrika*, 1908, **6,** 1–25.

8. Sandler, Joseph. A test of the significance of the difference between the means of correlated measures based on a simplification of Student's *t*. *Brit. J. Psychol.*, 1955, **46,** Part 3, 225–226.

9. Runyon, R. Note on use of the *A* statistic as a substitute for *t* in the one-sample case. *Psych. Rep.*, 1968, **22,** 361–362.

10. Anderson, N. On teaching *F* instead of *t*. *J. Expt'l. Educ.*, 1960, **28,** No. 3, 261–263.

11. Cohen, J. The statistical power of abnormal-social psychological research: a review. *J. of Abn. & Soc. Psychol.*, 1962, **65,** 145–153.

12. Walker, Helen M. Degrees of freedom. *J. Educ. Psychol.*, 1940, **31,** 253–269.

In 1908 a British statistician named William S. Gosset published an article which revolutionized hypothesis testing with small samples. In this article, entitled "The probable error of the mean," he demonstrated that the normal distribution does not adequately describe the distribution of means of small *N*'s.

Gosset published this article under the pseudonym of "Student" in compliance with the policies of the Guinness brewery where he served as an adviser. The well known t-distributions were introduced by this eminent statistician and the corresponding test statistic is often referred to as "Student's t-ratio."

Student's paper is included in its original form. Where the mathematical arguments are beyond the scope of the reader, they may be omitted without any loss in the continuity of the discussion.

Student developed the t-statistic for use with correlated as well as uncorrelated samples. Sandler's article provides a convenient mathematically equivalent substitute for the t-ratio whenever correlated samples are employed. The Runyon article extends the Sandler A statistic to the one-sample case.

The remaining articles in Block 2 deal with broad issues relating to hypothesis testing.

Anderson questions the need for the t-ratio since F is equivalent to t in the one-degree-of-freedom situation.

Cohen, turning his attention to the important concept of power, examined over 70 published research studies and found that the probability of rejecting a false null hypothesis in social psychological research is distressingly low.

The concept of degrees of freedom is lucidly discussed in Walker's paper, showing why it is important and how to determine degrees of freedom.

7

the probable error
of a mean

Student

Introduction

Any experiment may be regarded as forming an individual of a "population" of experiments which might be performed under the same conditions. A series of experiments is a sample drawn from this population.

Now any series of experiments is only of value in so far as it enables us to form a judgment as to the statistical constants of the population to which the experiments belong. In a great number of cases the question finally turns on the value of a mean, either directly, or as the mean differences between the two quantities.

If the number of experiments be very large, we may have precise information as to the value of the mean, but if our sample be small, we have two sources of uncertainty: (1) owing to the "error of random sampling" the mean of our series of experiments deviates more or less widely from the mean of the population, and (2) the sample is not sufficiently large to determine what is the law of distribution of individuals. It is usual, however, to assume a normal distribution, because, in a very large number of cases, this gives an approximation so close that a small sample will give no real information as to the

Reprinted from *Biometrika* 6, 1–25 (1908), by permission of the publisher.

manner in which the population deviates from normality: since some law of distribution must be assumed it is better to work with a curve whose area and ordinates are tabled, and whose properties are well known. This assumption is accordingly made in the present paper, so that its conclusions are not strictly applicable to populations known not to be normally distributed; yet it appears probable that the deviation from normality must be very extreme to lead to serious error. We are concerned here solely with the first of these two sources of uncertainty.

The usual method of determining the probability that the mean of the population lies within a given distance of the mean of the sample, is to assume a normal distribution about the mean of the sample with a standard deviation equal to $s/\sqrt{n}$, where s is the standard deviation of the sample, and to use the tables of the probability integral.

But, as we decrease the number of experiments, the value of the standard deviation found from the sample of experiments becomes itself subject to an increasing error, until judgments reached in this way may become altogether misleading.

In routine work there are two ways of dealing with this difficulty: (1) an experiment may be repeated many times, until such a long series is obtained that the standard deviation is determined once and for all with sufficient accuracy. This value can then be used for subsequent shorter series of similar experiments. (2) Where experiments are done in duplicate in the natural course of the work, the mean square of the difference between corresponding pairs is equal to the standard deviation of the population multiplied by $\sqrt{2}$. We can thus combine together several series of experiments for the purpose of determining the standard deviation. Owing however to secular change, the value obtained is nearly always too low, successive experiments being positively correlated.

There are other experiments, however, which cannot easily be repeated very often; in such cases it is sometimes necessary to judge of the certainty of the results from a very small sample, which itself affords the only indication of the variability. Some chemical, many biological, and most agricultural and large scale experiments belong to this class, which has hitherto been almost outside the range of statistical enquiry.

Again, although it is well known that the method of using the normal curve is only trustworthy when the sample is "large," no one has yet told us very clearly where the limit between "large" and "small' samples is to be drawn.

The aim of the present paper is to determine the point at which we may use the tables of the probability integral in judging of the significance of the mean of a series of experiments, and to furnish alternative tables for use when the number of experiments is too few.

The paper is divided into the following nine sections:

1. The equation is determined of the curve which represents the frequency distribution of standard deviations of samples drawn from a normal population.

2. There is shown to be no kind of correlation between the mean and the standard deviation of such a sample.

3. The equation is determined of the curve representing the frequency distribution of a quantity z, which is obtained by dividing the distance between the mean of a sample and the mean of the population by the standard deviation of the sample.

4. The curve found in (1) is discussed.

5. The curve found in (3) is discussed.

6. The two curves are compared with some actual distributions.

7. Tables of the curves found in (3) are given for samples of different size.

8 and 9. The tables are explained and some instances are given of their use.

10. Conclusions.

Section 1

Samples of n individuals are drawn out of a population distributed normally, to find an equation which shall represent the frequency of the standard deviations of these samples.

If s be the standard deviation found from a sample $x_1 x_2 \cdots x_n$ (all these being measured from the mean of the population), then

$$s^2 = \frac{S(x_1^2)}{n} - \left(\frac{S(x_1)}{n}\right)^2 = \frac{S(x_1^2)}{n} - \frac{S(x_1^2)}{n^2} - \frac{2S(x_1 x_2)}{n^2}.$$

Summing for all samples and dividing by the number of samples we get the mean value of s^2 which we will write $\bar{s}^2$,

$$\bar{s}^2 = \frac{n\mu_2}{n} - \frac{n\mu_2}{n^2} = \frac{\mu_2(n-1)}{n},$$

where μ_2 is the second moment coefficient in the original normal distribution of x: since x_1, x_2, etc., are not correlated and the distribution is normal, products involving odd powers of x_2 vanish on summing, so that $2S(x_1 x_2)/n^2$ is equal to 0.

If M'_n represent the Rth moment coefficient of the distribution of s^2 about the end of the range where $s^2 = 0$,

$$M'_1 = \mu_2 \frac{(n-1)}{n}.$$

Again

$$s^4 = \left\{ \frac{S(x_1^2)}{n} - \left(\frac{S(x_1)}{n} \right)^2 \right\}^2$$

$$= \left(\frac{S(x_1^2)}{n} \right)^2 - \frac{2S(x_1^2)}{n} \left(\frac{S(x_1)}{n} \right)^2 + \left(\frac{S(x_1)}{n} \right)^4$$

$$= \frac{S(x_1^4)}{n^2} + \frac{2S(x_1^2 x_2^2)}{n^2} - \frac{2S(x_1^4)}{n^3} - \frac{4S(x_1^2 x_2^2)}{n^3} + \frac{S(x_1^4)}{n^4}$$

$$+ \frac{6S(x_1^2 x_2^2)}{n^4} + \text{other terms involving odd powers of } x_1 \text{ etc.,}$$
$$\text{which will vanish on summation.}$$

Now $S(x_1^4)$ has n terms but $S(x_1^2 x_2^2)$ has $\frac{1}{2}n(n-1)$, hence summing for all samples and dividing by the number of samples we get

$$M'_2 = \frac{\mu_4}{n} + \mu_2^2 \frac{(n-1)}{n} - \frac{2\mu_4}{n^2} - 2\mu_2^2 \frac{(n-1)}{n^2} + \frac{\mu_4}{n^3} + 3\mu_2^2 \frac{(n-1)}{n^3}$$

$$= \frac{\mu_4}{n^3} \{n^2 - 2n + 1\} + \frac{\mu_2^2}{n^3}(n-1)\{n^2 - 2n + 3\}.$$

Now since the distribution of x is normal, $u_4 = 3\mu_2^2$, hence

$$M'_2 = \mu_2^2 \frac{(n-1)}{n^3} \{3n - 3 + n^2 - 2n + 3\} = \mu_2^2 \frac{(n-1)(n+1)}{n^2}.$$

In a similar tedious way I find:

$$M'_3 = \mu_2^3 \frac{(n-1)(n+1)(n+3)}{n^3},$$

and

$$M'_4 = \mu_2^4 \frac{(n-1)(n+1)(n+3)(n+5)}{n^4}.$$

The law of formation of these moment coefficients appears to be a simple one, but I have not seen my way to a general proof.

If now M_R be the Rth moment coefficient of s^2 about its mean, we have

$$M_2 = \mu_2^2 \frac{(n-1)}{n^2}\{(n+1)-(n-1)\} = 2\mu_2^2 \frac{(n-1)}{n^2},$$

$$M_3 = \mu_2^3 \left\{ \frac{(n-1)(n+1)(n+3)}{n^3} - \frac{3(n-1)}{n} \cdot \frac{2(n-1)}{n^2} - \frac{(n-1)^3}{n^3} \right\}$$

$$= \mu_2^3 \frac{(n-1)}{n^3}\{n^2 + 4n + 3 - 6n + 6 - n^2 + 2n - 1\}$$

$$= 8\mu_2^3 \frac{(n-1)}{n^3},$$

$$M_4 = \frac{\mu_2^4}{n^4}\{(n-1)(n+1)(n+3)(n+5)$$
$$- 32(n-1)^2 - 12(n-1)^3 - (n-1)^4\}$$

$$= \frac{\mu_2^4(n-1)}{n^4}\{n^3 + 9n^2 + 23n + 15 - 32n + 32$$
$$- 12n^2 + 24n - 12 - n^3 + 3n^2 - 3n + 1\}$$

$$= \frac{12\mu_2^4(n-1)(n+3)}{n^4}.$$

Hence

$$\beta_1 = \frac{M_3^2}{M_2^3} = \frac{8}{n-1}, \qquad \beta_2 = \frac{M_4}{M_2^2} = \frac{3(n+3)}{n-1},$$

$$\therefore \quad 2\beta_2 - 3\beta_1 - 6 = \frac{1}{n-1}\{6(n+3) - 24 - 6(n-1)\} = 0.$$

Consequently a curve of Professor Pearson's type III may be expected to fit the distribution of s^2.

The equation referred to an origin at the zero end of the curve will be

$$y = Cx^p e^{-\gamma x},$$

where

$$\gamma = 2\frac{M_2}{M_3} = \frac{4\mu_2^2(n-1)n^3}{8n^2\mu_2^3(n-1)} = \frac{n}{2\mu_2},$$

and

$$p = \frac{4}{\beta_1} - 1 = \frac{n-1}{2} - 1 = \frac{n-3}{2}.$$

Consequently the equation becomes

$$y = Cx^{(n-3)/2}e^{-nx/2\mu_2},$$

which will give the distribution of s^2.

The area of this curve is

$$C\int_0^\infty x^{(n-3)/2}e^{-nx/2\mu_2}\,dx = I \quad \text{(say)}.$$

The first moment coefficient about the end of the range will therefore be

$$\frac{C\int_0^\infty x^{(n-1)/2}e^{-nx/2\mu_2}\,dx}{I} = \frac{C[(-2\mu_2/n)x^{(n-1)/2}e^{-nx/2\mu_2}]_{x=0}^{x=\infty}}{I}$$
$$+ \frac{C\int_0^\infty [(n-1)/n]\mu_2 x^{(n-3)/2}e^{-nx/2\mu_2}\,dx}{I}.$$

The first part vanishes at each limit and the second is equal to

$$\frac{[(n-1)/n]\mu_2 I}{I} = \frac{n-1}{n}\mu_2,$$

and we see that the higher moment coefficients will be formed by multiplying successively by $[(n+1)/n]\mu_2$, $[(n+3)/n]\mu_2$, etc., just as appeared to be the law of formation of M_2', M_3', M_4', etc.

Hence it is probable that the curve found represents the theoretical distribution of s^2; so that although we have no actual proof we shall assume it to do so in what follows.

The distribution of s may be found from this, since the frequency of s is equal to that of s^2 and all that we must do is to compress the base line suitably.

Now if

$$y_1 = \phi(s^2) \text{ be the frequency curve of } s^2$$

and

$$y_2 = \psi(s) \text{ be the frequency curve of } s,$$

then

$$y_1\,d(s^2) = y_2\,ds,$$

or

$$y_2\,ds = 2y_1 s\,ds,$$

$$\therefore \quad y_2 = 2sy_1.$$

Hence

$$y_2 = 2Cs(s^2)^{(n-3)/2}e^{-ns^2/2\mu_2}$$

is the distribution of s.

This reduces to

$$y_2 = 2Cs^{n-2}e^{-ns^2/2\mu_2}.$$

Hence $y = Ax^{n-2}e^{-nx^2/2\sigma^2}$ will give the frequency distribution of standard deviations of samples of n, taken out of a population distributed normally with standard deviation σ. The constant A may be found by equating the area of the curve as follows:

$$\text{Area} = A\int_0^\infty x^{n-2}e^{-nx^2/2\sigma^2}\, dx. \quad \left(\text{Let } I_p \text{ represent } \int_0^\infty x^p e^{-nx^2/2\sigma^2}\, dx.\right)$$

Then

$$I_p = \frac{\sigma^2}{n}\int_0^\infty x^{p-1}\frac{d}{dx}\left(-e^{-nx^2/2\sigma^2}\right)\, dx$$

$$= \frac{\sigma^2}{n}\left[-x^{p-1}e^{-nx^2/2\sigma^2}\right]_{x=0}^{x=\infty} + \frac{\sigma^2}{n}(p-1)\int_0^\infty x^{p-2}e^{-nx^2/2\sigma^2}\, dx$$

$$= \frac{\sigma^2}{n}(p-1)I_{p-2x}$$

since the first part vanishes at both limits.

By continuing this process we find

$$I_{n-2} = \left(\frac{\sigma^2}{n}\right)^{(n-2)/2}(n-3)(n-5)\cdots 3\cdot 1 I_0$$

or

$$= \left(\frac{\sigma^2}{n}\right)^{(n-3)/2}(n-3)(n-5)\cdots 4\cdot 2 I_1$$

according as n is even or odd.

But I_0 is

$$\int_0^\infty e^{-nx^2/2\sigma^2}\, dx = \sqrt{\frac{\pi}{2n}}\,\sigma,$$

and I_1 is

$$\int_0^\infty xe^{-nx^2/2\sigma^2}\, dx = \left[-\frac{\sigma^2}{n}e^{-nx^2/2\sigma^2}\right]_{x=0}^{x=\infty} = \frac{\sigma^2}{n}.$$

Hence if n be even,

$$A = \frac{\text{Area}}{(n-3)(n-5)\cdots 3\cdot 1\sqrt{\frac{\pi}{2}}\left(\frac{\sigma^2}{n}\right)^{(n-1)/2}},$$

and if n be odd

$$A = \frac{\text{Area}}{(n-3)(n-5)\cdots 4\cdot 2\left(\frac{\sigma^2}{n}\right)^{(n-1)/2}}.$$

Hence the equation may be written

$$y = \frac{N}{(n-3)(n-5)\cdots 3\cdot 1}\sqrt{\frac{2}{\pi}}\left(\frac{n}{\sigma^2}\right)^{(n-1)/2}x^{n-2}e^{-nx^2/2\sigma^2} \quad (n\text{ even})$$

or

$$y = \frac{N}{(n-3)(n-5)\cdots 4\cdot 2}\left(\frac{n}{\sigma^2}\right)^{(n-1)/2}x^{n-2}e^{-nx^2/2\sigma^2} \quad (n\text{ odd})$$

where N as usual represents the total frequency.

Section 2

To show that there is no correlation between (a) the distance of the a sample from the mean of the population and (b) the standard deviation of a sample with normal distribution.

1. Clearly positive and negative positions of the mean of the sample are equally likely, and hence there cannot be correlation between the absolute value of the distance of the mean from the mean of the population and the standard deviation, but

2. there might be correlation between the square of the distance and the square of the standard deviation.

Let

$$u^2 = \left(\frac{S(x_1)}{n}\right)^2 \quad \text{and} \quad s^2 = \frac{S(x_1^2)}{n} - \left(\frac{S(x_1)}{n}\right)^2.$$

Then if m_1', M_1' be the mean values of u^2 and s^2, we have by the preceding part

$$M_1' = \mu_2\frac{(n-1)}{n} \quad \text{and} \quad m_1' = \frac{\mu_2}{n}.$$

Now

$$u^2 s^2 = \frac{S(x_1^2)}{n}\left(\frac{S(x_1)}{n}\right)^2 - \left(\frac{S(x_1)}{n}\right)^4$$

$$= \left(\frac{S(x_1^2)}{n}\right)^2 + 2\frac{S(x_1 x_2)\cdot S(x_1^2)}{n^3} - \frac{S(x_1^4)}{n^4}$$

$$- \frac{6x_1^2 x_2^2}{n^4} -\text{ other terms of odd order which will vanish on summation.}$$

Summing for all values and dividing by the number of cases we get

$$R_{u^2 s^2}\sigma_{u^2}\sigma_{s^2} + m_1 M_1 = \frac{\mu_4}{n^2} + \mu_2^2\frac{(n-1)}{n^2} - \frac{\mu_4}{n^3} - 3\mu_2^2\frac{(n-1)}{n^3},$$

where $R_{u^2 s^2}$ is the correlation between u^2 and s^2.

$$R_{u^2 s^2}\sigma_{u^2}\sigma_{s^2} + \mu_2^2\frac{(n-1)}{n^2} = \mu_2^2\frac{(n-1)}{n^3}\{3+n-3\} = \mu_2^2\frac{(n-1)}{n^2}.$$

Hence $R_{u^2 s^2}\sigma_{u^2}\sigma_{s^2} = 0$ or there is no correlation between u^2 and s^2.

Section 3

To find the equation representing the frequency distribution of the means of samples of n drawn from a normal population, the mean being expressed in terms of the standard deviation of the sample.

We have $y = (C/\sigma^{n-1})s^{n-2}e^{-ns^2/2\sigma^2}$ as the equation representing the distribution of s, the standard deviation of a sample of n, when the samples are drawn from a normal population with standard deviation σ.

Now the means of these samples of n are distributed according to the equation

$$y = \frac{\sqrt{n}\,N}{\sqrt{2\pi}\,\sigma}e^{-nx^2/2\sigma^2} *$$

and we have shown that there is no correlation between x, the distance of the mean of the sample, and s, the standard deviation of the sample.

Now let us suppose x measured in terms of s; i.e., let us find the distribution of $z = x/s$.

If we have $y_1 = \phi(x)$ and $y_2 = \psi(z)$ as the equations representing

---

*   Airy, *Theory of Errors of Observations*, Part II. §6.

the frequency of x and of z respectively, then

$$y_1 \, dx = y_2 \, dz = y_2 \frac{dx}{s},$$

$$\therefore \quad y_2 = sy_1.$$

Hence

$$y = \frac{N\sqrt{n}\, s}{\sqrt{2\pi}\,\sigma} e^{-ns^2 z^2/2\sigma^2}$$

is the equation representing the distribution of z for samples of n with standard deviation s.

Now the chance that s lies between s and $s + ds$ is:

$$\frac{\int_s^{s+ds} (C/\sigma^{n-1}) s^{n-2} e^{-ns^2/2\sigma^2} \, ds}{\int_0^{\infty} (C/\sigma^{n-1}) s^{n-2} e^{-ns^2/2\sigma^2} \, ds},$$

which represents the N in the above equation.

Hence the distribution of z due to values of s which lie between s and $s + ds$ is

$$y = \frac{\int_s^{s+ds} (C/\sigma^n) \sqrt{n/2\pi}\, s^{n-1} e^{-ns^2(1+z^2)/2\sigma^2} \, ds}{\int_0^{\infty} (C/\sigma^{n-1}) s^{n-2} e^{-ns^2/2\sigma^2} \, ds}$$

$$= \frac{\sqrt{n/2\pi} \int_s^{s+ds} s^{n-1} e^{-ns^2(1+z^2)/2\sigma^2} \, ds}{\sigma \int_0^{\infty} s^{n-2} e^{-ns^2/2\sigma^2} \, ds},$$

and summing for all values of s we have as an equation giving the distribution of z

$$y = \frac{\sqrt{n/2\pi}}{\sigma} \frac{\int_0^{\infty} s^{n-1} e^{-ns^2(1+z^2)/2\sigma^2} \, ds}{\int_0^{\infty} s^{n-2} e^{-ns^2/2\sigma^2} \, ds}.$$

By what we have already proved this reduces to

$$y = \frac{1}{2} \frac{n-2}{n-3} \cdot \frac{n-4}{n-5} \cdots \frac{5}{4} \cdot \frac{3}{2} (1 + z^2)^{-n/2} \qquad \text{if } n \text{ be odd,}$$

and to

$$y = \frac{1}{\pi} \frac{n-2}{n-3} \cdot \frac{n-4}{n-5} \cdots \frac{4}{3} \cdot \frac{2}{1} (1 + z^2)^{-n/2} \qquad \text{if } n \text{ be even.}$$

Since this equation is independent of σ it will give the distribution of the distance of the mean of a sample from the mean of the population expressed in terms of the standard deviation of the sample for any normal population.

Section 4

Some properties of the
standard deviation
frequency curve

By a similar method to that adopted for finding the constant we may find the mean and moments: thus the mean is at I_{n-1}/I_{n-2}, which is equal to

$$\frac{(n-2)}{(n-3)}\frac{(n-4)}{(n-5)}\cdots\frac{2}{1}\sqrt{\frac{2}{\pi}}\frac{\sigma}{\sqrt{n}} \qquad \text{if } n \text{ be even,}$$

or

$$\frac{(n-2)}{(n-3)}\frac{(n-4)}{(n-5)}\cdots\frac{3}{2}\sqrt{\frac{\pi}{2}}\frac{\sigma}{\sqrt{n}} \qquad \text{if } n \text{ be odd.}$$

The second moment about the end of the range is

$$\frac{I_n}{I_{n-2}} = \frac{(n-1)\sigma^2}{n}.$$

The third moment about the end of the range is equal to

$$\frac{I_{n+1}}{I_{n-2}} = \frac{I_{n+1}}{I_{n-1}} \cdot \frac{I_{n-1}}{I_{n-2}}$$
$$= \sigma^2 \times \text{the mean.}$$

The fourth moment about the end of the range is equal to

$$\frac{I_{n+2}}{I_{n-2}} = \frac{(n-1)(n+1)}{n^2}\sigma^4.$$

If we write the distance of the mean from the end of the range $D\sigma/\sqrt{n}$ and the moments about the end of the range v_1, v_2, etc., then

$$v_1 = \frac{D\sigma}{\sqrt{n}}, \qquad v_2 = \frac{n-1}{n}\sigma^2, \qquad v_3 = \frac{D\sigma^3}{\sqrt{n}}, \qquad v_4 = \frac{n^2-1}{n^2}\sigma^4.$$

From this we get the moments about the mean:

$$\mu_2 = \frac{\sigma^2}{n}(n - 1 - D^2),$$

$$\mu_3 = \frac{\sigma^3}{n\sqrt{n}}\{nD - 3(n - 1)D + 2D^3\} = \frac{\sigma^3 D}{n\sqrt{n}}\{2D^2 - 2n + 3\},$$

$$\mu_4 = \frac{\sigma^2}{n^2}\{n^2 - 1 - 4D^2n + 6(n - 1)D^2 - 3D^4\}$$

$$= \frac{\sigma^4}{n^2}\{n^2 - 1 - D^2(3D^2 - 2n + 6)\}.$$

It is of interest to find out what these become when n is large.

In order to do this we must find out what is the value of D.

Now Wallis's expression for π derived from the infinite product value of $\sin x$ is

$$\frac{\pi}{2}(2n + 1) = \frac{2^2 \cdot 4^2 \cdot 6^2 \cdots (2n)^2}{1^2 \cdot 3^2 \cdot 5^2 \cdots (2n - 1)^2}.$$

If we assume a quantity $\theta(= a_0 + (a_1/n) + \text{etc.})$ which we may add to the $2n + 1$ in order to make the expression approximate more rapidly to the truth, it is easy to show that $\theta = -(1/2) + (1/16n) - \text{etc.}$, and we get

$$\frac{\pi}{2}\left(2n + \frac{1}{2} + \frac{1}{16n}\right) = \frac{2^2 \cdot 4^2 \cdot 6^2 \cdots (2n)^2}{1^2 \cdot 3^2 \cdot 5^2 \cdots (2n - 1)^2}. \ *$$

From this we find that whether n be even or odd D^2 approximates to $n - (3/2) + (1/8n)$ when n is large.

Substituting this value of D we get

$$\mu_2 = \frac{\sigma^2}{2n}\left(1 - \frac{1}{4n}\right),$$

$$\mu_3 = \frac{\sigma^3\sqrt{1 - (3/2n) + (1/16n^2)}}{4n^2},$$

$$\mu_4 = \frac{3\sigma^4}{4n^2}\left(1 + \frac{1}{2n} - \frac{1}{16n^2}\right).$$

---

* This expression will be found to give a much closer approximation to π than Wallis's.

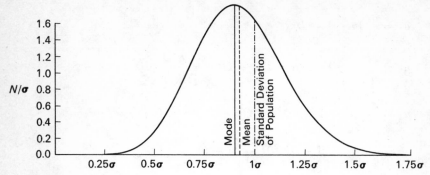

Fig. 1
Frequency curve giving the distribution of standard deviations of samples of 10 taken from a normal population.

Equation $y = \dfrac{N}{7 \cdot 5 \cdot 3} \dfrac{10^{9/2}}{\sigma^9} \sqrt{\dfrac{2}{\pi}} x^8 e^{-10x^2/2\sigma^2}.$

Consequently the value of the standard deviation of a standard deviation which we have found

$$\left(\frac{\sigma}{\sqrt{2n} \sqrt{1 - 1/4n}} \right)$$

becomes the same as that found for the normal curve by Professor Pearson $(\sigma/\sqrt{2n})$ when n is large enough to neglect the $1/4n$ in comparison with 1.

Neglecting terms of lower order than $1/n$ we find

$$\beta_1 = \frac{2n - 3}{n(4n - 3)}, \qquad \beta_2 = 3 \left(1 - \frac{1}{2n} \right)\left(1 + \frac{1}{2n} \right).$$

Consequently as n increases, β_2 very soon approaches the value 3 of the normal curve, but β_1 vanishes more slowly, so that the curve remains slightly skew.

Figure 1 shows the theoretical distribution of the S.D. found from samples of 10.

$$y = \frac{N10^{9/2}}{7 \cdot 5 \cdot 3} \sqrt{\frac{2}{\pi}} \frac{x^8}{\sigma^9} e^{-10x^2/2\sigma^2}.$$

Section 5

Some properties
of the curve

$$y = \frac{n-2}{n-3} \cdot \frac{n-4}{n-5} \cdots \left(\begin{array}{ll} \frac{4}{3} \cdot \frac{2}{\pi} & \text{if } n \text{ be even} \\[2mm] \frac{5}{4} \cdot \frac{3}{2} & \text{if } n \text{ be odd} \end{array} \right) (1 + z^2)^{-n/2}.$$

Writing $z = \tan \theta$ the equation becomes

$$y = \frac{n-2}{n-3} \cdot \frac{n-4}{n-5} \cdots \text{etc.} \times \cos^n \theta,$$

which affords an easy way of drawing the curve. Also $dz = d\theta/\cos^2 \theta$.
Hence to find the area of the curve between any limits we must find

$$\frac{n-2}{n-3} \cdot \frac{n-4}{n-5} \cdots \text{etc.} \times \int \cos^{n-2}\theta \, d\theta$$

$$= \frac{n-2}{n-3} \cdot \frac{n-4}{n-5} \cdots \text{etc.} \left\{ \frac{n-3}{n-2} \int \cos^{n-4} \theta \, d\theta + \left[\frac{\cos^{n-3} \theta \sin \theta}{n-2} \right] \right\}$$

$$= \frac{n-4}{n-5} \cdot \frac{n-6}{n-7} \cdots \text{etc.} \int \cos^{n-4} \theta \, d\theta$$

$$+ \frac{1}{n-3} \cdot \frac{n-4}{n-5} \cdots \text{etc.} \left[\cos^{n-3} \theta \sin \theta \right],$$

and by continuing the process the integral may be evaluated.
For example, if we wish to find the area between 0 and θ for $n = 8$ we have

$$\text{area} = \frac{6}{5} \cdot \frac{4}{3} \cdot \frac{2}{1} \cdot \frac{1}{\pi} \int_0^\theta \cos^6 \theta \, d\theta$$

$$= \frac{4}{3} \cdot \frac{2}{\pi} \int_0^\theta \cos^4 \theta \, d\theta + \frac{1}{5} \cdot \frac{4}{3} \cdot \frac{2}{\pi} \cos^5 \theta \sin \theta$$

$$= \frac{\theta}{\pi} + \frac{1}{\pi} \cos \theta \sin \theta + \frac{1}{3} \cdot \frac{2}{\pi} \cos^3 \theta \sin \theta + \frac{1}{5} \cdot \frac{4}{3} \cdot \frac{2}{\pi} \cos^5 \theta \sin \theta,$$

and it will be noticed that for $n = 10$ we shall merely have to add to this same expression the term

$$\frac{1}{7} \cdot \frac{6}{5} \cdot \frac{4}{3} \cdot \frac{2}{\pi} \cos^7 \theta \sin \theta.$$

The tables at the end of the paper give the area between $-\infty$ and z (or $\theta = -\pi/2$ and $\theta = \tan^{-1} z$).

This is the same as 5 plus the area between $\theta = 0$, and $\theta = \tan^{-1} z$, and as the whole area of the curve is equal to 1, the tables give the probability that the mean of the sample does not differ by more than z times the standard deviation of the sample from the mean of the population.

The whole area of the curve is equal to

$$\frac{n-2}{n-3} \cdot \frac{n-4}{n-5} \cdots \text{etc.} \times \int_{-\pi/2}^{+\pi/2} \cos^{n-2} \theta \, d\theta,$$

and since all the parts between the limits vanish at both limits this reduces to 1.

Similarly the second moment coefficient is equal to

$$\frac{n-2}{n-3} \cdot \frac{n-4}{n-5} \cdots \text{etc.} \times \int_{-\pi/2}^{+\pi/2} \cos^{n-2} \theta \tan^2 \theta \, d\theta$$

$$= \frac{n-2}{n-3} \cdot \frac{n-4}{n-5} \cdots \text{etc.} \times \int_{-\pi/2}^{+\pi/2} (\cos^{n-4} \theta - \cos^{n-2} \theta) \, d\theta$$

$$= \frac{n-2}{n-3} - 1$$

$$= \frac{1}{n-3}.$$

Hence the standard deviation of the curve is $1/\sqrt{n-3}$. The fourth moment coefficient is equal to

$$\frac{n-2}{n-3} \cdot \frac{n-4}{n-5} \cdots \text{etc.} \times \int_{-\pi/2}^{+\pi/2} \cos^{n-2} \theta \tan^4 \theta \, d\theta$$

$$= \frac{n-2}{n-3} \cdot \frac{n-4}{n-5} \cdots \text{etc.} \times \int_{-\pi/2}^{+\pi/2} (\cos^{n-6} \theta - 2 \cos^{n-4} \theta + \cos^{n-2} \theta) \, d\theta$$

$$= \frac{n-2}{n-3} \cdot \frac{n-4}{n-5} - \frac{2(n-2)}{n-3} + 1 = \frac{3}{(n-3)(n-5)}.$$

The odd moments are of course zero as the curve is symmetrical, so

$$\beta_1 = 0, \qquad \beta_2 = \frac{3(n-3)}{n-5} = 3 + \frac{2}{5}.$$

Hence as n increases the curve approaches the normal curve whose standard deviation is $1/\sqrt{n-3}$.

β_2 however is always greater than 3, indicating that large deviations are more common than in the normal curve.

I have tabled the area for the normal curve with standard deviation $1/\sqrt{7}$ so as to compare with my curve for $n = 10$.* It will be seen that

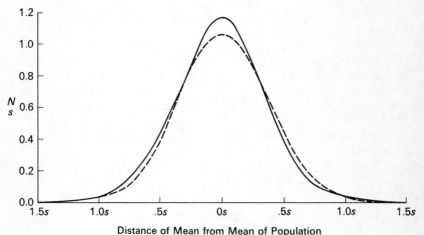

$\frac{N}{s}$

Distance of Mean from Mean of Population

Fig. 2
Solid curve:

$$y = \frac{N}{S} \times \frac{8}{7} \cdot \frac{6}{5} \cdot \frac{4}{3} \cdot \frac{2}{\pi} \cos^{10} \theta, \qquad x/s = \tan \theta.$$

Broken line curve:

$$y = \frac{\sqrt{7} \cdot N}{\sqrt{2\pi} \cdot s} e^{-7x^2/2s^2},$$

the normal curve with the same S.D.

---

* See p. 91.

odds laid according to either table would not seriously differ till we reach $z = .8$, where the odds are about 50 to 1 that the mean is within that limit z beyond that the normal curve gives a false feeling of security, for example, according to the normal curve it is 99,986 to 14 (say 7,000 to 1) that the mean of the population lies between $-\infty$ and $+1.3s$ whereas the real odds are only 99,819 to 181 (about 550 to 1).

Now 50 to 1 corresponds to three times the probable error in the normal curve and for most purposes would be considered significant; for this reason I have only tabled my curves for values of n not greater than 10, but have given the $n = 9$ and $n = 10$ tables to one further place of decimals. They can be used as foundations for finding values for larger samples.*

The table for $n = 2$ can be readily constructed by looking out $\theta = \tan^{-1} z$ in Chambers' Tables and then $.5 + \theta/\pi$ gives the corresponding value.

Similarly $\frac{1}{2} \sin \theta + .5$ gives the values when $n = 3$.

There are two points of interest in the $n = 2$ curve. Here s is equal to half the distance between the two observations. $\tan^{-1}(s/s) = \pi/4$ so that between $+s$ and $-s$ lies $2 \times (\pi/4) \times (1/\pi)$ or half the probability, i.e., if two observations have been made and we have no other information, it is an even chance that the mean of the (normal) population will lie between them. On the other hand the second moment coefficient is

$$\frac{1}{\pi} \int_{-\pi/2}^{+\pi/2} \tan^2 \theta \, d\theta = \frac{1}{\pi} \left[\tan \theta - \theta \right]_{-\pi/2}^{\pi/2} = \infty,$$

or the standard deviation is infinite while the probable error is finite.

Section 6

Practical test of the
foregoing equations

Before I had succeeded in solving my problem analytically, I had endeavoured to do so empirically. The material used was a correlation table containing the height and left middle finger measurements of 3,000 criminals, from a paper by W. R. Macdonell (*Biometrika*, **1**,

---

*   E.g., if $n = 11$, to the corresponding value for $n = 9$, we add $\frac{7}{8} \times \frac{5}{6} \times \frac{3}{4}$ $\times \frac{1}{2} \times \frac{1}{2} \cos^8 \theta \sin \theta$: if $n = 13$ we add as well $\frac{9}{10} \times \frac{7}{8} \times \frac{5}{6} \times \frac{3}{4} \times \frac{1}{2} \times \frac{1}{2}$ $\cos^{10} \theta \sin \theta$ and so on.

p. 219). The measurements were written out on 3,000 pieces of cardboard, which were then very thoroughly shuffled and drawn at random. As each card was drawn its numbers were written down in a book which thus contains the measurements of 3,000 criminals in a random order. Finally each consecutive set of 4 was taken as a sample—750 in all—and the mean, standard deviation, and correlation* of each sample determined. The difference between the mean of each sample and the mean of the population was then divided by the standard deviation of the sample, giving us the z of Section 3.

This provides us with two sets of 750 standard deviations and two sets of 750 z's on which to test the theoretical results arrived at. The height and left middle finger correlation table was chosen because the distribution of both was approximately normal and the correlation was fairly high. Both frequency curves, however, deviate slightly from normality, the constants being for height $\beta_1 = .0026$, $\beta_2 = 3.175$, and for left middle finger lengths $\beta_1 = .0030$, $\beta_2 = 3.140$, and in consequence there is a tendency for a certain number of larger standard deviations to occur than if the distributions were normal. This, however, appears to make very little difference to the distribution of z.

Another thing which interferes with the comparison is the comparatively large groups in which the observations occur. The heights are arranged in 1 inch groups, the standard deviation being only 2.54 inches: while the finger lengths were originally grouped in millimetres, but unfortunately I did not at the time see the importance of having a smaller unit, and condensed them into two millimetre groups, in terms of which the standard deviation is 2.74.

Several curious results follow from taking samples of 4 from material disposed in such wide groups. The following points may be noticed:

1.   The means only occur as multiples of .25.

2.   The standard deviations occur as the square roots of the following types of numbers n, $n + .19$, $n + .25$, $n + .50$, $n + .69$, $2n + .75$.

3.   A standard deviation belonging to one of these groups can only be associated with a mean of a particular kind; thus a standard deviation of $\sqrt{2}$ can only occur if the mean differs by a whole number from the group we take as origin, while $\sqrt{1.69}$ will only occur when the mean is at $n \pm .25$.

---

*   I hope to publish the results of the correlation work shortly.

4.   All the four individuals of the sample will occasionally come from the same group, giving a zero value for the standard deviation. Now this leads to an infinite value of z and is clearly due to too wide a grouping, for although two men may have the same height when measured by inches, yet the finer the measurements the more seldom will they be identical, till finally the chance that four men will have *exactly* the same height is infinitely small. If we had smaller grouping the zero values of the standard deviation might be expected to decrease, and a similar consideration will show that the smaller values of the standard deviation would also be likely to increase, such as .436, when 3 fall in one group and 1 in an adjacent group, or .50 when 2 fall in two adjacent groups. On the other hand when the individuals of the sample lie far apart, the argument of Sheppard's correction will apply, the real value of the standard deviation being more likely to be smaller than that found owing to the frequency in any group being greater on the side nearer the mode.

These two effects of grouping will tend to neutralise each other in their effect on the mean value of the standard deviation, but both will increase the variability.

Accordingly we find that the mean value of the standard deviation is quite close to that calculated, while in each case the variability is sensibly greater. The fit of the curve is not good, both for this reason and because the frequency is not evenly distributed owing to effects (2) and (3) of grouping. On the other hand the fit of the curve giving the frequency of z is very good and as that is the only practical point the comparison may be considered satisfactory.

The following are the figures for height:

Mean value of standard deviations: calculated $2.027 \pm .021$
Mean value of standard deviations: observed $\underline{2.026}$
$$\text{difference} = -.001$$

Standard deviation of standard deviations:

calculated $.8556 \pm .015$
observed $\underline{.9066}$
difference $= +.0510$

In tabling the observed frequency, values between .0125 and .0875 were included in one group, while between .0875 and .0125 they were divided over the two groups. As an instance of the irregularity due

Comparison of fit. Theoretical equation:

$$y = \frac{16 \times 750}{\sqrt{2\pi}\,\sigma^3}\, x^2 e^{-2x^2/\sigma^2}.$$

Scale in Terms of Standard Deviation of Population	0 to .1	.1 to .2	.2 to .3	.3 to .4	.4 to .5	.5 to .6	.6 to .7	.7 to .8	.8 to .9
Calculated frequency	$1\frac{1}{2}$	$10\frac{1}{2}$	27	$45\frac{1}{2}$	$64\frac{1}{2}$	$78\frac{1}{2}$	87	88	$81\frac{1}{2}$
Observed frequency	3	$14\frac{1}{2}$	$24\frac{1}{2}$	$37\frac{1}{2}$	107	67	73	77	$77\frac{1}{2}$
Difference	$+1\frac{1}{2}$	$+4$	$-2\frac{1}{2}$	-8	$+42\frac{1}{2}$	$-11\frac{1}{2}$	-14	-11	-4

Scale in Terms of Standard Deviation of Population	.9 to 1.0	1.0 to 1.1	1.1 to 1.2	1.2 to 1.3	1.3 to 1.4	1.4 to 1.5	1.5 to 1.6	1.6 to 1.7	Greater Than 1.7
Calculated frequency	71	58	45	33	23	15	$9\frac{1}{2}$	$5\frac{1}{2}$	7
Observed frequency	64	$52\frac{1}{2}$	$49\frac{1}{2}$	35	28	$12\frac{1}{2}$	9	$11\frac{1}{2}$	7
Difference	-7	$-5\frac{1}{2}$	$+4\frac{1}{2}$	$+2$	$+5$	$-2\frac{1}{2}$	$-\frac{1}{2}$	$+6$	0

whence $\chi^2 = 48.06$, $P = .00006$ (about).

to grouping I may mention that there were 31 cases of standard deviations 1.30 (in terms of the grouping) which is .5117 in terms of the standard deviation of the population, and they were therefore divided over the groups .4 to .5 to .6. Had they all been counted in groups .5 to .6, χ^2 would have fallen to 29.85 and P would have risen to .03. The χ^2 test presupposes *random* sampling from a frequency following the given law, but this we have not got owing to the interference of the grouping.

When, however, we test the z's where the grouping has not had so much effect we find a close correspondence between the theory and the actual result.

There were three cases of infinite values of z which, for the reasons given above, were given the next largest values which occurred, namely $+6$ or -6. The rest were divided into groups of .1, .04, .05, and .06, being divided between the two groups on either side.

The calculated value for the standard deviation of the frequency curve was 1 ($\pm.017$) while the observed was 1.039. The value of the standard deviation is really infinite, as the fourth moment coefficient is infinite, but as we have arbitrarily limited the infinite cases we may take as an approximation

Comparison of fit. Theoretical equation:

$$y = \frac{2}{\pi}\cos^4 \theta, \qquad z = \tan \theta.$$

Scale of z	Less Than −3.05	−3.05 to −2.05	−2.05 to −1.55	−1.55 to −1.05	−1.05 to −.75	−.75 to −.45	−.45 to −.15	−.15 to +.15
Calculated frequency	5	$9\frac{1}{2}$	$13\frac{1}{2}$	$34\frac{1}{2}$	$44\frac{1}{2}$	$78\frac{1}{2}$	119	141
Observed frequency	9	$14\frac{1}{2}$	$11\frac{1}{2}$	33	$43\frac{1}{2}$	$70\frac{1}{2}$	$119\frac{1}{2}$	$151\frac{1}{2}$
Difference	$+4$	$+5$	-2	$-1\frac{1}{2}$	-1	-8	$+\frac{1}{2}$	$+10\frac{1}{2}$

Scale of z	+.15 to +.45	+.45 to +.75	+.75 to +1.05	+1.05 to +1.55	+1.55 to +2.05	+2.05 to +3.05	More Than +3.05
Calculated frequency	119	$78\frac{1}{2}$	$44\frac{1}{2}$	$34\frac{1}{2}$	$13\frac{1}{2}$	$9\frac{1}{2}$	5
Observed frequency	122	$67\frac{1}{2}$	49	$26\frac{1}{2}$	16	10	6
Difference	$+3$	-11	$+4\frac{1}{2}$	-8	$+2\frac{1}{2}$	$+\frac{1}{2}$	$+1$

whence $\chi^2 = 12.44$, $P = 56$.

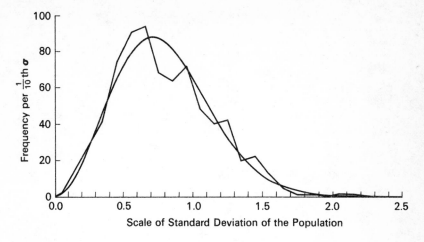

Fig. 3
Comparison of calculated standard deviation frequency curve with 750 actual standard deviations.

This is very satisfactory, especially when we consider that as a rule observations are tested against curves fitted from the mean and one or more other moments of the observations, so that considerable correspondence is only to be expected; while this curve is exposed to the full errors of random sampling, its constants having been calculated quite apart from the observations.

The left middle finger samples show much the same features as those of the height, but as the grouping is not so large compared to the variability the curves fit the observations more closely. Figures 3* and 4 give the standard deviations and the z's for this set of samples. The results are as follows:

Mean value of standard deviations: calculated 2.186 ± .023
Mean value of standard deviations; observed   2.179

$$\text{difference} = -.007$$

Standard deviation of standard deviations:

calculated	.9224 ± .016
observed	.9802

difference = + .0578

---

*   There are three small mistakes in plotting the observed values in Fig. 3, which make the fit appear worse than it really is.

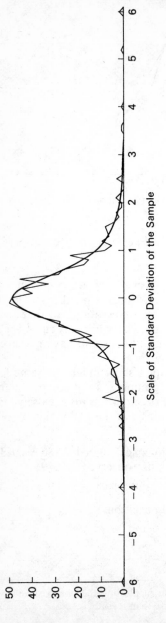

Fig. 4
Comparison of the theoretical frequency curve

$$y = \frac{1{,}500}{\pi}\left(1 + \frac{x^2}{s^2}\right)^{-2},$$

with an actual sample of 750 cases.

Comparison of fit. Theoretical equation:

$$y = \frac{16 \times 750}{\sqrt{2\pi}\,\sigma^3}\, x^2 e^{-2x^2/\sigma^2}.$$

Scale in Terms of Standard Deviation of Population	0 to .1	.1 to .2	.2 to .3	.3 to .4	.4 to .5	.5 to .6	.6 to .7	.7 to .8	.8 to .9
Calculated frequency	$1\frac{1}{2}$	$10\frac{1}{2}$	27	$45\frac{1}{2}$	$64\frac{1}{2}$	$78\frac{1}{2}$	87	88	$81\frac{1}{2}$
Observed frequency	2	14	$27\frac{1}{2}$	51	$64\frac{1}{2}$	91	$94\frac{1}{2}$	$68\frac{1}{2}$	$65\frac{1}{2}$
Difference	$+\frac{1}{2}$	$+3\frac{1}{2}$	$+\frac{1}{2}$	$+5\frac{1}{2}$	—	$+12\frac{1}{2}$	$+7\frac{1}{2}$	$-19\frac{1}{2}$	-16

Scale in Terms of Standard Deviation of Population	.9 to 1.0	1.0 to 1.1	1.1 to 1.2	1.2 to 1.3	1.3 to 1.4	1.4 to 1.5	1.5 to 1.6	1.6 to 1.7	Greater Than 1.7
Calculated frequency	71	58	45	33	23	15	$9\frac{1}{2}$	$5\frac{1}{2}$	7
Observed frequency	73	$48\frac{1}{2}$	$40\frac{1}{2}$	$42\frac{1}{2}$	20	$22\frac{1}{2}$	12	5	$7\frac{1}{2}$
Difference	$+2$	$-9\frac{1}{2}$	$-4\frac{1}{2}$	$+9\frac{1}{2}$	-3	$+7\frac{1}{2}$	$+2\frac{1}{2}$	$-\frac{1}{2}$	$+\frac{1}{2}$

whence $\chi^2 = 21.80$, $P = .19$.

Calculated value of standard deviation 1 ($\pm.017$)
Observed value of standard deviation   .982
difference $= -.018$

Comparison of fit. Theoretical equation:

$$y = \frac{2}{\pi} \cos^4 \theta, \qquad z = \tan \theta.$$

Scale of z	Less Than −3.05	−3.05 to −2.05	−2.05 to −1.55	−1.55 to −1.05	−1.05 to −.75	−.75 to −.45	−.45 to −.15	−.15 to +.15
Calculated frequency	5	$9\frac{1}{2}$	$13\frac{1}{2}$	$34\frac{1}{2}$	$44\frac{1}{2}$	$78\frac{1}{2}$	119	141
Observed frequency	4	$15\frac{1}{2}$	18	$33\frac{1}{2}$	44	75	122	138
Difference	−1	+6	$+4\frac{1}{2}$	−1	$-\frac{1}{2}$	$-3\frac{1}{2}$	+3	−3

Scale of z	+.15 to +.45	+.45 to +.75	+.75 to +1.05	+1.05 to +1.55	+1.55 to +2.05	+2.05 to +3.05	More Than +3.05
Calculated frequency	119	$78\frac{1}{2}$	$44\frac{1}{2}$	$34\frac{1}{2}$	$13\frac{1}{2}$	$9\frac{1}{2}$	5
Observed frequency	$120\frac{1}{2}$	71	$46\frac{1}{2}$	36	11	9	6
Difference	$+1\frac{1}{2}$	$-7\frac{1}{2}$	+2	$+1\frac{1}{2}$	$-2\frac{1}{2}$	$-\frac{1}{2}$	+1

whence $\chi^2 = 7.39$, $P = .92$.

A very close fit.

We see then that if the distribution is approximately normal our theory gives us a satisfactory measure of the certainty to be derived from a small sample in both the cases we have tested; but we have an indication that a fine grouping is of advantage. If the distribution is not normal, the mean and the standard deviation of a sample will be positively correlated, so that although both will have greater variability, yet they will tend to counteract each other, a mean deviating largely from the general mean tending to be divided by a larger standard deviation. Consequently I believe that the tables at the end of the present paper may be used in estimating the degree of certainty arrived at by the mean of a few experiments, in the case of most laboratory or biological work where the distributions are as a rule of a "cocked hat" type and so sufficiently nearly normal.

Section 7
Tables of

$$\frac{n-2}{n-3} \frac{n-4}{n-5} \cdots \left(\begin{array}{l} \dfrac{3 \cdot 1}{2 \cdot 2} \; n \text{ odd} \\[2ex] \dfrac{2}{1} \cdot \dfrac{1}{\pi} \; n \text{ even} \end{array} \right) \int_{-\pi/2}^{\tan^{-1}z} \cos^{n-2} \theta \, d\theta$$

for values of n from 4 *to* 10 *inclusive*
together with

$$\frac{\sqrt{7}}{\sqrt{2\pi}} \int_{-\infty}^{x} e^{-7x^2/2} \, dx$$

for comparison when n = 10.

$z\left(=\dfrac{x}{s}\right)$	$n=4$	$n=5$	$n=6$	$n=7$	$n=8$	$n=9$	$n=10$	For Comparison $\left(\dfrac{\sqrt{7}}{\sqrt{2\pi}}\int_{-\infty}^{x} e^{-7x^2/2}\,dx\right)$
.1	.5633	.5745	.5841	.5928	.6006	.60787	.61462	.60411
.2	.6241	.6458	.6634	.6798	.6936	.70705	.71846	.70159
.3	.6804	.7096	.7340	.7549	.7733	.78961	.80423	.78641
.4	.7309	.7657	.7939	.8175	.8376	.85465	.86970	.85520
.5	.7749	.8131	.8428	.8667	.8863	.90251	.91609	.90691
.6	.8125	.8518	.8813	.9040	.9218	.93600	.94732	.94375
.7	.8440	.8830	.9109	.9314	.9468	.95851	.96747	.96799
.8	.8701	.9076	.9332	.9512	.9640	.97328	.98007	.98253
.9	.8915	.9269	.9498	.9652	.9756	.98279	.98780	.99137
1.0	.9092	.9419	.9622	.9751	.9834	.98890	.99252	.99592

(cont.)

$z\left(=\dfrac{x}{s}\right)$	$n = 4$	$n = 5$	$n = 6$	$n = 7$	$n = 8$	$n = 9$	$n = 10$	For Comparison $\left(\dfrac{\sqrt{7}}{\sqrt{2\pi}}\displaystyle\int_{-\infty}^{x} e^{-7x^2/2}\,dx\right)$
1.1	.9236	.9537	.9714	.9821	.9887	.99280	.99539	.99819
1.2	.9354	.9628	.9782	.9870	.9922	.99528	.99713	.99925
1.3	.9451	.9700	.9832	.9905	.9946	.99688	.99819	.99971
1.4	.9531	.9756	.9870	.9930	.9962	.99791	.99885	.99989
1.5	.9598	.9800	.9899	.9948	.9973	.99859	.99926	.99996
1.6	.9653	.9836	.9920	.9961	.9981	.99903	.99951	.99999
1.7	.9699	.9864	.9937	.9970	.9986	.99933	.99968	
1.8	.9737	.9886	.9950	.9977	.9990	.99953	.99978	
1.9	.9770	.9904	.9959	.9983	.9992	.99967	.99985	
2.0	.9797	.9919	.9967	.9986	.9994	.99976	.99990	
2.1	.9821	.9931	.9973	.9989	.9996	.99983	.99993	
2.2	.9841	.9941	.9978	.9992	.9997	.99987	.99995	
2.3	.9858	.9950	.9982	.9993	.9998	.99991	.99996	
2.4	.9873	.9957	.9985	.9995	.9998	.99993	.99997	
2.5	.9886	.9963	.9987	.9996	.9998	.99995	.99998	
2.6	.9898	.9967	.9989	.9996	.9999	.99996	.99999	
2.7	.9908	.9972	.9991	.9997	.9999	.99997	.99999	
2.8	.9916	.9975	.9992	.9998	.9999	.99998	.99999	
2.9	.9924	.9978	.9993	.9998	.9999	.99998	.99999	
3.0	.9931	.9981	.9994	.9998	—	.99999	—	—

Section 8

Explanation of tables

The tables give the probability that the value of the mean, measured from the mean of the population, in terms of the standard deviation of the sample, will lie between $-\infty$ and z. Thus, to take the table for samples of six, the probability of the mean of the population lying between $-\infty$ and once the standard deviation of the sample is .9622 or the odds are about 24 to 1 that the mean of the population lies between these limits.

The probability is therefore .0378 that it is greater than once the standard deviation and .0756 that it lies outside ± 1.0 times the standard deviation.

Section 9

Illustrations of method

Illustration 1. As an instance of the kind of use which may be made of the tables, I take the following figures from a table by A. R. Cushny and A. R. Peebles in the *Journal of Physiology* for 1904, showing the different effects of the optical isomers of hyoscyamine hydrobromide in producing sleep. The sleep of 10 patients was measured without hypnotic and after treatment (1) with D. hyoscyamine hydrobromide, (2) with L. hyoscyamine hydrobromide. The average number of hours' sleep gained by the use of the drug is tabulated below.

The conclusion arrived at was that in the usual dose, 2 was, but 1 was not, of value as a soporific.

Additional hours' sleep gained by the use of hyoscyamine hydrobromide.

Patient	(Dextro-)	2 (Laevo-)	Difference (2–1)
1.	+ .7	+1.9	+1.2
2.	−1.6	+ .8	+2.4
3.	− .2	+1.1	+1.3
4.	−1.2	+ .1	+1.3
5.	−1	− .1	0
6.	+3.4	+4.4	+1.0
7.	+3.7	+5.5	+1.8
8.	+ .8	+1.6	+ .8
9.	0	+4.6	+4.6
10.	+2.0	+3.4	+1.4
	Mean + .75	Mean +2.33	Mean +1.58
	S.D. 1.70	S.D. 1.90	S.D. 1.17

First let us see what is the probability that 1 will on the average give increase of sleep; i.e., what is the chance that the mean of the population of which these experiments are a sample is positive. $+.75/1.70 = .44$ and looking out $z = .44$ in the table for ten experiment we find by interpolating between .8697 and .9161 that .44 corresponds to .8873, or the odds are .887 to .113 that the mean is positive.

That is about 8 to 1 and would correspond in the normal curve to about 1.8 times the probable error. It is then very likely that 1 gives an increase of sleep, but would occasion no surprise if the results were reversed by further experiments.

If now we consider the chance that 2 is actually a soporific we have the mean increase of sleep = 2.33/1.90 or 1.23 times the S.D. From the table the probability corresponding to this is .9974, i.e., the odds are nearly 400 to 1 that such is the case. This corresponds to about 4.15 times the probable error in the normal curve. But I take it the real point of the authors was that 2 is better than 1. This we must test by making a new series, subtracting 1 from 2. The mean value of this series is +1.58 while the S.D. is 1.17, the mean value being +1.35 times the S.D. From the table the probability is .9985 or the odds are about 666 to 1 that 2 is the better soporific. The low value of the S.D. is probably due to the different drugs reacting similarly on the same patient, so that there is correlation between the results.

Of course odds of this kind make it almost certain that 2 is the better soporific, and in practical life such a high probability is in most matters considered as a certainty.

Illustration 2.   Cases where the tables will be useful are not uncommon in agricultural work, and they would be more numerous if the advantages of being able to apply statistical reasoning were borne in mind when planning the experiments. I take the following instances from the accounts of the Woburn farming experiments published yearly by Dr. Voelcker in the *Journal of the Agricultural Society*.

A short series of pot culture experiments were conducted in order to determine the causes which lead to the production of hard (glutinous) wheat or soft (starchy) wheat. In three successive years a bulk of seed corn of one variety was picked over by hand and two samples were selected, one consisting of "hard" grains and the other of "soft." Some of each of these were planted in both heavy and light soil and the resulting crops were weighed and examined for hard and soft corn.

The conclusion drawn was that the effect of selecting the seed was negligible compared with the influence of the soil.

This conclusion was thoroughly justified, the heavy soil producing in each case nearly 100 percent of hard corn, but still the effect of selecting the seed could just be traced in each year.

But a curious point, to which Dr. Voelcker draws attention in the second year's report, is that the soft seeds produced the higher yield of both corn and straw. In view of the well-known fact that the *varieties* which have a high yield tend to produce soft corn, it is interesting to see how much evidence the experiments afford as to the correlation between softness and fertility in the same *variety*.

Further, Mr. Hooker* has shown that the yield of wheat in one year is largely determined by the weather during the preceding harvest. Dr. Voelcker's results may afford a clue as to the way in which the seed is affected, and would almost justify the selection of particular soils for growing seed wheat.†

The figures are given in the table on p. 96, the yields being expressed in grammes per pot.

If we wish to find the odds that soft seed will give a better yield of corn on the average, we divide the average difference by the standard deviation, giving us

$$z = .88.$$

Looking this up in the table for $n = 6$ we find $p = .9465$ or the odds are .9465 : 535, about 18 : 1.

Similarly for straw $z = 1.20$, $p = .9782$, and the odds about 45 : 1.

In order to see whether such odds are sufficient for a practical man to draw a definite conclusion, I take another set of experiments in which Dr. Voelcker compares the effects of different artificial manures used with potatoes on the large scale.

The figures represent the difference between the crops grown with the use of sulphate of potash and kainit respectively in both 1904 and 1905.

	cwt.	qr.	lb.		ton	cwt.	qr.	lb.	
1904	+ 10	3	20	:	+ 1	10	1	26	(two experiments
1905	+ 6	0	3	:	+	13	2	8	in each year).

The average gain by the use of sulphate of potash was 15.25 cwt. and the S.D. 9 cwt., whence, if we want the odds that the conclusion given below is right, $z = 1.7$, corresponding, when $n = 4$, to $p = .9698$ or odds of 32 : 1; this is midway between the odds in the former example. Dr. Voelcker says "It may now fairly be concluded that for the potato crop on light land 1 cwt. per acre of sulphate of potash is a better dressing than kainit."

As an example of how the tables should be used with caution, I take the following pot culture experiments to test whether it made any difference whether large or small seeds were sown.

---

*   *Journal of Royal Statistical Society*, 1907.

†   And perhaps a few experiments to see whether there is a correlation between yield and "mellowness" in barley.

Year	1899		1900		1901		Average	Standard Deviation	z
Soil	*Light*	*Heavy*	*Light*	*Heavy*	*Light*	*Heavy*			
Yield of corn from:									
soft seed	7.85	8.89	14.81	13.55	7.48	15.39	11.328		
hard seed	7.27	8.32	13.81	13.36	7.97	13.13	10.643		
Difference	+.58	+.57	+1.00	+.19	−.49	+2.26	+.685	.778	.88
Yield of straw from:									
soft seed	12.81	12.87	22.22	20.21	13.97	22.57	17.442		
hard seed	10.71	12.48	21.64	20.26	11.71	18.96	15.927		
Difference	+2.10	+.39	+.78	−.05	+2.66	+3.61	+1.515	1.261	1.20

Illustration 3. In 1899 and in 1903 "head corn" and "tail corn" were taken from the same bulks of barley and sown in pots. The yields in grammes were as follows:

	1899	1903
Large seed	13.9	7.3
Small seed	14.4	8.7
	+.5	+.6

The average gain is thus .55 and the S.D. .05, giving $z = 11$. Now the table for $n = 2$ is not given, but if we look up the angle whose tangent is 11 in Chambers' tables,

$$p = \frac{\tan^{-1} 11}{180°} + .5 = \frac{84° 47'}{180°} + .5 = .971,$$

so that the odds are about 33:1 that small corn gives a better yield than large. These odds are those which would be laid, and laid rightly, by a man whose only knowledge of the matter was contained in the two experiments. Anyone conversant with pot culture would however know that the difference between the two results would generally be greater and would correspondingly moderate the certainty of his conclusion. In point of fact a large scale experiment confirmed the result, the small corn yielding about 15 percent more than the large.

I will conclude with an example which comes beyond the range of the tables, there being eleven experiments.

To test whether it is of advantage to kiln-dry barley seed before sowing, seven varieties of barley were sown (both kiln-dried and not kiln-dried) in 1899 and four in 1900; the results are given in the table.

It will be noticed that the kiln-dried seed gave on an average the larger yield of corn and straw, but that the quality was almost always inferior. At first sight this might be supposed to be due to superior germinating power in the kiln-dried seed, but my farming friends tell me that the effect of this would be that the kiln-dried seed would produce the better quality barley. Dr. Voelcker draws the conclusion "In such seasons as 1899 and 1900 there is no particular advantage in kiln-drying before sowing." Our examination completely justifies this and adds "and the quality of the resulting barley is inferior though the yield may be greater."

In this case I propose to use the approximation given by the normal curve with standard deviation $s/\sqrt{(n-3)}$ and therefore use Sheppard's tables, looking up the difference divided by $s/\sqrt{8}$. The probability in the case of yield of corn per acre is given by looking up $33.7/22.3 = 1.51$

	lbs. Head Corn per Acre			Price of Head Corn in Shillings per Quarter			cwts. Straw per Acre			Value of Crop per Acre in Shillings*		
	N.K.D.	K.D.	Diff.	N.K.D.	K.D.	Diff.	N.K.D.	K.D.	Diff.	N.K.D.	K.D.	Diff.
1899	1903	2009	$+106$	$26\frac{1}{2}$	$26\frac{1}{2}$	0	$19\frac{1}{4}$	25	$+5\frac{3}{4}$	$140\frac{1}{2}$	152	$+11\frac{1}{2}$
	1935	1915	$-\ 20$	28	$26\frac{1}{2}$	$-1\frac{1}{2}$	$22\frac{3}{4}$	24	$+1\frac{1}{4}$	$152\frac{1}{2}$	145	$-7\frac{1}{2}$
	1910	2011	$+101$	$29\frac{1}{2}$	$28\frac{1}{2}$	-1	23	24	$+1$	$158\frac{1}{2}$	161	$+2\frac{1}{2}$
	2496	2463	$-\ 33$	30	29	-1	23	28	$+5$	$204\frac{1}{2}$	$199\frac{1}{2}$	-5
	2108	2180	$+\ 72$	$27\frac{1}{2}$	27	$-\frac{1}{2}$	$22\frac{1}{2}$	$22\frac{1}{2}$	0	162	164	$+2$
	1961	1925	$-\ 36$	26	26	0	$19\frac{3}{4}$	$19\frac{1}{2}$	$-\frac{1}{4}$	142	$139\frac{1}{2}$	$-2\frac{1}{2}$
	2060	2122	$+\ 62$	29	26	-3	$24\frac{1}{2}$	$22\frac{1}{4}$	$-2\frac{1}{4}$	168	155	-13
1900	1444	1482	$+\ 38$	$29\frac{1}{2}$	$28\frac{1}{2}$	-1	$15\frac{1}{2}$	16	$+\frac{1}{2}$	118	$117\frac{1}{2}$	$-\frac{1}{2}$
	1612	1542	$-\ 70$	$28\frac{1}{2}$	28	$-\frac{1}{2}$	18	$17\frac{1}{4}$	$-\frac{3}{4}$	$128\frac{1}{2}$	121	$-7\frac{1}{2}$
	1316	1443	$+127$	30	29	-1	$14\frac{1}{4}$	$15\frac{3}{4}$	$+1\frac{1}{2}$	$109\frac{1}{2}$	$116\frac{1}{2}$	$+7$
	1511	1535	$+\ 24$	$28\frac{1}{2}$	28	$-\frac{1}{2}$	17	$17\frac{1}{4}$	$+\frac{1}{4}$	120	$120\frac{1}{2}$	$+\frac{1}{2}$
Average	1841.5	1875.2	$+\ 33.7$	28.45	27.55	$-.91$	19.95	21.05	$+1.10$	145.82	144.68	$+1.14$
Standard deviation	—	—	63.1	—	—	.79	—	—	2.25	—	—	6.67
Standard deviation $\div \sqrt{8}$	—	—	22.3	—	—	.28	—	—	.80	—	—	2.40

* Straw being valued at 15s. per ton.

in Sheppard's tables. This gives $p = .934$, or the odds are about $14:1$ that kiln-dried corn gives the higher yield.

Similarly $.91/.28 = 3.25$, corresponding to $p = .9994,$* so that the odds are very great that kiln-dried seed gives barley of a worse quality than seed which has not been kiln-dried.

Similarly it is about 11 to 1 that kiln-dried seed gives more straw and about $2:1$ that the total value of the crop is less with kiln-dried seed.

Section 10

Conclusions

1. A curve has been found representing the frequency distribution of standard deviations of samples drawn from a normal population.

2. A curve has been found representing the frequency distribution of values of the means of such samples, when these values are measured from the mean of the population in terms of the standard deviation of the sample.

3. It has been shown that this curve represents the facts fairly well even when the distribution of the population is not strictly normal.

4. Tables are given by which it can be judged whether a series of experiments, however short, have given a result which conforms to any required standard of accuracy or whether it is necessary to continue the investigation.

Finally I should like to express my thanks to Professor Karl Pearson, without whose constant advice and criticism this paper could not have been written.

---

* As pointed out in Section 5 the normal curve gives too large a value for p when the probability is large. I find the true value in this case to be $p = .9976$. It matters little however to a conclusion of this kind whether the odds in its favor are $1,660:1$ or merely $416:1$.

8

a test of the significance of the difference between the means of correlated measures, based on a simplification of Student's t

Joseph Sandler

Psychologists have often to compare the means of two distinct sets of scores, where there is a correlation between the two sets. This is usually done when:

1. Two groups have been matched with respect to some extraneous variable, such as age or intelligence. Each person in one group is paired with a person in the other.
2. A set of persons has been given a test twice, in different circumstances (e.g., before and after training, or the administration of a drug).

The appropriate test of significance of the difference between the two means is Student's t by the method of differences (or by the more laborious method in which the correlation between the two sets of scores is actually calculated and then corrected for). t by the method of differences is given as follows (Johnson, 1949):

$$t = \frac{\bar{d}}{\text{S.E.}_{\bar{d}}},$$

Reprinted from *British Journal of Psychology* **46**, Part 3, 225–226 (1955), by permission of the author and the publisher. Copyright © 1955 by J. Sandler.

where $\bar{d}$ is the mean difference between the pairs of scores, and S.E.$_d$ is the standard error of the mean difference. t has $N - 1$ degrees of freedom, where N is the number of cases in each group.

It is the purpose of this paper to present a statistic A, which yields exactly the same results as Student's t, being rigorously derived from it, but which is extremely simple to calculate. If, as is commonly the case, two matched groups are compared with respect to a large number of variables, the use of A results in a considerable saving of time and labor. It is found as follows:

$$A = \frac{\text{The sum of the squares of the differences}}{\text{The square of the sum of the differences}} = \frac{\Sigma D^2}{(\Sigma D)^2}.$$

A table of A has been constructed, and is appended. The table is entered with $N - 1$ degrees of freedom, and a value of A is significant at any given level if it is equal to or *less* than the tabled value. It corresponds to the two-tail form of t.

If we write t as

$$t = \frac{(\Sigma d)/N}{\sqrt{\dfrac{\Sigma d^2 - (\Sigma d)^2/N}{N(N - 1)}}},$$

taking the square of both sides gives us

$$t^2 = \frac{N - 1}{N} \frac{(\Sigma d)^2}{\Sigma d^2 - (\Sigma d)^2/N}.$$

Hence,

$$\frac{N - 1}{Nt^2} = \frac{\Sigma d^2}{(\Sigma d)^2} - \frac{1}{N}.$$

From this we may write A in terms of t:

$$A = \frac{N - 1}{Nt^2} + \frac{1}{N};$$

t can be written in terms of A as follows:

$$t = \sqrt{\frac{N - 1}{AN - 1}}.$$

The table of A has been constructed from published tables of Student's t (Fisher and Yates, 1948) and the tables of the inverted beta (F) distribution, computed by Merrington and Thompson (1943).

Table of A
(*For any given value of N − 1, the table shows the values of A*
corresponding to various levels of probability. A is significant at
a given level if it is equal to or less than the value shown in the table.)

N − 1	.10	.05	.02	.01	.001	N − 1
			Probability			
1	.5125	.5031	.50049	.50012	.5000012	1
2	.412	.369	.347	.340	.334	2
3	.385	.324	.286	.272	.254	3
4	.376	.304	.257	.238	.211	4
5	.372	.293	.240	.218	.184	5
6	.370	.286	.230	.205	.167	6
7	.369	.281	.222	.196	.155	7
8	.368	.278	.217	.190	.146	8
9	.368	.276	.213	.185	.139	9
10	.368	.274	.210	.181	.134	10
11	.368	.273	.207	.178	.130	11
12	.368	.271	.205	.176	.126	12
13	.368	.270	.204	.174	.124	13
14	.368	.270	.202	.172	.121	14
15	.368	.269	.201	.170	.119	15
16	.368	.268	.200	.169	.117	16
17	.368	.268	.199	.168	.116	17
18	.368	.267	.198	.167	.114	18
19	.368	.267	.197	.166	.113	19
20	.368	.266	.197	.165	.112	20
21	.368	.266	.196	.165	.111	21
22	.368	.266	.196	.164	.110	22
23	.368	.266	.195	.163	.109	23
24	.368	.265	.195	.163	.108	24
25	.368	.265	.194	.162	.108	25
26	.368	.265	.194	.162	.107	26
27	.368	.265	.193	.161	.107	27
28	.368	.265	.193	.161	.106	28
29	.368	.264	.193	.161	.106	29
30	.368	.264	.193	.160	.105	30
40	.368	.263	.191	.158	.102	40
60	.369	.262	.189	.155	.099	60
120	.369	.261	.187	.153	.095	120
∞	.370	.260	.185	.151	.092	∞

References

Fisher, R. A. and F. Yates. *Statistical Tables.* London: Oliver and Boyd, 1948.

Johnson, Palmer O. *Statistical Methods in Research.* New York: Prentice Hall, 1949.

Merrington, Maxine and Catherine M. Thompson. Tables of the inverted beta (*F*) distribution. *Biometrika,* **33,** 73–88, 1943.

9

note on use of the A statistic as a substitute for t in the one-sample case

Richard P. Runyon

Several years ago, Joseph Sandler demonstrated a statistic, A, which is rigorously derived from the Student t ratio for correlated samples but which requires only a fraction of the time to compute (1955). The statistic, A, is defined as:

$$A = \frac{\text{the sum of the squares of the differences}}{\text{the square of the sum of the differences}} = \frac{\Sigma D^2}{(\Sigma D)^2}.$$

Expressed in terms of t,

$$A = [(N - 1)/(Nt^2)] + (1/N).$$

Also,

$$t = \sqrt{(N - 1)/(NA - 1)}.$$

One and two-tailed critical values of the A statistic may be found in Runyon and Haber (1967) and two-tailed critical values in Sandler (1955).

Reprinted with permission of author and publisher:

Runyon, R. Note on use of the A statistic as a substitute for t in the one-sample case. *Psychological Reports*, 1968, **22,** 361–362.

Table 1
Use of the sandler A statistic to test $H_0: \mu = \mu_0$

Test Score	μ_0	D	D^2	
105	106	−1	1	
109	106	3	9	
115	106	9	81	
112	106	6	36	
124	106	18	324	$A = \Sigma D^2/(\Sigma D)^2 = 967/(57)^2$
115	106	9	81	$= .298;$
103	106	−3	9	$df = 9.$
110	106	4	16	
125	106	19	361	
99	106	−7	49	
ΣD		57	967	

The present paper demonstrates the generalization of the Sandler A statistic to test hypotheses in situations where the Student t ratio, one-sample case, i.e., $t = (M - \mu_0)/S_M$, is appropriate. The procedure consists of subtracting the value of the parameter hypothesized under H_0 from each score, summing the differences and squaring, squaring the differences and summing, and substituting these values in the formula for A.

To illustrate, imagine the scores in Table 1 were obtained at random from a group of S's. We wish to test the null hypothesis that the sample was drawn from a population in which the mean, μ, is equal to 106.

Reference to the table of critical values of A reveals that an $A \leq .276$ is required to reject the null hypothesis at the .05 level, two-tailed test. Since the calculated A of .298 exceeds this value, the null hypothesis must be regarded as tenable.

The Student t ratio calculated from these data is 2.134, which also falls short of the .05 significance level. This is as it should be since the two tests are algebraically equivalent.

References

Runyon, R. P. and A. Haber. *Fundamentals of behavioral statistics.* Reading, Mass.: Addison-Wesley, 1967.

Sandler, J. A test of the significance of the difference between the means of correlated measures, based on a simplification of Student's *t*. *Brit. J. Psychol.*, 1955, **46**, 225–226.

10

on teaching F instead of t

Norman H. Anderson

It is well known that the square of a *t* ratio on *n* *df* is interpretable as an *F* ratio on 1 and *n* *df*. For the case of one or two means then, the values of *t* and *F* are equivalents, and lead to identical probability and inferential statements. Since *F* is the more general, applying as well to the case of more than two means, one might well suspect that the *t* test could be retired from use. Because the *t* test constitutes such a large part of current statistical pedagogy and practice, it may be useful to consider the matter in more detail. The main considerations which seem to the writer to be relevant are summarized briefly below.[1] These considerations are applicable principally to the first few statistics courses in the applied sciences and have less relevance to more theoretical courses.

In favor of *t*, it can be argued that it has greater intuitive appeal. To measure the difference between two means against its standard error may be simpler to comprehend and result in easier learning than does the variance partitioning technique of *F*. However, as soon as it is admitted that *t* is insufficient to meet everyday needs, so that *F* must

---

Reprinted from *Journal of Experimental Education* **28,** No. 3, 261–263 (1960), by permission of the author and the publisher.

1. For the purposes of this note, the terms "*F* test" and "analysis of variance" will be taken as synonymous although this is not strictly correct. It will be necessary to allude to a number of uses of the analysis of variance, but these uses are well known and will not be documented.

be taught anyway, this argument loses its power. It may also be suggested that whatever greater immediacy of meaning may attach to *t* is not entirely its natural due, but rather a product of the present organization of statistics courses.

The *t* test may also be preferred because of its relation to some of the problems arising in estimation, such as the construction of confidence intervals. Algebraically, of course, it makes little difference whether one proceeds from *t* or from *F*. Thus, with *F*, the 95 percent confidence interval is obtained using $\sqrt{s_m^2 F(.95; 1, n)}$. The interpretation of the confidence interval could then be taken on faith (and even serve usefully as the basis for the significance test for the case of one or two means). However, it must be admitted that the confidence interval idea seems easier to comprehend when it is based on the standard picture of the symmetrical *t* distribution. This possible advantage of *t* must be measured against its shortcomings in problems of significance testing which are discussed below.

A further point in favor of *t* stems from a danger of the analysis of variance. Ordinarily, when pair-wise comparisons among several conditions are to be made, the error mean square from the overall *F* analysis is used throughout. When the condition variances are reasonably equal, this procedure gives increased sensitivity since the error is estimated more precisely. If there is marked heterogeneity of variance, however, such tests may be biased, and it may be preferable to test each pair of conditions using only the data from that pair (although this does not entirely escape the difficulty). Of course, the two condition *F* could be used here as easily as *t*. Nevertheless, it must be admitted that routine application of the analysis of variance does facilitate overlooking the problem.

Against these arguments must be set a number of negative aspects of *t*. For situations with just one or two conditions, of course, it is a matter of statistical indifference whether *t* or *F* is used. Either yields the same inferences, as noted above. Moreover, since $t^2 = F$, there need be little difference in computational efficiency. It may be noted, however, that the standard computing rules for *t*, in contrast to those for *F*, are not efficient and thus more liable to arithmetical error.

When more than two conditions are involved, piece-meal *t* testing presents certain dangers.[2] The one commonly emphasized is the

---

2. A specific comparison based on some reasonably firm rational or empirical ground may always be tested, of course. However, unless it is based on a single degree of freedom, it will require an *F* ratio in its own right. It should also be specifically noted that multiple comparison procedures will be superior to *F* (and *t*) in certain situations.

increased risk of thereby obtaining "significant" differences which the data do not in fact support. Curiously enough, the *t* test approach also increases the likelihood of the obverse error, namely, failing to detect results which the data are quite adequate to declare real. This can happen in a number of ways, which trend tests may serve to illustrate. In investigations in which one of the independent variables is numerical, the between conditions variation can often be expected on prior grounds to reside largely in the linear, or linear + quadratic, component of the curve. Pair-wise comparisons of means may fail to reveal even a fairly strong real effect which a trend analysis *F* will elucidate with ease.

A more fundamental objection to the *t* test approach concerns the original planning of the investigation. The researcher who thinks in terms of *t* is less likely to use as incisive and informative a design as can be had for the allotted time and effort. Even when the basic plan is sound, a poor superstructure can, and not infrequently does, prejudice the analysis and interpretation, or entail considerable extra computational cost.

Fisher's commendation of the use of factorial designs for controlling extraneous variation may be cited in illustration of this last point. Even with only two main experimental conditions, it is often desirable to counterbalance a second variable, not of great interest in itself, in order to obtain added generality. Unless set up so that the two-way analysis can be and is used, however, the counterbalancing may do more harm than good.

In a similar way, it is often possible to use as a second independent variable some individual difference measure which is correlated with the response measure under study. This procedure, essentially a "randomized blocks" factorial design, may generally be expected not only to increase the sensitivity of the experiment, but also to yield information on the organismic variables.

That the *F* test is a desirable piece of statistical machinery hardly needs even the incidental justification given here. But if *F* is to be taught at all, then it evidently follows, since *F* is the more general, that *F* alone should be taught. To require the mastery of two sets of rules where one will do is an improvident use of the student's time.

For statistics courses in which time is insufficient for both tests, the choice of *F* would accomplish the same ends as the choice of *t*. If more time were available, the elimination of *t* would permit the development of some of the simpler ramifications of the analysis of variance, such as two-way designs, specific comparisons, and trend tests. Moreover, teaching *F* from the start would set up conditions for maximal positive transfer later in learning since the computing rules for F follow a uniform and elegant logic in all situations. It might also be noted in this connection that the computational procedures for correlation and regression analysis can be subsumed under the analysis of variance format as well.

Finally, it may be questioned whether learning the t test does not produce a fair amount of negative transfer. The evidence available to the writer, admittedly anecdotal in nature, suggests that students who have learned t are reluctant to abandon this skill when necessary. Having a technique which may actually, if not always advisedly, be used, they tend to regard even workaday designs as "fancy" or "not worth the trouble at this stage of investigation." Thus, if they use the design at all, they do so only with pain, and so fail to acquire the familiarity with the new technique that would come were it regarded as just another application of the F test they already knew.

It would thus appear that t is superfluous, since F may always be computed instead; inadequate, since it does not apply as generally as does F; dangerous, since its use may increase errors of inference, as well as lead to weak experiments; and a waste of time, since teaching F will provide more transfer to later learning. On the balance, it seems fair to conclude that the t test should be struck from the curriculum.

More practical experience is needed in order to integrate the analysis of variance with beginning statistics on the conceptual level. However, it is appropriate to sketch briefly the sequence of computational routines which is indicated by the argument of this note.

1. Computation of the sample variance is done using the analysis of variance table:

Source	df	SS	MS
Mean	1	T^2/N	
Error (variability)	$N - 1$	$\Sigma X^2 - T^2/N$	

The entry, MS error, then furnishes an unbiased estimate of the population variance. The scaffolding provided by the tabular format is unnecessary, of course, but seems to serve a useful mnemonic function. Its real benefit accrues in Step 2.

2. The test of significance for a single sample is most appropriately carried out on difference scores, or on other scores which have a mean of 0 under the null hypothesis. A single division appended to the Step 1 routine yields the relevant F ratio.

3. With two samples of difference scores, the analysis of variance table is extended one step further:

Source	df	SS	MS	F
Mean	1			
Between groups	1			
Error	$N-2$			

4. It is straightforward to extend Step 3 to the case of several samples and it seems advisable to do so promptly in order to avoid the development of a superstition that the technique only works for one or two. The routine remains the same when the scores are arbitrary rather than difference scores. It is only necessary to observe that the F for Mean is no longer meaningful or important and may be omitted from the table.

5. A simple extension of the computing routine yields the calculation of r for a single sample:

Source	XX	XY	YY
Mean	T_X^2/N	$T_X T_Y/N$	T_Y^2/N
Error	$\Sigma X^2 - T_X^2/N$	$\Sigma XY - T_X T_Y/N$	$\Sigma Y^2 - T_Y^2/N$

The square of the correlation coefficient is estimated from the entries in the Error line, $r^2 = SS_{XY}^2/SS_{XX}SS_{YY}$. The test for significance may be made by consulting a table for r or, with an additional calculation, by using F. When the calculation of r is taught this way, there is less likelihood of confusedly agglomerating the between and within samples regressions when more than a single sample is involved.

It is suggested that $\Sigma X2$ be given for most of the homework problems. This will greatly decrease the time spent on each problem and, by thus allowing a greater variety of problems to be assigned, increase the learning efficiency. Whether or not further applications of the analysis of variance are given in the first course will depend on the available time, and on whether the course is oriented toward experimental or observational research.

11

the statistical power of abnormal-social psychological research: a review*

Jacob Cohen

Given an experimental effect in a population, how likely is the null hypothesis to be rejected? Equivalently, what is the power of the statistical test? What is the expectation that the (false) null hypothesis will be sustained and thus a Type II error committed?

It is a remarkable phenomenon that the research which is reported by psychological investigators rarely refers to this issue, and even more rarely actually investigates it. On the other hand, issues concerning Type I error or "significance," i.e., the validity of the *rejection* of the null hypothesis, are more or less conscientiously attended to. This marked asymmetry of sophistication and attention to these two types

From: J. Cohen, "The statistical power of abnormal-social psychological research: a review," *Journal of Abnormal and Social Psychology* **65,** No. 3, 1962, 145–153. Copyright © 1962 by the American Psychological Association, and reproduced by permission.

* This study was primarily supported by Grant M-5174(A) from the National Institute of Mental Health, United States Public Health Service, which support is gratefully acknowledged. I am also grateful to Catherine Henderson for her expert assistance in preparing the manuscript, and to the New York University Faculty Research Fund for supplementary assistance.

of error is mirrored, and largely determined, by the exposition of these issues in the statistics textbooks used in the graduate training of the investigators. These texts are characterized by an early explanation of Type I and Type II errors, followed by a neglect of the latter throughout the remainder of the text. Thus, every statistical test is described with careful attention to issues of significance, and typically no attention to power. (For a partial exception, see Walker and Lev, 1953.)

The problem of power is occasionally approached indirectly by concern with the sample size to be used in an investigation. Other things equal, power is a monotonic function of sample size, but decisions as to sample size are typically reached by recourse to local tradition, ready availability of data, unaided intuition, usually called "experience," and negotiation (the latter usually between doctoral candidate and sponsor, or author and editor) and rarely on the basis of a Type II error analysis, which can always be performed *prior* to the collection of data. These nonrational bases for setting sample size must often result in investigations being undertaken which have little chance of success despite the actual falsity of the null hypothesis, and probably less often in the use of a far larger sample than is necessary. Either of these circumstances is wasteful of research effort.

Stemming from these considerations, a program of investigation, computation, and reportage has been undertaken whose major aims are as follows:

1. To call these issues to the attention of investigators, consumers of research, and evaluators of research planned or completed (sponsors, agency panels, journal editors).

2. To provide tables and conventional standards which will facilitate the performance of power analyses for the most common statistical tests.

3. To conduct surveys of the psychological research literature to assess its current status with regard to power.

The present report is the first of the investigation, and seeks to achieve partially the first and third aim.[1] Specifically, it describes the results of a survey, of the *Journal of Abnormal and Social Psychology*, 1960, **61,** from the viewpoint of the power of the statistical tests employed. Less formally, it seeks to answer the question, "What kind of chance did these investigators have of rejecting false null hypotheses?"

---

1. A more detailed description of the statistical rationale, as well as the resulting power tables, is presently in preparation for separate publication.

Method

The statistical literature was searched for formulae and nomographs of power functions of the most commonly used statistical tests, from which tables were prepared relating power to the conditions of which it is a function: (a) size of effect (degree of departure in the population from the null hypothesis), (b) significance (Type I error) criterion, (c) sample size, and (d) choice of critical region (i.e., directional or nondirectional). The tests and the sources of the formulae or nomographs are given in Table 1.[2]

Standard conditions

For the purpose of the survey, it was necessary to formulate a set of reasonable standard conditions on the basis of which the power of each test could be computed. Whether or not other significance criteria were indicated, the .05 Type I error level was used uniformly.[3] Further, whether or not otherwise specified, the nondirectional version of the null hypothesis was used throughout. This means a two-sided test for normal, binomial, and *t* distributions, and the logically equivalent one-sided (high) value test for χ^2 and F distributions, as they are usually tabled and used in hypothesis testing. Although this criterion may lead to underestimating power in some cases, it avoids the more serious problem of inflated significance levels and the embarrassment of large effects in the nonpredicted direction.

Size of effect

The most difficult problem for the psychological investigator in performing a power analysis on an experimental plan is the formulation of an answer to the question, "How large an effect (a difference, correlation coefficient, etc.) in the population do I expect actually exists, or want to be able to detect?" Only rarely in the abnormal-social area are theoretical models well enough specified to be of help in answering this question, yet the question must be answered. In the present study, this problem was further complicated by the need

---

2. See Footnote 1.

3. With few exceptions, the articles provided no evidence of a significance level being set prior to data collection, either because it was not deemed worth mentioning, or none had indeed been set. In any case, and rightly or wrongly, the .05 level has trickled down from agronomy as a conventional standard, and is usually understood to be the significance criterion if no other is mentioned.

Table 1
*Statistical tests and sources of formulae and nomographs
of power functions.*

Test of Null Hypothesis	Source
1. *t* test: difference between means	Dixon and Massey, 1957, formula p. 253
2. Normal deviate test: difference between proportions (via arc sine transformation)	Dixon and Massey, 1957, p. 251 and Table A-28, p. 465
3. Normal deviate test for difference between Pearson *r*'s (via Fisher *z* transformation)	Dixon and Massey, 1957, p. 251 and Table A-30b, p. 468
4. *t* test: Pearson *r* is zero	Dixon and Massey, 1957, formula p. 253 (adapted)
5. Binomial and normal deviate test: proportion equals .50 (sign test)	Mosteller, Rourke, and Thomas, Table IV, pp. 369–388; Walker and Lev, 1953, pp. 60–63, 67–69
6. *F* test in analysis of variance designs: *k* means are equal	Eisenhart, Hastay, and Wallis, 1947, pp. 256–259; Dixon and Massey, 1957, pp. 426–453 (nomographs)
7. χ^2 test: (a) *k* proportions are equal, or (b) *kr* proportions are independent (contingency test)	Patnaik, 1949; Fix, Hodges, and Lehmann, 1959

to answer it for diverse content areas, utilizing a large variety of dependent variables and many different types of statistical tests. A solution was needed for the present survey which would make possible a reasonable basis for integration across this diversity. Finally, in the hope of facilitating the performance of power analyses as a routine practice in research planning, a solution was sought which could serve, at least provisionally, as a standard set of conventional criteria in such analyses.

The solution which evolved took the following form:

1. For each type of statistical test where it was necessary, size of effect was expressed quantitatively in terms not dependent on the specific metric of the variable(s) involved, e.g., differences in means were expressed in units of standard deviation (the usual z scores), departures of true population from null hypothetical k category percentage distributions were formulated as constant proportions of $1/k$, etc.

2. Three levels of size of effect to be detected were conceived: small, medium, and large.

3. Each of these levels was operationally defined for each type of statistical test, by assigning to them values of the relevant metric-free population parameter. These values are necessarily somewhat arbitrary, but were chosen so as to seem reasonable. The reader can render his own judgment as to their reasonableness from a study of Table 2 and the ensuing discussion, which set them forth, but whatever his judgment, he may at least be willing to accept them as conventional.

Discussion is necessary to amplify, exemplify, and perhaps justify the decisions summarized in Table 2 for each type of statistical test of the null hypothesis in turn:

1. t test for two means. Consider the medium level: it posits the existence of a difference between population means amounting to one-half of the population sigma. In more generally familiar terms, this would be exemplified by a research plan that sought to detect a difference of 8 points between the mean IQ's of two populations. Similarly, small and large IQ mean differences would amount to 4 and 16 points, respectively. These values seem reasonable. For example, an 8-point mean IQ difference is large enough to be noticeable; this is the order of magnitude of the difference between people in professional and managerial occupations and also between clerical and semiskilled workers (Super, 1949, p. 98). Differences half this size (small) would not be readily perceptible; e.g., the mean IQ difference between twins and nontwins (Husén, 1959); differences twice this size (large) would be so obvious as to virtually render a statistical test superfluous, e.g., the mean IQ difference between college graduates and those with only a 50–50 chance of passing in an academic high school curriculum (Cronbach, 1960, p. 174).

2. Normal test for two proportions. The detectability of a population difference in proportions of any given magnitude is not constant for

Table 2
Values of population parameters which define the levels of size of effect for the various statistical tests

Test	Population Parameter	Values		
		Small	Medium	Large
1. t (two means are equal)	$\lvert M_1 - M_2 \rvert / \sigma$	.25	.50	1.00
2. Normal (two proportions are equal)	$\lvert P_1 - P_2 \rvert$	.10	.20	.30
3. Normal (two r's are equal)	$\lvert r_1 - r_2 \rvert$	.10	.20	.30
4. $t(r = 0)$	$\lvert r \rvert$	.20	.40	.60
5. Sign test	$\lvert P - .50 \rvert$	.10	.20	.30
6. F (k means are equal)	σ_{M_i} / σ	.125	.25	.50
7a. χ^2 (k proportions are equal)	Ratio: $\dfrac{\text{Largest } P}{\text{Smallest } P}$	3:2	2:1	4:1
7b. χ^2 (contingency test)	$\displaystyle\sum_{i=1}^{kr} \frac{(P_{0i} - P_{1i})^2}{P_{0i}} = l$	Varies with table size, but uses criteria equivalent, for equal degrees of freedom, to 7a (see text).		

any given research plan, but increases as the average of the two proportions departs in either direction from .50. Thus, for example, with two samples of 50 cases each the power under our standard conditions to detect a difference between population proportions of .40 and .60 is .52, while for .70 and .90 (or .10 and .30) it is .73. In the survey, the level of average population proportion at which the power of the test was computed was the average of the sample proportions found. Although this procedure was tedious, the alternative was to use as the parameter the difference between the arc sine transformations of the population proportions, for which power is invariant over levels, but general unfamiliarity and awkwardness in thinking about differences between proportions in these terms led to its rejection.

Similar reasoning as detailed for t tests for means led to the selection of the values for the difference in population proportions to define small, medium, and large effects (Table 2). It was felt that a population incidence difference of .20 (medium) would be a fairly noticeable phenomenon, and the other levels were defined symmetrically about it.

3. *Normal test for two r's.* An analogous problem to that of two proportions exists here: a given population difference between two Pearson correlation coefficients is of varying detectability as a function of their level, even more so than in the case of proportions, e.g., with two samples of 50 cases each, the power under our standard conditions to detect a difference between population r's of .10 and .30 is .17, while for .70 and .90 it is .83. An exactly parallel solution was used, i.e., the sample values were used to approximate the level of population correlation of the test. Again, the problem was avoidable by using the difference in Fisher z transformation values to define size of effect— these are invariant for level of population r's—but again considerations of awkwardness and unfamiliarity led to the rejection of this alternative.

The argument of perceptibility for the definition of a correlation difference of .20 as medium (Table 2) is not uniformly convincing. At high and possibly at moderate levels of correlation, such a population difference would be noticeable, but not, say, when the population r's were .10 and .30. This difficulty, too, could have been avoided by definition via differences in Fisher z transformation values. In any case, this decision could not affect the results of the survey, since only a few minor instances of this statistical test were encountered. Small and large effects were again symmetrically defined as differences of .10 and .30.

4. *t test of $r = 0$.* There were no technical complications here, but the choice of "reasonable" values defining the levels of size of effect

proved troublesome. Initially, for the sake of comparability, it was planned to use the values of the r which are implied by those selected for the t test between means, since any difference between (standardized) means can be expressed as a (point biserial) correlation coefficient, or vice versa. This led (on the assumption of populations of equal size,[4] to values of .125, .25, and .50 for the respective levels of size of effect. On the generally untenable further assumption that the populations result from the dichotomization of a normally distributed variable, the resulting biserial r values are somewhat larger, .16, .31, and .63. Thus, from this point of view we have as candidates for the definition of a medium effect, coefficients of .25 or (more questionably) .31.

On the other hand, conventional verbal descriptions would consider a "small" correlation, one between .20 and .40, a "moderate" one between .40 and .70, and a "high" one between .70 and .90 (Guilford, 1956, p. 145). Guilford points out that these verbal terms may be misleading, and points out that "the validity coefficient for a single test may be expected in the range from .00 to .60, with most of them in the lower half of that range" (p. 146).

Thus, the medium correlation defined for compatability with the criterion for a t test between means would be about .25–.30, in conventional abstract terms about .50–.60, and in specific application as test validity coefficients, perhaps about .30–.40. A compromise among these considerations was struck: a medium effect size was defined as .40, with small and large effects, respectively, as .20 and .60. These are smaller than would be dictated by the abstract conventions, but rather more generous (i.e., give higher power estimates) than the criteria of the other statistical tests, and are reasonably in keeping with at least one common application of correlation, validity coefficients.

5. *Sign test.* This is more generally a test of the hypothesis that the population proportion having a given characteristic equals .5, and is accomplished by reference to the binomial distribution for small samples and the normal distribution for $n > 25$, where it gives an adequate approximation to the binomial. The same criteria were used for levels of size of effect here as were used for the hypothesis that two population proportions differ, i.e., .10, .20, and .30 for small, medium, and large effects, respectively (Table 2), and on the basis of the same considerations.

6. *F test for k means.* The population parameter f (Table 2) used to define degree of departure from the null hypothesis was the standard deviation of the k standardized population means, i.e., of the means

---

4. Assumptions of inequality lead to smaller values.

expressed in units of the common population sigma, or as z scores. For the t test for two means, the parameter was the absolute difference between the two means so expressed; here, for k means, it is their standard deviation which measures their departure from each other, and therefore from the null hypothesis which holds them to be equal.

Since t is merely a special case of F (i.e., its square root when the numerator has 1 df) it was possible to define the levels of the parameter f to make them consistent with those of t. Expressed in terms of f, the t criteria are, respectively, .125, .25, and .50 (Table 2). Taking the medium level, .25, we illustrate for varying numbers of samples, the population means implied. For this illustration the means are equally spaced[5] and are expressed in both standard terms and IQ units (M 100, σ 16):

$k = 2$		$k = 3$		$k = 4$	
+.25	104	+.306	104.9	+.335	105.4
−.25	96	0	100.0	+.112	101.8
		−.306	95.1	−.112	98.2
				−.335	94.6

Note that for two samples, the difference between means is .50, as defined for the medium level of the t test for means. Note also that the standard deviation of each column of standardized means is .25, and of IQ means $(.25)(16) = 4$.

The illustration serves as a guide as to the size of the disparities between means defined as a medium effect. Small effects are arrived at by halving the gaps between means, large effects by doubling them.

7a. χ^2 test that k proportions are equal. This test created the greatest problem in the selection of a parameter to define degree of departure from the null hypothesis. A plan to follow the same procedure as for k means, namely, a fixed standard deviation of the population proportions, was frustrated by the fact that proportions are bounded by zero and one, so that as the number of samples increases, with sigma fixed and $1/k$ decreasing toward zero, negative values are called for.

---

5. When there are more than two means, specifying f does not fix the standard mean values. To concretize the exposition, the further specification of their distribution is necessary, and equal spacing is chosen because it leads to maximum separation of the extreme means as well as for its intuitive simplicity. The power computed, however, is independent of the spacing, but is simply a function of f (Dixon and Massey, 1957, p. 257).

After further exploration with other approaches, the problem was finally solved by choosing as a parameter of size of effect the ratio of the largest population proportion to the smallest, with equal spacing of the k proportions. So specified, this leads in turn (for any given value of k) to the standard departure function used with the noncentral χ^2 distribution (Patnaik, 1949, and formula for l given in 7b, Table 2).

Once the parametric function was chosen, specific values were then selected to define the levels (Table 2). Focusing again on the critical medium level, a ratio of 2:1 leads to the following specification of population departures from the null hypothesis of equiproportionality for some illustrative values of k:

$k = 2$	$k = 3$	$k = 4$	$k = 5$
.667	.444	.333	.267
.333	.333	.289	.233
	.222	.222	.200
		.167	.167
			.133

It should be noted that by this criterion as k increases, other things equal, the departure function l and hence the power decreases. Note, too, that for $k = 2$, this criterion is *not* quite the same as for the statistically equivalent sign test (Table 2), which calls for populations of .70 and .30 and hence a criterion of $2\frac{1}{3}:1$, instead of the 2:1 value used. This incompatibility was tolerated both because of the greater simplicity of the latter, and also because the former gave rise to discrepancies between proportions for larger values of k which seemed intuitively too large to be deemed medium.

A large effect is defined as a ratio twice as large as those illustrated above (i.e., 4:1) and a small effect as one three-quarters as large (i.e., 3:2), since a ratio half as large defines *no* effect (i.e., 1:1).

7b. χ^2 contingency test. A definition of size of population contingency which was both simple and direct could not be achieved, in contrast to the other tests. Instead, the same criteria values l were used here as those which resulted from the ratio of largest to smallest proportion in the simpler one-dimensional χ^2 test (Table 2, line 7a). Thus, for any given number of degrees of freedom, medium contingency is implicitly defined as departure from null association (as measured by l) equal to that of medium departure from the equiproportionality hypothesis of 7a, i.e., a 2:1 ratio of extremes (Table 2). This results in l values which vary as a function of *df*. What this leads to, as a definition of medium size of contingency, is perhaps more clearly illustrated by examples than described. Following are some contingency tables of varying degrees of freedom whose proportions exemplify medium contingency (decimal points omitted):

111	167	222			167	139	111	083
222	167	111			083	111	139	167

$df = 2, \quad l = .0741$ $\qquad\qquad df = 3, \quad l = .0617$

067	083	100	117	133	084	098	152
133	117	100	083	067	098	138	098
					152	098	084

$df = 4, \quad l = .0556$ $\qquad\qquad df = 4, \quad l = .0556$

Note that in the $2 \times k$ tables above the extreme columns' cells are in $2:1$ ratio and the values in each row are equally spaced. Of course, other tables of equal size of effect (therefore leading to equal power) can be constructed, provided that they yield the l value appropriate to the df involved.

Limitations of space preclude the presentation of tables which exemplify small and large contingency effects, but the interested reader can construct his own by analogy with the material presented.

Survey procedure

With power tables prepared for .05 level nondirectional tests for varying values of n for each statistical test type, and the size of effect levels chosen, the next step was the survey of articles in the volume. Each article was read in turn, and the nature of each statistical test performed (or implied) in the article was noted. Generally, when sample sizes (and for F tests and χ^2, df) were added to the standard conditions, the power of the test for small, medium, and large effect size could be read directly from the appropriate prepared tables, or by interpolation between tabled values. The statistical tests given in Table 1 are not inclusive of all used in the volume, most noteworthily, nonparametric tests based on ranks could not be studied from the point of view of power due to unavailability of systematic studies of this issue in the literature. In the relatively few instances where such tests had been used, the power was determined for the analogous parametric test, e.g., the t test for means for the Mann-Whitney U test and for the Wilcoxon matched-pairs signed-ranks test, and the F test for the Kruskal-Wallis H test and for the Friedman test (Siegel,

1956). Note that the effect of this substitution was to slightly over-estimate the power of the tests on the usual assumption that the conditions required by the parametric tests obtained. Even if this assumption is questioned, it is quite unlikely that the substitution results in an underestimation of power. In general, in the few instances where statistical tests were so described as to leave a doubt about the exact details, the doubt was resolved in favor of higher power estimates. For example, if a group of n cases was divided into two subgroups for comparison, but the subgroup sizes were not given, it was assumed they were equal, which then leads to a maximum power estimate for that value of n.

In this way, the power was determined for the 4,829 statistical tests[6] in the volume. But it was desired to characterize the power of each of the research studies in the volume. The typical article involved a number of tests not all of equal relevance to its major hypotheses. To determine an average set of power values across all the statistical tests of an article might lead to a distorted result, if, for example, a few hypothesis relevant tests were performed on the total data followed by a large number of subsidiary exploratory tests on only a portion of the cases. The latter would be less powerful (since sample sizes are smaller), more numerous, and less relevant to the issues central to the investigation. These considerations led to the classification of all tests performed either as bearing directly on the status of the major hypotheses or experimental issues, of which there were 2,088, or as being peripheral to these issues, an additional 2,741. The latter typically included such things as exploratory tests, routine tests of the significance of all correlation coefficients in a factor analysis, significance tests of reliability coefficients of dependent variables, tests of "by-product" control variables or unhypothesized interactions in analysis of variance designs, etc.

Once the tests were so classified, the mean power of the major tests was determined at the three levels of size of effect for each research study.[7] By this procedure, no matter what the number of tests a

---

6. Fortunately, this did not demand that many separate determinations. In these characteristically multivariable studies, a single test, e.g., the significance of an r for a given n might be applied as many as 861 times, i.e., to each intercorrelation of a 42×42 matrix (to take the most extreme example) which counts as 861 statistical tests, but requires only a single power determination.

7. The less important mean power for all tests, both major and peripheral, was also found for each article.

particular study might involve, all articles count equally in the description of the total volume. The mean power values of the studies at hypothesized small, medium, and large population effects were then distributed and their central tendency and variability determined.

Results

There are, in all, 78 articles in the *Journal of Abnormal and Social Psychology*, 1960, **61.** Of these, 6 involved no statistical tests at all (case reports, factor analytic studies, etc.) and two additional articles (both factor analytic) involved no major tests as above defined. The frequency and cumulative percentage distributions and relevant descriptive statistics of the (mean) power to detect small, medium, and large effects of the remaining 70 articles are given in Table 3. As can

Table 3
Frequency and cumulative percentage distributions of the power of the 70 articles[a] to detect small, medium, and large population effects under nondirectional .05 level conditions

Power	Small Effect		Medium Effect		Large Effect	
	Frequency	Cumulative Percentage	Frequency	Cumulative Percentage	Frequency	Cumulative Percentage
.99–					9	100
.95–.98					7	87
.90–.94			2	100	18	77
.80–.89			4	97	14	51
.70–.79			4	91	7	31
.60–.69			8	86	7	21
.50–.59			12	74	6	11
.40–.49	3	100	15	57	0	3
.30–.39	6	96	10	36	2	3
.20–.29	14	87	13	21		
.10–.19	39	67	2	3		
.05–.09	8	11				
	—		—		—	
n	70		70		70	
M	.18		.48		.83	
Median	.17		.46		.89	
σ	.08		.20		.16	
Q_1	.12		.32		.73	
Q_3	.23		.60		.94	

[a]   From the *Journal of Abnormal and Social Psychology*, 1960, **61.**

be seen from the distributions and their summarizing statistics, given .05 level nondirectional statistical tests of the major hypothesis, the power to detect the size of effect levels previously defined are as follows:

Small Effects. On the average, the studies reviewed had only about one chance in five or six of detecting small effects. About a fourth of the articles had as much as one chance in four of yielding significant results, and another fourth had no more than one chance in eight under these conditions. Not one of the studies had as much as a 50–50 chance of detecting a slight effect!

Medium Effects. When one posits medium effects in the population (generally of the order of twice as large as small effects) the studies average slightly less than a 50–50 chance of successfully rejecting their major null hypotheses. No more than one-quarter of these studies have as good as three chances in five of succeeding under these conditions, and another quarter have less than one chance in three.

Large Effects. Only when one assumes large effects (roughly twice as large as medium) does one find typically a good chance of rejecting the major null hypotheses, about five out of six. Even under these most favorable circumstances, a quarter of the studies have less than three chances in four of succeeding.

Another way of viewing these results is to determine the proportion of the studies which would meet the criterion of a Type II error level as small as the conventional Type I level, namely, .05 (power, therefore, would be at .95 or higher). None of the studies meet this criterion when one posits small or even medium effects, and only 23 % (i.e., 16 of 70) meet it under conditions of large effect.

Incidentally, if the reader questions the validity of the author's judgment in classifying the statistical tests into major and peripheral (see above, Survey Procedure) or is for any reason curious about the power of the researches when all tests, major and peripheral, are considered, the power means for small, medium, and large effects are .20, .50, and .83, respectively, hardly different from the means in Table 3.

Discussion

The results indicate that the investigators contributing to Volume 61 of the *Journal of Abnormal and Social Psychology* had, on the average, a relatively (or even absolutely) poor chance of rejecting their major null hypotheses, unless the effect they sought was large. This surprising (and discouraging) finding needs some further consideration to be seen in full perspective.

First, it may be noted that with few exceptions, the 70 studies *did* have significant results. This may then suggest that perhaps the definitions of size of effect were too severe, or perhaps, accepting the definitions, one might seek to conclude that the investigators were operating under circumstances wherein the effects were actually large, hence their success. Perhaps, then, research in the abnormal-social area is not as "weak" as the above results suggest. But this argument rests on the implicit assumption that the research which is *published* is representative of the research *undertaken* in this area. It seems obvious that investigators are less likely to submit for publication unsuccessful than successful research, to say nothing of a similar editorial bias in accepting research for publication. Consider this paradigm: 100 investigations are undertaken in which, in fact, there is actually a medium population effect. From the above findings, about 50 get positive results and are likely to come to publication; the other 50 fail to reject their (assumed false) null hypotheses and are unlikely to come to publication. Thus, the general success of the articles in the volume under review does not successfully argue for their antecedent probabilities of success being any higher than the results of the analysis suggest, or, equivalently, that the criteria for size of effect used were overly stringent.[8]

On the contrary, there is a line of argument that suggests that the criteria were not stringent enough. Assume that a medium effect exists in the population with regard to some psychological construct or constructs, e.g., a correlation between two (pure factor) *attitudes* of .40. By the time we have measured each, the variance of our scores contains error and other construct irrelevant variance which serve to attenuate the population effect we seek to a correlation of perhaps .20 to .30 between fallible attitude *scores*. We always must draw inferences from variables containing error and irrelevant variance while we normally conceptualize our problems in terms of constructs. The net effect of the fallibility of our measurement and classification is to attenuate the effects we seek. Thus, the size of effect criteria, relating as they do to fallible observations, imply even larger construct

---

8. The paradigm can be continued: assume that at the same time another 100 investigations are undertaken in which, in fact, there is *no* effect, i.e., the null hypothesis is true. At the .05 level, these will contribute, on the average, another five candidates for publication. This reduces even further the strength of this argument.

effects, and from the viewpoint of the latter, are on the generous side.

If we then accept the diagnosis of general weakness of the studies, what treatment can be prescribed? Formally, at least, the answer is simple: increase sample sizes. The mean of the maximum sample sizes used to test major hypotheses in the 70 studies was 68.[9] The power of a statistical test depends formally on several parameters, but unless one is to increase the significance level (i.e., increase the risk of Type I errors) or use directional tests (e.g., a one-sided test for *t*), power can generally be increased only by an increase in sample size. Taking 68 cases, it is instructive (and chastening) to see how much power they provide for various tests under standard conditions (.05 significance criterion, nondirectional) assuming the existence of a *medium* population effect:

1. *t test for a difference between two means.* Assuming samples of 34 cases each, the power is .52. If the sample was unequally divided, say for 50 and 18, power would be only .42.[10]

2. *Normal deviate test for a difference between two proportions.* With two samples of 34 cases, assuming extreme population proportions, say .70 and .90 (or .10 and .30), power is .57; assuming population proportions of .40 and .60, power is only .38.

3. *Normal deviate test for a difference between r's.* Again dividing the 68 cases equally for maximum power, with high population *r*'s, say .70 and .90, power is .66; with low *r*'s differing by the same amount, say .10 and .30, power is only .13!

4. *t test that a population r = 0.* If it is, in fact, .40 (medium), 68 cases give the high power value of .93. This high power is a consequence of the definition of medium as .40, rather than a lower value which compatability with the other test criteria would dictate (see above, Size of Effect).

5. *Normal deviate test that a population proportion is .50 (sign test).* If the population proportion is actually .70 (or .30), 68 cases give the high power value of .92, provided that the design yields 68 differences. If, however, the 68 cases are set up to yield 34 matched pairs, *n* is effectively 34, and power is only .63.

---

9. Since the distribution is positively skewed, as evidenced by a standard deviation of 55, the median would be considerably less than 68.

10. It is demonstrable that for the statistical test of *any* difference between or among samples which total *n* cases, power is at a maximum when the *n* cases are equally divided.

6.   F test for k means.   Power here depends upon the number of groups. Assuming three groups of 23 cases each, power is .41; with four groups of 17 cases each, .36; with seven groups of 10 cases each, power drops to .31. The *F* test in the analysis of variance is, indeed, a most versatile statistical tool (*cf.* Anderson, 1961) but investigators may lose sight of the fact that, following the discovery of a significant *F* ratio involving several groups, they are usually left with a multiple comparison problem where the means are no more stable than the sample size on which each is based. Thus, if in the last example (seven groups of 10 cases each) *F* is found significant, the determination of which group differs significantly from which then depends on means based on 10 cases. Even if one then follows the overliberal practice of performing *t* tests between pairs of these means at the tabled, but actually higher, .05 level (using the within-group error term based on 63 *df*) the power of each test under medium effect conditions is only .19, despite the overall *F* test power of .31!

7a. χ^2 test that k proportions are equal.   This parallels the situation for *F* tests, power varying with *k*. For three groups of 23, power to detect a medium effect is .38; for four groups of 17, .30; for seven groups of 10, .21. The same considerations apply when it is necessary to follow-up the overall χ^2 test.

7b. χ^2 contingency test.   As above, power varies with *df*. For example, for the contingency tables illustrated above (Size of Effect) assuming 68 cases in each, power is as follows: *df* = 2, .50; *df* = 3, .37; *df* = 4 (both tables) .30.

Given these generally meager power values for 68 cases, it is not surprising to find a mean power value assuming medium effect size over the 70 articles of only .48. Are these studies representative of abnormal-social research undertaken? It follows from our earlier reasoning that, if anything, published studies are more powerful than those which do not reach publication, certainly not less powerful. Therefore, the going antecedent probability of success of current abnormal-social research is much lower than one would like to see it, a situation which is capable of improvement by increasing the size of the samples customarily employed.[11] The investigator on

---

11. Other means for increasing power: improving experimental design efficiency and/or experimental control, and renouncing a slavish adherence to a standard Type I level, usually .05. In some investigations, an increase in the latter may result in so large an increase in power as to justify the greater Type I risk. However, normal scientific conservatism would not tolerate too long a trip on this road. Increased sample size is likely to prove the most effective general prescription for improving power.

the track of a subtle issue in the area of subception who plans to study 30 cases would do well to take heed!

The consequences of this state of affairs are fairly obvious. If many investigators are running high risks of failing to detect substantial population effects, much research is resulting in spuriously "negative" results. One can only speculate on the number of potentially fruitful lines of investigation which have been abandoned because Type II errors were made, a situation which is substantially remediable by using double or triple the original sample size. A generation of researchers could be profitably employed in repeating interesting studies which originally used inadequate sample sizes. Unfortunately, the ones most needing such repetition are least likely to have appeared in print.

It is quite likely that similar conditions prevail in other areas of psychological research. It is recommended that psychological investigators attend to issues of power in their planning of experiments, and that the definitions of size of effect employed in this survey be used conventionally. In the absence of any basis for specifying an alternative to the null hypothesis for purposes of power analysis, the criterion values for a medium effect (Table 2) are offered as a convention.

Summary

The purpose of the study was to survey the articles of the *Journal of Abnormal and Social Psychology*, 1960, **61,** from the point of view of the power of their statistical tests to reject their major null hypotheses, for defined levels of departure of population parameters from null conditions, i.e., size of effect. Conventional test conditions were employed in power determination: nondirectional tests at the .05 level of significance.

For this purpose, extensive tables for the common statistical tests were prepared from which the power of a test could be read as a function of sample size and size of effect. From these tables, the power to detect small, medium, and large effects of each statistical test employed in each article was determined, and the mean power values for the major tests of each article were used to characterize that article. The distributions of these values were presented and summarized.

It was found that the average power (probability of rejecting false null hypotheses) over the 70 research studies was .18 for small effects, .48 for medium effects, and .83 for large effects.

These values are deemed to be far too small and suggest that much research in the abnormal-social area has lead to the failure to reject null hypotheses which are in fact false. This in turn may have lead to frequent premature abandonment of useful lines of investigation.

Since power is a direct monotonic function of sample size, it is recommended that investigators use larger sample sizes than they customarily do. It is further recommended that research *plans* be routinely subjected to power analysis, using as conventions the criteria of population effect size employed in this survey.

References

Anderson, N. H. Scales and statistics: Parametric and nonparametric. *Psychol. Bull.*, 1961, **58**, 305–316.

Cronbach, L. J. *Essentials of psychological testing.* (2nd ed.) New York: Harper, 1960.

Dixon, W. J. and F. J. Massey, Jr. *Introduction to statistical analysis.* (2nd ed.) New York: McGraw-Hill, 1957.

Eisenhart, C., M. W. Hastay, and W. A. Wallis. *Techniques of statistical analysis.* New York: McGraw-Hill, 1947.

Fix, E., J. L. Hodges, Jr., and E. L. Lehmann. The restricted χ^2 test. In *Studies in probability and statistics dedicated to Harald Cramér.* Stockholm: Almquist and Wiksell, 1959.

Guilford, J. P. *Fundamental statistics in psychology and education.* (3rd ed.) New York: McGraw-Hill, 1956.

Husén, T. *Psychological twin research.* Stockholm: Almquist and Wiksell, 1959.

Mosteller, F., R. E. K. Rourke, and G. B. Thomas, Jr. *Probability and statistics.* Reading, Mass.: Addison-Wesley, 1961.

Patnaik, P. B. The noncentral χ^2 and F-distributions and their applications. *Biometrika*, 1949, **36**, 202–232.

Siegel, S. *Nonparametric statistics for the behavioral sciences.* New York: McGraw-Hill, 1956.

Super, D. E. *Appraising vocational fitness.* New York: Harper, 1949.

Walker, Helen M. and J. Lev. *Statistical inference.* New York: Holt, 1953.

12

degrees of freedom

Helen M. Walker

A concept of central importance to modern statistical theory which few textbooks have attempted to clarify is that of "degrees of freedom." For the mathematician who reads the original papers in which statistical theory is now making such rapid advances, the concept is a familiar one needing no particular explanation. For the person who is unfamiliar with N-dimensional geometry or who knows the contributions to modern sampling theory only from secondhand sources such as textbooks, this concept often seems almost mystical, with no practical meaning.

Tippett, one of the few textbook writers who attempt to make any general explanation of the concept, begins his account (p. 64) with the sentence, "This conception of *degrees of freedom* is not altogether easy to attain, and we cannot attempt a full justification of it here; but we shall show its reasonableness and shall illustrate it, hoping that as a result of familiarity with its use the reader will appreciate it." Not only do most texts omit all mention of the concept but many actually give incorrect formulas and procedures because of ignoring it.

Reprinted from the *Journal of Educational Psychology* **31,** 253–269 (1940), by permission of the author and the publisher.

In the work of modern statisticians, the concept of degrees of freedom is not found before "Student's" paper of 1908, it was first made explicit by the writings of R. A. Fisher, beginning with his paper of 1915 on the distribution of the correlation coefficient, and has only within the decade or so received general recognition. Nevertheless the concept was familiar to Gauss and his astronomical associates. In his classical work on the *Theory of the Combination of Observations* (Theoria Combinationis Observationum Erroribus Minimis Obnoxiae) and also in a work generalizing the theory of least squares with reference to the combination of observations (Ergänzung zur Theorie der den kleinsten Fehlern unterworfen Combination der Beobachtungen, 1826), he states both in words and by formula that the number of observations is to be decreased by the number of unknowns estimated from the data to serve as divisor in estimating the standard error of a set of observations, or in our terminology

$$\sigma^2 = \frac{\Sigma\, x^2}{N - r},$$

where r is the number of parameters to be estimated from the data.

The present paper is an attempt to bridge the gap between mathematical theory and common practice, to state as simply as possible what degrees of freedom represent, why the concept is important, and how the appropriate number may be readily determined. The treatment has been made as nontechnical as possible, but this is a case where the mathematical notion is simpler than any nonmathematical interpretation of it. The paper will be developed in four sections: (1) The freedom of movement of a point in space when subject to certain limiting conditions, (2) The representation of a statistical sample by a single point in N-dimensional space, (3) The import of the concept of degrees of freedom, and (4) Illustrations of how to determine the number of degrees of freedom appropriate for use in certain common situations.

**The freedom of movement
of a point in space when
subject to certain limiting
conditions**

As a preliminary introduction to the idea, it may be helpful to consider the freedom of motion possessed by certain familiar objects, each of which is treated as if it were a mere moving point without size. A drop of oil sliding along a coil spring or a bead on a wire has only one degree of freedom for it can move only on a one-dimensional path, no matter how complicated the shape of that path may be. A drop of mercury on a plane surface has two degrees of freedom, moving freely on a two-dimensional surface. A mosquito moving freely in three-dimensional space, has three degrees of freedom.

Considered as a moving point, a railroad train moves backward and forward on a linear path which is a one-dimensional space lying on a two-dimensional space, the earth's surface, which in turn lies within a three-dimensional universe. A single coordinate, distance from some origin, is sufficient to locate the train at any given moment of time. If we consider a four-dimensional universe in which one dimension is of time and the other three dimensions of space, two coordinates will be needed to locate the train, distance in linear units from a spatial origin and distance in time units from a time origin. The train's path which had only one dimension in a space universe has two dimensions in a space-time universe.

A canoe or an automobile moves over a two-dimensional surface which lies upon a three-dimensional space, is a section of a three-dimensional space. At any given moment, the position of the canoe, or auto, can be given by two coordinates. Referred to a four-dimensional space-time universe, three coordinates would be needed to give its location, and its path would be a space of three dimensions, lying upon one of four.

In the same sense an airplane has three degrees of freedom in the usual universe of space, and can be located only if three coordinates are known. These might be latitude, longitude, and altitude; or might be altitude, horizontal distance from some origin, and an angle; or might be direct distance from some origin, and two direction angles. If we consider a given instant of time as a section through the space-time universe, the airplane moves in a four-dimensional path and can be located by four coordinates, the three previously named and a time coordinate.

The degrees of freedom we have been considering relate to the motion of a point, or freedom of translation. In mechanics freedom of *rotation* would be equally important. A point, which has position only, and no size, can be translated but not rotated. A real canoe can turn over, a real airplane can turn on its axis or make a nose dive, and so these real bodies have degrees of freedom of rotation as well as of translation. The parallelism between the sampling problems we are about to discuss and the movement of bodies in space can be brought out more clearly by discussing freedom of translation, and disregarding freedom of rotation, and that has been done in what follows.

If you are asked to choose a pair of numbers (x, y) at random, you have complete freedom of choice with regard to each of the two numbers, have two degrees of freedom. The number pair may be represented by the coordinates of a point located in the x, y plane, which is a two-dimensional space. The point is free to move anywhere in the horizontal direction parallel to the xx' axis, and is also free to move anywhere in the vertical direction, parallel to the yy' axis. There are two independent variables and the point has two degrees of freedom.

Now suppose you are asked to choose a pair of numbers whose sum is 7. It is readily apparent that only one number can be chosen freely, the second being fixed as soon as the first is chosen. Although there are two variables in the situation, there is only one independent variable. The number of degrees of freedom is reduced from two to one by the imposition of the condition $x + y = 7$. The point is not now free to move anywhere in the xy plane but is constrained to remain on the line whose graph is $x + y = 7$, and this line is a one-dimensional space lying in the original two-dimensional space.

Suppose you are asked to choose a pair of numbers such that the sum of their squares is 25. Again it is apparent that only one number can be chosen arbitrarily, the second being fixed as soon as the first is chosen. The point represented by a pair of numbers must lie on a circle with center at the origin and radius 5. This circle is a one-dimensional space lying in the original two-dimensional plane. The point can move only forward or backward along this circle, and has one degree of freedom only. There were two numbers to be chosen ($N = 2$) subject to one limiting relationship ($r = 1$) and the resultant number of degrees of freedom is $N - r = 2 - 1 = 1$.

Suppose we simultaneously impose the two conditions $x + y = 7$ and $x^2 + y^2 = 25$. If we solve these equations algebraically we get only two possible solutions, $x = 3$, $y = 4$, or $x = 4$, $y = 3$. Neither variable can be chosen at will. The point, once free to move in two directions, is now constrained by the equation $x + y = 7$ to move only along a straight line, and is constrained by the equation $x^2 + y^2 = 25$ to move only along the circumference of a circle, and by the two together is confined to the intersection of that line and circle. There is no freedom of motion for the point. $N = 2$ and $r = 2$. The number of degrees of freedom is $N - r = 2 - 2 = 0$.

Consider now a point (x, y, z) in three-dimensional space ($N = 3$). If no restrictions are placed on its coordinates, it can move with freedom in each of three directions, has three degrees of freedom. All three variables are independent. If we set up the restriction $x + y + z = c$, where c is any constant, only two of the numbers can be freely chosen, only two are independent observations. For example, let $x - y - z = 10$. If now we choose, say, $x = 7$ and $y = 9$, then z is forced to be -12. The equation $x - y - z = c$ is the equation of a plane, a two-dimensional space cutting across the original three-dimensional space, and a point lying on this space has two degrees of freedom. ($N - r = 3 - 1 = 2$.) If the coordinates of the (x, y, z) point are made to conform to the condition $x^2 + y^2 + z^2 = k$, the point will be forced to lie on the surface of a sphere whose center is at the origin and whose radius is $\sqrt{k}$. The surface of a sphere is a two-dimensional space. ($N = 3, r = 1, N - r = 3 - 1 = 2$.)

If both conditions are imposed simultaneously, the point can lie only on the intersection of the sphere and the plane, that is, it can move only along the circumference of a circle, which is a one-dimensional figure lying in the original space of three dimensions. ($N - r = 3 - 2 = 1$.) Considered algebraically, we note that solving the pair of equations in three variables leaves us a single equation in two variables. There can be complete freedom of choice for one of these, no freedom for the other. There is one degree of freedom.

The condition $x = y = z$ is really a pair of independent conditions, $x = y$ and $x = z$, the condition $y = z$ being derived from the other two. Each of these is the equation of a plane, and their intersection gives a straight line through the origin making equal angles with the three axes. If $x = y = z$, it is clear that only one variable can be chosen arbitrarily, there is only one independent variable, the point is constrained to move along a single line, there is one degree of freedom.

These ideas must be generalized for N larger than 3, and this generalization is necessarily abstract. Too ardent an attempt to visualize the outcome leads only to confusion. Any set of N numbers determine a single point in N-dimensional space, each number providing one of the N coordinates of that point. If no relationship is imposed upon these numbers, each is free to vary independently of the others, and the number of degrees of freedom is N. Every necessary relationship imposed upon them reduces the number of degrees of freedom by one. Any equation of the first degree connecting the N variables is the equation of what may be called a hyperplane (Better not try to visualize it!) and is a space of $N - 1$ dimensions. If, for example, we consider only points such that the sum of their coordinates is constant, $\Sigma X = c$, we have limited the point to an $N - 1$ space. If we consider only points such that $\Sigma (X - M)^2 = k$, the locus is the surface of a hypersphere with center at the origin and radius equal to $\sqrt{k}$. This surface is called the locus of the point and is a space of $N - 1$ dimensions lying within the original N space. If r such conditions should be imposed simultaneously, the point would be confined to the intersection of the various loci, which would be a space of $N - r$ dimensions lying within the original N space. The number of degrees of freedom would be $N - r$.

The representation of a statistical sample by a point in N-dimensional space

If any N numbers can be represented by a single point in a space of N dimensions, obviously a statistical sample of N cases can be so represented by a single sample point. This device, first employed by R. A. Fisher in 1915 in a celebrated paper ("Frequency distribution of the values of the correlation coefficient in samples from an indefinitely large population") has been an enormously fruitful one, and must be understood by those who hope to follow recent developments.

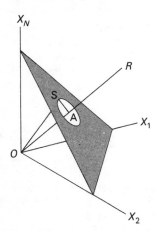

Fig. 1

Let us consider a sample space of N dimensions, with the origin taken at the true population mean, which we will call μ, so that $X_1 - \mu = x_1$, $X_2 - \mu = x_2$, etc., where $X_1, X_2, \ldots X_N$ are the raw scores of the N individuals in the sample. Let M be the mean and s the standard deviation of a sample of N cases. Any set of N observations determines a single sample point, such as S. This point has N degrees of freedom if no conditions are imposed upon its coordinates.

All samples with the same mean will be represented by sample points lying on the hyperplane

$$(X_1 - \mu) + (X_2 - \mu) + \cdots + (X_N - \mu) = N(M - \mu),$$

or $\Sigma X = NM$, a space of $N - 1$ dimensions.

If all cases in a sample were exactly uniform, the sample point would lie upon the line

$$X_1 - \mu = X_2 - \mu = X_3 - \mu = \cdots = X_N - \mu = M - \mu$$

which is the line OR in Fig. 1, a line making equal angles with all the coordinate axes. This line cuts the plane $\Sigma X = NM$ at right angles at a point we may call A. Therefore, A is a point whose coordinates are each equal to $M - \mu$. By a well-known geometric relationship,

$$\overline{OS}^2 = (X_1 - \mu)^2 + (X_2 - \mu)^2 + \cdots + (X_N - \mu)^2$$

$$\overline{OA}^2 = N(M - \mu)^2$$

$$\overline{OS}^2 = \overline{OA}^2 + \overline{AS}^2$$

$$\overline{AS}^2 = \sum (X - \mu)^2 - N(M - \mu)^2 = \sum X^2 - NM^2 = Ns^2$$

Therefore, $OA = (M - \mu)\sqrt{N}$ and $AS = s\sqrt{N}$.

The ratio OA/AS is thus $(M - \mu)/s$ and is proportional to the ratio of the amount by which a sample mean deviates from the population mean to its own standard error. The fluctuation of this ratio from sample to sample produces what is known as the t-distribution.

For computing the variability of the scores in a sample around a population mean which is known *a priori*, there are available N degrees of freedom because the point S moves in N-dimensional space about O; but for computing the variability of these same scores about the mean of their own sample, there are available only $N - 1$ degrees of freedom, because one degree has been expended in the computation of that mean, so that the point S moves about A in a space of only $N - 1$ dimensions.

Fisher has used these spatial concepts to derive the sampling distribution of the correlation coefficient. The full derivation is outside the scope of this paper but certain aspects are of interest here. When we have N individuals each measured in two traits, it is customary to represent the N pairs of numbers by a correlation diagram of N points in two-dimensional space. The same data can, however, be represented by two points in N-dimensional space, one point representing the N values of X and the other the N values of Y. In this frame of reference the correlation coefficient can be shown to be equal to the cosine of the angle between the vectors to the two points, and to have $N - 2$ degrees of freedom.

The import of the concept

If the normal curve adequately described all sampling distributions, as some elementary treatises seem to imply, the concept of degrees of freedom would be relatively unimportant, for this number does not appear in the equation of the normal curve, the shape of the curve being the same no matter what the size of the sample. In certain other important sampling distributions—as for example the Poisson—the same thing is true, that the shape of the distribution is independent of the number of degrees of freedom involved. Modern statistical analysis, however, makes much use of several very important sampling distributions for which the shape of the curve changes with the effective size of the sample. In the equations of such curves, the number of degrees of freedom appears as a parameter (called n in the equations which follow) and probability tables built from these curves must be entered with the correct value of n. If a mistake is made in determining n from the data, the wrong probability value will be obtained from the table, and the significance of the test employed will be wrongly interpreted. The Chi-square distribution, the t-distribution, and the F and z distributions are now commonly used even in elementary work, and the table for each of these must be entered with the appropriate value of n.

Let us now look at a few of these equations to see the role played in them by the number of degrees of freedom. In the formulas which follow, C represents a constant whose value is determined in such a way as to make the total area under the curve equal to unity. Although this constant involves the number of degrees of freedom, it does not need to be considered in reading probability tables because, being a constant multiplier, it does not affect the proportion of area under any given segment of the curve, but serves only to change the scale of the entire figure.

Normal curve

$$y = C_1 e^{-x^2/2\sigma^2}.$$

The number of degrees of freedom does not appear in the equation, and so the shape of the curve is independent of it. The only variables to be shown in a probability table are x/σ and y or some function of y such as a probability value.

Chi-square

$$y = C_2 (\chi^2)^{(n-2)/2} e^{-x^2/2}.$$

The number of degrees of freedom appears in the exponent. When $n = 1$, the curve is J-shaped. When $n = 2$, the equation reduces to $y = C_2 e^{-x^2/2}$ and has the form of the positive half of a normal curve. The curve is always positively skewed, but as n increases it becomes more and more nearly like the normal, and becomes approximately normal when n is 30 or so. A probability table must take account of three variables, the size of Chi-square, the number of degrees of freedom, and the related probability value.

t-distribution

$$y = C_3\left(1 + \frac{t^2}{n}\right)^{-(n+1)/2}$$

The number of degrees of freedom appears both in the exponent and in the fraction t^2/n. The curve is always symmetrical, but is more peaked than the normal when n is small. This curve also approaches the normal form as n increases. A table of probability values must be entered with the computed value of t and also with the appropriate value of n. A few selected values will show the comparison between estimates of significance read from a table of the normal curve and a t-table.

For a normal curve, the proportion of area in both tails of the curve beyond 3σ is .0027. For a t-distribution the proportion is as follows:

n	1	2	5	10	20
p	.204	.096	.030	.014	.007

Again, for a normal curve, the point such that .01 of the area is in the tails, is 2.56σ from the mean.

For a t-distribution, the position of this point is as follows:

n	1	2	3	5	10	20	30
x/σ	63.6	9.9	5.8	4.0	3.2	2.8	2.75

F-distribution and z-distribution

$$y = C_4\frac{F^{(n_1-2)/2}}{(n_1F + n_2)^{(n_1+n_2)/2}} \quad \text{and} \quad y = C_5\frac{e^{n_1s}}{(n_1e^{2s} + n_2)^{(n_1+n_2)/2}}$$

In each of these equations, which provide the tables used in analysis of variance problems, there occurs not only the computed value of F (or of z), but also the two parameters n_1 and n_2, n_1 being the number of degrees of freedom for the mean square in the numerator of F and n_2 the number of degrees of freedom for that in the denominator. Because a probability table must be entered with all three, such a table often shows the values for selected probability values only. The tables published by Fisher give values for $p = .05$, $p = .01$, and $p = .001$; those by Snedecor give $p = .05$ and $p = .01$.

Sampling distribution of r

This is a complicated equation involving as parameters the true correlation in the population, ρ; the observed correlation in the sample, r; and the number of degrees of freedom. If $\rho = 0$ the distribution is symmetrical. If $\rho = 0$ and n is large, the distribution becomes normal. If $\rho \neq 0$ and n is small the curve is definitely skewed. David's *Tables of the Correlation Coefficient* (issued by the Biometrika Office, University College, London, 1938) must be entered with all three parameters.

Determining the appropriate number of degrees of freedom in certain typical problems

A universal rule holds: The number of degrees of freedom is always equal to the number of observations minus the number of necessary relations obtaining among these observations. In geometric terms, the number of observations is the dimensionality of the original space and each relationship represents a section through that space restricting the sample point to a space of one lower dimension. Imposing a relationship upon the observations is equivalent to estimating a parameter from them. For example, the relationship $\Sigma X = NM$ indicates that the mean of the population has been estimated from observations. The number of degrees of freedom is also equal to the number of independent observations, which is the number of original observations minus the number of parameters estimated from them.

Standard Error of a Mean. This is $\sigma_{\text{mean}} = \sigma/\sqrt{N}$ when σ is known for the population. As σ is seldom known *a priori*, we are usually forced to make use of the observed standard deviation in the sample, which we will call s. In this case $\sigma_{\text{mean}} \doteq s/\sqrt{N-1}$, one degree of freedom being lost because deviations have been taken around the sample mean, so that we have imposed one limiting relationship, $\Sigma X = NM$, and have thus restricted the sample point to a hyperplane of $N - 1$ dimensions.

Without any reference to geometry, it can be shown by an algebraic solution that $s\sqrt{N} \doteq \sigma\sqrt{N-1}$. (The symbol $\doteq$ is to be read "tends to equal" or "approximates.")

Goodness of Fit of Normal Curve to a Set of Data. The number of observations is the number of intervals in the frequency distribution for which an observed frequency is compared with the frequency to be expected on the assumption of a normal distribution. If this normal curve has an arbitrary mean and standard deviation agreed upon in advance, the number of degrees of freedom with which we enter the Chi-square table to test goodness of fit is one less than the number of intervals. In this case one restriction is imposed; namely $\Sigma f = \Sigma f'$, where f is an observed and f' a theoretical frequency. If, however, as is more common, the theoretical curve is made to conform to the observed data in its mean and standard deviation, two additional restrictions are imposed; namely $\Sigma fX = \Sigma f'X$ and $\Sigma f(X - M)^2 = \Sigma f'(X - M)^2$, so that the number of degrees of freedom is three less than the number of intervals compared. It is clear that when the curves are made to agree in mean and standard deviation, the discrepancy between observed and theoretical frequencies will be reduced, so the number of degrees of freedom in relation to which that discrepancy is interpreted should also be reduced.

Relationship in a Contingency Table. Suppose we wish to test the existence of a relationship between trait A, for which there are three categories, and trait B, for which there are five, as shown in Fig. 2. We have fifteen cells in the table, giving us fifteen observations, inasmuch as an "observation" is now the frequency in a single cell. If we want to ask whether there is sufficient evidence to believe that in the population from which this sample is drawn A and B are independent, we need to know the cell frequencies which would be expected under that hypothesis. There are then fifteen comparisons to be made between observed frequencies and expected frequencies. But are all fifteen of these comparisons independent?

If we had *a priori* information as to how the traits would be distributed theoretically, then all but one of the cell comparisons would be independent, the last cell frequency being fixed in order to make up the proper total of one hundred fifty, and the degrees of freedom would be $15 - 1 = 14$. This is the situation Karl Pearson had in mind when he first developed his Chi-square test of goodness of fit, and Table XII in Vol. I of his *Tables for Statisticians and Biometricians* is made up on the assumption that the number of degrees of freedom is one less than the number of observations. To use it when that is not the case we merely readjust the value of n with which we enter the table.

In practice we almost never have *a priori* estimates of theoretical frequencies, but must obtain them from the observations themselves, thus imposing restrictions on the number of independent observations and reducing the degrees of freedom available for estimating reliability. In this case, if we estimate the theoretical frequencies from the data, we would estimate the frequency $f'_{11} = (20)(40)/150$ and others in similar fashion. Getting the expected cell frequencies from the observed marginal frequencies imposes the following relationships:

$$f_{11} + f_{21} + f_{31} + f_{41} + f_{51} = 40 \tag{a}$$
$$f_{12} + f_{22} + f_{32} + f_{42} + f_{52} = 60$$
$$f_{13} + f_{23} + f_{33} + f_{43} + f_{53} = 50$$

$$f_{11} + f_{12} + f_{13} = 20 \tag{b}$$
$$f_{21} + f_{22} + f_{23} = 20$$
$$f_{31} + f_{32} + f_{33} = 35$$
$$f_{41} + f_{42} + f_{43} = 30$$
$$f_{51} + f_{52} + f_{53} = 50$$

$$f_{11} + f_{21} + \cdots + f_{51} + f_{12} + \cdots + f_{53} = 150 \tag{c}$$

	A_1	A_2	A_3	
B_1	12	3	5	20
B_2	3	6	11	20
B_3	3	30	2	35
B_4	9	14	7	30
B_5	13	7	25	45
	40	60	50	150

Fig. 2
Observed joint frequency distribution of two traits A and B.

	A_1	A_2	A_3	
B_1	f_{11}	f_{12}	f_{13}	20
B_2	f_{21}	f_{22}	f_{23}	20
B_3	f_{31}	f_{32}	f_{33}	35
B_4	f_{41}	f_{42}	f_{43}	30
B_5	f_{51}	f_{52}	f_{53}	45
	40	60	50	150

Fig. 3
Observed marginal frequencies of two traits A and B.

At first sight, there seem to be nine relationships, but it is immediately apparent that (c) is not a new one, for it can be obtained either by adding the three (a) equations or the five (b) equations. Also any one of the remaining eight can be obtained by appropriate manipulation of the other seven. There are then only seven independent necessary relationships imposed upon the cell frequencies by requiring them to add up to the observed marginal totals. Thus $n = 15 - 7 = 8$, and if we compute Chi-square, we must enter the Chi-square table with

eight degrees of freedom. The same result can be obtained by noting
that two entries in each row and four in each column can be chosen
arbitrarily and there is then no freedom of choice for the remaining
entries.

In general in a contingency table, if c = number of columns and
r = number of rows, the number of degrees of freedom is

$$n = (c - 1)(r - 1) \quad \text{or} \quad n = rc - (r + c - 1).$$

Variance in a Correlation Table. Suppose we have a scatter diagram
with c columns, the frequencies in the various columns being n_1,
$n_2, \ldots, n_c$, the mean values of Y for the columns being $m_1, m_2, \ldots, m_c$,
and the regression values of Y estimated from X being $\tilde{Y}_1, \tilde{Y}_2, \ldots, \tilde{Y}_c$.
Thus for any given column, the sum of the Y's is

$$\sum_1^{n_i} fY = n_i m_i.$$

For the entire table $N = n_1 + n_2 + \cdots + n_c$,

$$NM = \sum_1^c \sum_1^{n_i} fY,$$

so that $NM = n_1 m_1 + n_2 m_2 + \cdots + n_c m_c$.

Now we may be interested in the variance of all the scores about
the total mean, of all the scores about their own column means, of
all the scores about the regression line, of regressed values about the
total mean, of column means about the total mean, or of column means
about the regression line, and we may be interested in comparing two
such variances. It is necessary to know how many degrees of freedom
are available for such comparisons.

a.   Total variance. For the variance of all scores about the total mean,
this is

$$s^2 = \frac{1}{N} \sum_1^N (Y - M)^2,$$

we have N observations and only one restriction; namely, $\Sigma fY = NM$.
Thus there are $N - 1$ degrees of freedom.

b.   Variance of regressed values about total mean. The equation for
the regressed values being

$$\tilde{Y} - M_y = r \frac{s_x}{s_y}(X - M_x),$$

it is clear that as soon as x is known, y is also known. The sample point can move only on a straight line. There is only one degree of freedom available for the variance of regressed values.

c.   *Variance of scores about regression line.* There are N residuals of the form $Y - \tilde{Y}$ and their variance is the square of the standard error of estimate, or $s_y^2(1 - r_{xy}^2)$. There are N observations and two restrictions; namely,

$$\sum f(Y - \tilde{Y}) = 0$$

and

$$\sum f(Y - Y)^2 = Ns_y^2(1 - r_{xy}^2).$$

Thus there are $N - 2$ degrees of freedom available.

d.   *Variance of scores about column means.* If from each score we subtract not the regression value but the mean of the column in which it stands, the variance of the residuals thus obtained will be $s_y^2(1 - E^2)$ where E is the correlation ratio obtained from the sample. There are N such residuals. For each column we have the restriction

$$\sum_1^{n_i} fY = n_i m_i$$

making c restrictions in all. The number of degrees of freedom for the variance within columns is therefore $N - c$.

e.   *Variance of column means about total means.* To compute this variance we have c observations, i.e., the means of c columns, restricted by the single relation

$$NM = \sum_1^c n_i m_i,$$

and therefore have $c - 1$ degrees of freedom. The variance itself can be proved to be $s_y^2 E^2$, and represents the variance among the means of columns.

f.   *Variance of column means about regression line.* If for each column we find the difference $m_i - \tilde{Y}_i$ between the column mean and the regression value, and then find

$$\frac{1}{N} \sum_1^c f_i(m_i - \tilde{Y}_i)^2,$$

the result will be $s_y^2(E^2 - r^2)$ which is a variance representing the departure of the means from linearity. There is one such difference for each column, giving us c observations, and these observations are restricted by the two relationships,

$$\sum_1^c f_i(m_i - \tilde{Y}_i) = 0$$

and

$$\sum_1^c f_i(m_i - \tilde{Y}_i)^2 = Ns_y^2(E^2 - r^2).$$

Therefore, we have $c - 2$ degrees of freedom.

The following scheme shows these relationships in summary form.

Source of Variation	Formula	Degrees of Freedom
d. Scores about column means	$s^2(1 - E^2)$	$N - c$
e. Means about total mean	s^2E^2	$c - 1$
a. Total	s^2	$N - 1$
c. Scores about regression line	$s^2(1 - r^2)$	$N - 2$
b. Regressed values about total mean	s^2r^2	1
a. Total	s^2	$N - 1$
d. Scores about column means	$s^2(1 - E^2)$	$N - c$
f. Column means about regression line	$s^2(E^2 - r^2)$	$c - 2$
c. Scores about regression line	$s^2(1 - r^2)$	$N - 2$
b. Regressed values about total mean	s^2r^2	1
f. Column means about regression line	$s^2(E^2 - r^2)$	$c - 2$
e. Column means about total mean	s^2E^2	$c - 1$
b. Regressed values about total mean	s^2r^2	1
f. Column means about regression line	$s^2(E^2 - r^2)$	$c - 2$
d. Scores about column means	$s^2(1 - E^2)$	$N - c$
a. Total	s^2	$N - 1$

It is apparent that these variances have additive relationships and that their respective degrees of freedom have exactly the same additive relationships.

Tests Based on Ratio of Two Variances.   From any pair of these additive variances, we may make an important statistical test. Thus, to test whether linear correlation exists in the population or not, we may divide $s^2 r^2/1$ by $s^2(1 - r)^2/(N - 2)$ obtaining $r^2(N - 2)/(1 - r^2)$. To test whether a relationship measureable by the correlation ratio exists in the population, we may divide $s^2 E^2/(c - 1)$ by $s^2(1 - E^2)/(N - c)$ obtaining

$$\frac{E^2}{1 - E^2} \cdot \frac{N - c}{c - 1}.$$

To test whether correlation is linear, we may divide $s^2(E^2 - r^2)/(c - 2)$ by $s^2 r^2/1$ obtaining $(E^2 - r^2)/r^2(c - 2)$ or may divide $s^2(E^2 - r^2)/(c - 2)$ by $s^2(1 - E^2)/(N - c)$ obtaining

$$\frac{E^2 - r^2}{1 - E^2} \cdot \frac{N - c}{c - 2}.$$

In each case, the resulting value is referred to Snedecor's *F*-table which must be entered with the appropriate number of degrees of freedom for each variance. Or we may find the logarithm of the ratio to the base *e*, take half of it, and refer the result to Fisher's *z*-table, which also must be entered with the appropriate number of degrees of freedom for each variance.

Partial Correlation.   For a coefficient of correlation of zero order, there are $N - 2$ degrees of freedom. This is obvious, since a straight regression line can be fitted to any two points without residuals, and the first two observations furnish no estimate of the size of *r*. For each variable that is held constant in a partial correlation, one additional degree of freedom is lost, so that for a correlation coefficient of the *p*th order, the degrees of freedom are $N - p - 2$. This places a limit upon the number of meaningful interrelationships which can be obtained from a small sample. As an extreme illustration, suppose twenty-five variables have been measured for a sample of twenty-five cases only, and all the intercorrelations computed, as well as all possible partial correlations—the partials of the twenty-third order will of necessity be either $+1$ or -1, and thus are meaningless. Each such partial will be associated with $25 - 23 - 2$ degrees of freedom. If the partial were not $+1$ or -1 the error variance $\sigma^2(1 - r^2)/(N - p - 2)$ would become infinite, a fantastic situation.

References

Dawson, S.: *An Introduction to the Computation of Statistics.* University of London Press, 1933. Pp. 114. No general discussion. Gives rule for χ^2 only.

Ezekiel, M.: *Methods of Correlation Analysis.* John Wiley & Sons, 1930, p. 121.

Fisher, R. A.: "Frequency distribution of the values of the correlation coefficient in samples from an indefinitely large population." *Biometrika,* 1915, **10,** 507–521. First application of n-dimensional geometry to sampling theory.

Fisher, R. A.: *Statistical Methods for Research Workers.* Oliver and Boyd. This has now gone through seven editions. The term "degrees of freedom" does not appear in the index, but the concept occurs constantly throughout the book.

Goulden, C. H.: *Methods of Statistical Analysis.* John Wiley & Sons, Inc., 1939. See index.

Guilford, J. P.: *Psychometric Methods.* McGraw-Hill, 1936. P. 308.

Mills, F. C.: *Statistical Methods Applied to Economics and Business.* Henry Holt & Co., 2nd ed., 1938. See index.

Rider, P. R.: "A survey of the theory of small samples." *Annals of Mathematics.* 1930, **31,** 577–628. Published as a separate monograph by Princeton University Press. Gives geometric approach to sampling distributions.

Rider, P. R.: *An Introduction to Modern Statistical Methods.* John Wiley & Sons, Inc., 1939. See index. While there is no general explanation of the meaning of degrees of freedom, this book gives a careful and detailed explanation of how the number of degrees of freedom is to be found in a large variety of situations.

Snedecor, G. W.: *Statistical Methods.* Collegiate Press, Inc., 1937, 1938. See index.

Snedecor, G. W.: *Calculation and Interpretation of Analysis of Variance and Covariance.* Collegiate Press, Inc., 1934, pp. 9–10.

Tippett, L. H. C.: *The Methods of Statistics.* Williams and Norgate, Ltd., 1931. One of the few attempts to treat the concept of degrees of freedom in general terms, but without geometric background, is made on pages 64–65.

Yule and Kendall: *Introduction to the Theory of Statistics.* Charles Griffin & Co. London, 1937. Pp. 415–416, 436.

block 3

13. Moses, L. E. Non-parametric statistics for psychological research. *Psychol. Bull*, 1952, **49,** 122–143.

¹4. Boneau, C. A. A comparison of the power of the *U* and *t* tests. *Psychol. Rev.*, 1962, **69,** 246–256.

15. Bresnahan, Jean L., and M. M. Shapiro. A general equation and technique for the exact partitioning of chi-square contingency tables. *Psychol. Bull.*, 1966, **66,** 252–262.

16. McNemar, Q. Note on the sampling error of the difference between correlated proportions or percentages. *Psychometrika*, 1947, **12,** 153–157.

17. Edwards, A. L. Note on the "correction for continuity" in testing the significance of the difference between correlated proportions. *Psychometrika*, 1948, **13,** 185–187.

18. Gaito, J. Non-parametric methods in psychological research. *Psych. Reports*, 1959, **5,** 115–125.

19. Boneau, C. A. The effects of violations of assumptions underlying the *t* test. *Psych. Bull.*, 1960, **57,** 49–64.

The relationship between numerical scale and choice of statistical test was examined in Block 1. Another aspect of the overall question relating to the choice of statistical test concerns the effects of violations of the assumptions underlying parametric tests relative to nonparametric tests.

Gaito's article presents a theoretical discussion of the advantages and disadvantages of nonparametric techniques relative to parametric techniques.

Boneau (1960) presents an empirical study demonstrating the robustness of the t-test when several of the underlying assumptions are violated.

An excellent overview of nonparametric statistical techniques is presented in Moses' article.

Interestingly, Boneau, whom we have previously identified as an advocate of the "strong statistics" school, presents an empirical study in which he concludes that the Mann-Whitney U test compares favorably in power with the t-test.

The two articles by Gaito (1959) and Boneau (1960) raise serious doubts about the necessity of nonparametric techniques in situations where there is an alternative parametric test. However, there are many situations in which there is no appropriate parametric technique. The other articles in Block 3 present significant facets of the use of nonparametric statistics and deal with specific aspects relating to nonparametric techniques.

13

non-parametric statistics
for psychological research

Lincoln E. Moses

It has been said that "everybody believes in the law of errors [the normal distribution], the experimenters because they think it is a mathematical theorem, the mathematicians because they think it is an experimental fact."[1] There are excellent theoretical reasons to explain the preeminent position which the normal distribution has held in the development of statistical theory.[2]

On the other hand, at some time or other nearly every experimenter must work with samples which he knows do not come from a normal distribution. If he knows what the distribution actually is then he

From: L. E. Moses, "Non-parametric statistics for psychological research," *Psychological Bulletin* **49**, 1952, 122–143. Copyright © 1952 by the American Psychological Association, and reproduced by permission.

1. Cramér cites Poincare's quotation of this famous remark by Lippman. (Cramér, H., *Mathematical methods of statistics*, Princeton Univ. Press, 1946. P. 232.)

2. Perhaps the most outstanding of these is the so-called Central Limit Theorem which specifies (roughly) that means of "large" (enough) samples from *any* population (except for some pathological cases which cannot occur in practice) are normally distributed. The discussion in this paper is not concerned with the "large sample case."

may find a transformation such that his transformed data *are* observations from a normal distribution, or he may find a special theory already worked out (as for, say, the Poisson distribution). More often he has no such knowledge of the population distribution, and then he must choose between applying the textbook methods in violation of their underlying assumptions, or of finding valid techniques which have no underlying assumptions concerning the shape of the parent population.

Until about fifteen years ago this was merely Hobson's choice, since about the only distribution-free methods were rank correlation and χ^2 tests. But there has recently been a great growth in statistical methodology which provides the experimenter with tools free of assumptions about the population distribution. These techniques are generally referred to as non-parametric methods, or sometimes, distribution free methods.

It is the purpose of this paper to present some of the principal methods, and an intuitive explanation of their rationale, properties, and applicability, with a view to facilitating their use by workers in psychological research.

In many, but not all, of the methods discussed, the data to which the tests are applied are not the original measurements in the sample but simply their ranks, or perhaps only their signs. This feature of the methods arouses some criticism. It is intuitively obvious that a statistical procedure that replaces each of the two sets of numbers below by the *same* set of plus and minus signs:

$-8, -3, -2.1, -1.6, .3$ $- - - - +$

$-14, -14, -9.4, -.2, 5.7$ $- - - - +$

is not using all the information the data provide—is "throwing away" information. This is a less telling indictment than it seems to be. The relevant question is not "How much information does a certain statistical procedure throw away?", but rather "Of the methods available—classical, or non-parametric—which best uses the information in the sample?" Since the answer to the question will depend on the sort of population from which the sample comes, no general answer can be given. In the literature of mathematical statistics [3, 23, 26] there are examples of distributions where a non-parametric test which "throws away information" is clearly superior to a *t*-test, for instance. How the comparison would work in any given case is a matter of conjecture. The following advantages and disadvantages of the non-parametric methods should be considered:

*Advantages of non-
parametric methods*

1. Whatever may be the form of the distribution from which the sample has been drawn, a non-parametric test of a specified significance level actually *has* that significance level (provided that the sample has been drawn at random; in certain cases as will be noted, it is also necessary to assume that the distribution is continuous).

2. If samples are very small, e.g., six, there is in effect no alternative to a non-parametric test (unless the parent distribution really is known).

3. If the sample consists of observations from several *different* populations there may be a suitable non-parametric treatment.

4. The methods are usually easier to apply than the classical techniques.

5. If the data are inherently of the nature of ranks, not measurements, they can be treated directly by non-parametric methods without precariously assuming some special form for the underlying distribution.

6. In certain cases data can only be taken as "better" or "worse," that is, an observation can only be characterized as a plus or minus. Obviously, the classical tests are not directly applicable to such data.

*Disadvantages of non-
parametric methods*

1. If non-parametric tests rather than normal-theory tests are applied to normal data then they are wasteful of data. The degree of wastefulness is measured by the "efficiency" of the non-parametric test. If, for example, a test has 80 percent efficiency this means that *where the data are from a normal distribution*, the appropriate classical test would be just as effective with a sample of 20 percent smaller size. The efficiency thus expresses the relative merits of the non-parametric test and the classical test under the conditions *where the normal test is correct*, but does not tell us how the tests will compare on nonnormal data.

2. The non-parametric tests and tables of significance values are widely scattered in the periodical literature.

3.   For large samples some of the non-parametric methods require a great amount of labor, unless approximations are employed.

Tests based on plus or minus

The Sign Test. One of the best known and most widely applicable of the techniques to be discussed in this paper is the statistical sign test. A complete treatment will be found in [2]. In many cases where an experimenter wishes to establish that two treatments are different (or that a particular one of the two is better) he is able to employ matched pairs, one member of each pair being assigned (at random) to treatment *A*, the other to treatment *B*. The classical technique is to apply a *t*-test to the differences; the underlying assumptions are that the differences are normally distributed with the same variance. The assumptions underlying the sign test are simply: (a) that the variable under consideration has a continuous distribution and (b) that both members of any pair are treated similarly—except for the experimental variable. There is an assumption neither of normality nor of similar treatment of the various pairs. Thus the different pairs may be of different socio-economic status, age, IQ, etc., so long as within each pair such relevant extranea are comparable. The hypothesis tested is that "The median difference is zero."[3] The test is performed by considering the differences $X_{Ai} - X_{Bi}$ and noting whether the sign is plus or minus. If the null hypothesis is true we expect about an equal number of plus and minus signs. The hypothesis is rejected if there are too few of one sign. The probability level of any result can be evaluated by the binomial expansion with $p = \frac{1}{2}$ and *N* equals the number of pairs. Tables of significance values for various sample sizes are available [1]. A table of sample sizes necessary to detect with probability .95 a departure from the null hypothesis of various degrees (e.g., that $P(X_A > X_B) = .3$) at significance levels .01, .05, .10, .25 is given by Dixon and Mood [2]. For $N \geq 30$ the normal approximation to the binomial will suffice.

If it is desired to test not merely that treatments *A* and *B* differ, but that the treatment *A* is actually better than treatment *B*, a significant result can arise only if the number of minus signs is too small.

---

3.   The hypothesis is also properly expressed:

$$P(X_A > X_B) = P(X_B > X_A) = \tfrac{1}{2}.$$

This is read in words: the probability that X_A will exceed X_B is equal to the probability that X_B will exceed X_A (and thus equal to $\frac{1}{2}$). X_A and X_B are two members of a pair.

An extension of the sign test will permit one to determine whether A is better than B by, say, 5 points. Formally the null hypothesis is:

$$P(X_A > X_B + 5) \leq \tfrac{1}{2}.^4$$

In this case one considers the differences

$$X_{Ai} - (X_{Bi} + 5)$$

and rejects the null hypothesis for too few minus signs.

Another extension enables one to determine whether A is better than B by some specified percentage—say 10 percent. The null hypothesis is: $P(X_A > 1.10X_B) \leq \tfrac{1}{2}$. If a significantly small number of the differences $X_{Ai} - (X_{Bi})(1.10)$ are negative the null hypothesis is rejected. Both these extensions are applicable only where the numbers are additive and the second is legitimate only if there is a zero point on the scale.

The efficiency of the sign test (in the sense defined) declines from around 95 percent for $N = 6$ [**25**] to 62 percent for very large samples. Where data are easily gotten, the extraordinary simplicity of computation sometimes justifies taking a larger sample and using the sign test, even though the classical methods would be justified and more efficient. In certain cases there is no substitute for the sign test, as where a pair of protocols can be assessed as to which exhibits more "cooperation" but there is little hope of a numerical evaluation.

The Median Test. In some cases where two treatments (or groups) are to be compared as to whether they are drawn from populations having the same median (or to determine whether a particular one of the two populations has a smaller median), it is not possible to work with matched pairs. The hypothesis can be tested by the median test (16, p. 394). The samples need not be of equal size. Suppose there are n X's and m Y's. Compute the median for the combined sample of $n + m$ observations. If the samples do come from populations with the same median then we should expect about half of the X's to be above the common median and about half below, similarly for the Y's. If the relative proportions are too discrepant, we reject the hypothesis of equality.

To perform the test, record a plus for any observation above the common median, a minus for any observation below the median. Then

---

4.   In words this is read: the probability is at most $\tfrac{1}{2}$ that X_A will exceed X_B by 5. The null hypothesis can also be expressed: the median difference $X_A - X_B$ is equal to at most 5 in the population.

construct a 2 × 2 contingency table. For instance, suppose that an experiment yielded the following data:

Control Group: (X) 10, 15, 13, 12, 12, 14, 11, 9

Experimental Group: (Y) 7, 7, 8, 6, 13, 9

All observations greater than or equal to 11 are +'s; all 10 or less are −'s.

	+	−
Experimental Group	1	5
Control Group	6	2

The significance of the data is evaluated in the same manner as if this were a 2 × 2 test of independence. For such small frequencies as these Fisher's exact method must be used [5, Sec. 21.02]; for large enough frequencies χ^2 with one degree of freedom is the test statistic, Yates's correction being used unless the number of cases is large. If the hypothesis is being tested against an alternative on one side only, i.e., the question asked of the data is not "are the two medians equal," but "is Md $(X) \geq$ Md (Y)," the ordinary techniques associated with χ^2 and one-sided test apply.

The assumptions underlying this test are that the X's and Y's are random samples from their respective populations, and that the population distributions are of the same form, differing only by a translation up or down the scale. Although the test is derived using the second assumption, Mood states that the test "is sensitive primarily to differences in location and very little to differences in shape."

Tests based on rank order

There is a group of important methods which deal with the data in terms of their ranks. Four of the most important will be discussed here: a rank test for matched pairs [27, 28]; the "T" test of Wilcoxon for two unmatched samples [27, 28], together with its extension by Mann and Whitney [13]; the analysis of variance by ranks [6]; the run test.

Wilcoxon's Matched Pairs Signed Ranks Test. Where the experimenter has paired scores X_{Ai} under treatment A and X_{Bi} under treatment B, he can rank the differences *in order of absolute size;* he may be unable to give numerical scores to the observations in each pair and still be able to rank the differences in order of absolute size. The ranking is done by giving rank 1 to the numerically *least* difference, rank 2 to the next least, etc. If methods *A* and *B* are equivalent, that is, if there is no difference and the null hypothesis is true, he should expect some of the larger, and some of the smaller, absolute deviations to arise with *A* being superior, some with *B* superior. That is, the sum of the ranks where *A* is favored should be about equal to the sum of the ranks where *B* is favored. If the sum of the ranks for the negative differences is too small, or if the sum of the ranks for the positive differences is too small, the null hypothesis is to be rejected. Tables of significance values for the smaller sum of ranks will be found in [27] for *n* (the number of pairs) equal to 7 through 16. Tables for *n* from 7 to 25 are available in [29]. For $n \geq 25$ the sum of ranks T may be taken as normally distributed with mean = $\bar{T} = n(n + 1)/4$ and standard deviation $\sqrt{(2n + 1)\bar{T}/6}$. For example: suppose that seven pairs of rats are divided into a control and an experimental group. Suppose that the data are their times to run a certain maze and are as shown in Table 1.

Table 1
Illustrative data for test of significance using Wilcoxon's matched pairs signed ranks test.

Pair	Exp.	Control	Diff. Exp-Control	Rank Diff.	Ranks with Less Frequent Sign
(a)	65	51	14	6	
(b)	60	44	16	7	
(c)	71	64	7	4	
(d)	52	55	-3	1	1
(e)	62	49	13	5	
(f)	43	38	5	2	
(g)	58	52	6	3	
Total of ranks with less frequent sign					1

First, it is worth noting that these data are amenable to treatment by the sign test. Six of the differences have the same sign. The probability of six or more signs alike, if in fact the median difference is zero, is equal to $16/128 = 1/8$. Therefore, these data would not be regarded as cause for rejection using the sign test. But a closer examination of the data shows not only that there was only one negative difference but that it was the smallest difference in the set. These data argue more strongly against the null hypothesis than would the same set of differences with, say, pair (e) being the sole negative difference (or indeed any other one difference) though any of these possible samples would be treated identically by the sign test. It turns out that application of the rank test under consideration will adjudge these data as significant; essentially the different answer arises from exactly the considerations just sketched—the *size* of the sole negative difference is taken into account.

Wilcoxon's tables tell us that for $n = 7$ a rank total of 2 or less for one of the groups is significant at level .05, and the null hypothesis of equality of treatments is rejected. The tables referred to are for two-sided tests. If one desires to test a one-sided hypothesis he may use the .05 level to determine a test of significance level .025, provided that the observed values lie in the direction of rejecting the one-sided hypothesis. Similar remarks apply to other significance levels.

Mann-Whitney "U" Test. Where the observations are not made on matched pairs, but two unmatched groups are to be compared, the Mann-Whitney "U" test (or in the case of equal sized groups, its equivalent, the Wilcoxon "T" test) for two samples can be applied.

The null hypothesis which is tested is that the two groups of observations—say n X's and m Y's—have been drawn from a common population (that is, "there is no difference"). The test is designed to detect (roughly stated) whether one population has a larger mean than the other. Precisely stated, it is designed to guard against the alternative hypotheses that for every a,

$$P(X > a) \geq P(Y > a) \qquad \text{or} \qquad P(X > a) \leq P(Y > a).$$

A special case (unnecessarily restrictive) is where X and Y are assumed to have the same distribution except for a translation along the scale, so that the X's are all smaller—or all larger—than the "corresponding" Y's; here the null hypothesis says that there is no translation at all, and the test has the property that if in fact there is a positive or negative translation, then with a sufficiently large sample the test will reject the null hypothesis with any desired degree of probability.

To apply the test one arranges the $m + n$ observations in increasing order of size (algebraic sign not being ignored) and substitutes their ranks (1 for the smallest, $m + n$ for the largest). If the two samples were of equal size, so that $m = n$, the sum of the ranks for the X's should about equal the sum of the ranks for the Y's under the null hypothesis. If $m \neq n$ then the sums would be roughly proportional to the sizes m and n. The test consists in determining whether the observed discrepancy is too large to have arisen reasonably by chance, with the null hypothesis being true.

Tables of significance values for all possible pairs of sample sizes with $m \leq 8$, $n \leq 8$ are given in [13]. For m and n both greater than 8 the test statistic is nearly normally distributed and the test of significance is made by employing this fact. If m, $n \geq 8$, then U is normally distributed with mean $mn/2$ and standard deviation $\sqrt{mn(n + m + 1)/12}$; one has merely to rank the $m + n$ observations from least to greatest, find T, the sum of the Y ranks, and from this calculate U, and see whether it is too many standard deviations removed from its expected value, $mn/2$.

As an example, suppose that there were 8 X's and 6 Y's, so that $m = 6$, $n = 8$ and that the data arranged in order of size were as shown in Table 2. The tables of significance are given in terms of U where

$$U = mn + \frac{m(m + 1)}{2} - T.$$

Here $U = 6 \times 8 + (6 \times 7/2) - 54 = 15$.

The table for $n = 8$ tells us that a U as small as 15 has a probability level of .141; so that the null hypothesis is accepted.

In using these tables the reader will find that the probability of small values of U is given. To find the probability $U \geq k$ where k is a number larger than those given in the tables he uses the identity:

$$P(U \geq k \mid n\ X\text{'s}, m\ Y\text{'s}) = P(U \leq mn - k \mid n\ X\text{'s}, m\ Y\text{'s}).$$

Table 2
Illustration for the Mann-Whitney "U" test

Variable	Observation	Rank
X	10.2	1
X	12.8	2
Y	13.4	3
X	13.5	4
X	16.0	5
Y	17.1	6
Y	17.3	7
X	18.0	8
X	18.2	9
X	19.0	10
Y	19.4	11
X	19.5	12
Y	21.3	13
Y	24.0	14

ΣX ranks = 51.

$T = \Sigma Y$ ranks = 54.

It is further to be noted that m and n are entirely symmetrical, so that

$$P\{U = k \mid n \; X\text{'s}, m \; Y\text{'s}\} = P\{U = k \mid m \; X\text{'s}, n \; Y\text{'s}\}.$$

As an example, suppose that an experimenter has 5 X's and 8 Y's and that the sum of the Y ranks, T, is 39. Then

$$U = 6 \times 8 + \frac{8(8 + 1)}{2} - 39 = 45.$$

This is a large value of U and is not tabled; to decide whether or not it is significantly large we note that

$$P(U \geq 45) = P(U \leq 6 \times 8 - 45) = P(U \leq 3).$$

The tables tell us that this probability is .002.

Analysis of Variance with Ranked Data. The assumptions underlying the analysis of variance are: the observations are independent; they are drawn from normal populations all of which have the same variance; the means in these normal populations are linear combinations of "effects" due to row and/or columns, etc., that is, effects are additive.

Correlation among the observations would be perhaps the most dangerous assumption failure; but careful design should usually eliminate this. In some cases both normality of distribution and homogeneity of variance can be approximated either in the data, or by some transformation. In other cases this cannot be done. The analysis of variance by ranks is a very easy procedure and does not depend on such assumptions. It has the further advantage of enabling data which are inherently only ranks to be examined for significance.

Let there be n replications of an experiment where each subject undergoes a different one of p treatments. In each replication there are a different p subjects. Data from such an experiment might be as follows:

Table 3
Illustration for analysis of variance with ranked data

	Treatment				
	A	B	C	D	E
Group 1	11(2)	14(4)	13(3)	9(1)	20(5)
Group 2	12(3)	11(2)	13(4)	10(1)	18(5)
Group 3	16(3)	17(4)	14(2)	13(1)	19(5)
Group 4	9(1)	11(3)	14(4)	10(2)	16(5)
Rank totals	9	13	13	5	20

The numbers appearing in parentheses are the ranks from least to greatest *within each row* (replication). If the treatments A, B, C, D, E ($p = 5$) are not different, then the rank totals would be expected to turn out about equal. In the present example there seems to be a marked disparity. To evaluate its significance we compute the statistic χ_r^2, done below, which has approximately the χ^2 distribution with $p - 1$ degrees of freedom.

$$\chi_r^2 = \frac{12}{np(p + 1)} \times \text{Sum (rank totals)}^2 - 3n(p + 1).$$

Here $n = 4$, $p = 5$ and the statistic becomes:

$$\chi_r^2 = \frac{12}{120}(844) - 12(6) = 12.4.$$

For 4 degrees of freedom this is significant at level .02 but not .01.

If the groups 1, 2, 3, 4 in the example themselves represented four treatments, or age levels, etc., then a test of the equality of those four treatments could also be made by interchanging rows and columns. For that test χ_r^2 would have 3 degrees of freedom since then $p = 4$, $n = 5$.

A full treatment of the mathematical basis for the test is given by Friedman [6]. Kendall and Smith [12] give exact probabilities for small m and n, and a detailed consideration of the closeness of approximation and recommendation for evaluation of significance levels are given in Friedman's article [7]. Wilcoxon [29] gives several instructive illustrations showing, among other things, how interactions can be tested.

Wald-Wolfowitz Run Test. The final test employing ranked data which will be considered is the Wald-Wolfowitz run test. This is a test of the hypothesis that two samples (not necessarily of equal size) have been drawn from a common population. It has the property that if the X's and Y's are not from a common population then, no matter in what way the populations differ (dispersion, median, skewness, etc.) the test will—for sufficiently large samples—reject the null hypothesis with probability as near to 1 as is desired. The application of the test is extremely simple.

Just as for the U test, arrange the combined sample of m Y's and n X's in increasing order. Then a run is defined as a sequence of letters of the same kind which cannot be extended by incorporating an adjacent observation. Thus there are 9 runs below:

$$\underline{X_1 \ X_2} \ Y_1 \ \underline{X_3} \ Y_2 \ Y_3 \ Y_4 \ Y_5 \ \underline{X_4 \ X_5} \ Y_6 \ \underline{X_6 \ X_7 \ X_8} \ Y_7 \ \underline{X_9 \ X_{10}}.$$

The X runs are underlined; the Y runs stand between them.

Now if the two samples are from a common population then the X's and Y's will generally be well mixed and the number of runs will be large. But if the X population has a much higher median, then there is to be expected a long run of Y's at one end, a long run of X's at the other, and consequently a reduced total number of runs. If the X's come from a population with much greater dispersion then there should be a long run of X's at each end, and a reduced total number of runs. Similar arguments apply to opposite skewness, etc. Generally, then, rejection of the null hypothesis will be indicated if the runs are too few in number. An important application of the run test is to test randomness of grouping; in some such cases *either* too many or too few runs might be basis for rejection. A nice example is given by Swed and Eisenhart [24] where the question at issue is, are seats at a lunch counter a half hour before the rush hour occupied at random? Very many runs of occupied and empty seats would clearly be an *a priori* cause for rejection. So would too few runs if the possibility of friends coming together was to be considered. In the example to which the U test was earlier applied, only too few runs would be reasonable cause for rejection if the X's and Y's represented, say, examination scores for two different statistics classes.

The run test can also be applied to a series of events ordered in time. Let there be n observations arranged in order of the time at which they were taken. Let those greater than the median be denoted by X, those less than the median by Y. If one suspects a time trend—like gradual increase—or a "bunching" in time due to change in attitude, etc., he would reject for too few runs.

Tables of significance for the run test are given by Swed and Eisenhart [24], for $m, n \leq 20$. For larger samples the number of runs d can be taken as being normally distributed with

mean $= (2mn/m + n) + 1$

and

standard deviation $= \sqrt{\dfrac{2mn(2mn - m - n)}{(m + n)^2(m + n - 1)}}$.

Mood [16] states that for practical purposes this approximation will suffice for $m, n \geq 10$. To apply this large sample theory one merely decides before taking the sample whether rejection is indicated by too many, or too few, (or either) runs and then sees whether d is too many standard deviations removed from its expected value in the rejection direction.

Mathematical investigations of this test indicate that because it guards against *all* kinds of difference between the distribution functions of X and Y it is not very powerful against any particular class of alternatives. Thus, if one were interested in detecting whether one population had a greater median than another he would do better to employ a test such as the U test. A related point is that when one rejects the null hypothesis on the basis of the run test, he can assert that the two populations differ—but he has little if any clue as to *how* they differ. Often the purpose is to establish that there is a difference in *means*, or *dispersion*, and the run test gives an answer which is not easy to interpret.

The only assumption involved in the run test is that the common population is continuous. This assumption is involved in all the tests depending on rank presented here. Generally, if there is a small number of ties the average rank for each set of tied observations may be given to each and the test carried through.

Randomization tests

There is a variety of non-parametric tests which employ the numerical values of the data themselves. Among the most important of these are techniques based on the method of randomization. This kind of test was proposed by Fisher [**4,** Sec. 21], and has received extended treatment and development by Pitman [**21, 22**].

Matched Pairs. All the randomization tests are based on parallel logic. The simplest with which to exhibit the rationale is the matched pair case. Suppose, for example, that we have two observations (one under condition A, the other under condition B) on each of seven individuals. The null hypothesis is that conditions A and B are no different; the data are shown in Table 4. The average difference is

Table 4
Illustration for randomization test using matched pairs

i	X_{Ai}	X_{Bi}	$d_i = X_{Ai} - X_{Bi}$
1	14.9	15.5	$-.6$
2	17.3	16.5	.8
3	14.9	13.2	1.7
4	18.1	16.0	2.1
5	12.0	12.1	$-.1$
6	19.4	18.1	1.3
7	15.6	11.4	4.2
			9.4 $= S$

1.34, but is it significantly different from zero at, say, the 5 percent level? To answer this with the t-test we would assume that the differences were normally distributed with a common unknown variance. We can get an exact test assuming only that the d_i are random samples from a common population. If the null hypothesis is true, then conditions A and B are experimentally indistinguishable, and for any individual the distinction between his X_A and X_B is merely a convention of labelling; in particular, the difference $X_{A3} - X_{B3} = 1.7$, say, is just exactly as likely as that $X_{B3} - X_{A3} = 1.7$. This means that associated with this sample are many other possible ones, all of which (under the null hypothesis) were exactly as likely to occur as this. For instance, the sample might just as well have turned out: $+.6$, $-.8$, -1.7, -2.1, $+.1$, -1.3, $+4.2$ or $+.6$, $+.8$, $+1.7$, $+2.1$, $+.1$, -1.3, -4.2, etc. In all, there are $2^7 = 128$ such outcomes, all equally likely under the null hypothesis that the treatments A and B are experimentally indistinguishable. With each of these is associated an $S = \Sigma \, d_i$. Some of these 128 S's are just about what one would expect if the null hypothesis were true, i.e., near zero. A few are well removed from zero—and much like what we expect under an alternative hypothesis such as the population mean of A exceeding that of B—or vice versa; we write these $\mu_A > \mu_B$ and $\mu_B > \mu_A$ in the sequel. To get an exact test of, say, level .05, we select of the samples which we can thus generate, that 5 percent of them most likely under the alternatives we wish to guard against, and constitute these chosen possible samples as our rejection region. In the present case, $.05(128) = 6.4$, so we choose six possibilities. The probability of getting one of these six samples under the null hypothesis is $6/128 = .047$. Then if the sample we actually drew is one of these listed for the rejection region we reject the hypothesis of equality of A and B. In our numerical example, if the investigator's "experimental hypothesis" had been: condition B leads to larger scores on the average than does condition A, he would test the null hypothesis of equality of A and B but would reject it only if the d_i were predominantly negative. If they were predominantly positive *or* well balanced he would have to regard the data as failing to support his experimental hypothesis. His rejection region would be six samples giving the greatest negative S. If he actually desired only to determine whether the two conditions yield different average scores then he must regard either a large positive S or a large negative S as cause for rejection, and his rejection region would consist of the three samples yielding greatest $+S$ and the negatives of these samples, which will yield the greatest $-S$.

Let us find the two-sided region just described. If all the d_i were positive then S would be 10.8, its maximum value. The next largest possible value for S (10.6) would be where all but $d_5 = .1$ were positive.

Such considerations lead to the following list of the first 5 positive samples in order of size of S:

							S
.6	.8	1.7	2.1	.1	1.3	4.2	10.8
.6	.8	1.7	2.1	−.1	1.3	4.2	10.6
−.6	.8	1.7	2.1	.1	1.3	4.2	9.6
−.6	.8	1.7	2.1	−.1	1.3	4.2	9.4
.6	−.8	1.7	2.1	.1	1.3	4.2	9.2

Thus the sample we obtained, which has been starred, lies in the acceptance region and the null hypothesis stands. If, however, only the alternative $\mu_A > \mu_B$ was being tested against, then the top six positive values would be the 5 percent rejection region, and our sample, being 4th, would lie in it.

For large n, say 20, the number of possible samples which we can generate by altering signs on the given numbers is large ($2^{20} > 1,000,000$) and even listing a 1 percent rejection region is a massive undertaking. There are two principal alternatives. Wilcoxon's T test, where ranks are substituted for numbers, may be used (in fact, the T test may be regarded as a randomization test on the ranks—and this clue should enable the reader to find the one-sided significance points for the T test where n is small). The second alternative is that where $n \geq 12$ (roughly), and where the d_i are of roughly the same size (as a rule it might be safe to require $(d_k^2/\Sigma\, d_i^2) \leq 5/2n$, where d_k is the largest difference in the set) a normal approximation can be used.

Each d_i, under the null hypothesis, is a chance variable taking the values $\pm d_i$ each with probability $\frac{1}{2}$. The d_i are independent. One form of the central limit theorem ensures that under the conditions given, the exact distribution of $z = S/\sqrt{\Sigma\, d_i^2}$ in the "randomization distribution" will be very closely approximated by the unit normal distribution. This test is obviously easy to apply. On data which are in fact normally distributed it is 100 percent efficient for large samples. Examples of nonnormal populations can be given where despite this efficiency it is an inferior test as compared with the rank T test (which has large sample efficiency of 95 percent).

Two Sample Test. A randomization significance test for two samples has the same underlying logic. Let there be n X's and m Y's. If there is "no difference" then the fact that in the pooled ordered sample a *particular* n observations are labelled X is, so to speak, one of many equally likely accidents. All together there are

$$\binom{m+n}{n} = \frac{(m+n)!}{m!\, n!}$$

equally likely ways in which the relabelling might be done. For certain of these the "spread" or difference between $\Sigma\,X$ and $\Sigma\,Y$ is extreme. The construction of the test consists in choosing a number k of these for a rejection region. If α is the significance level then k is chosen so that

$$k = \alpha \binom{m + n}{n},$$

as nearly as is possible. The choice of *which k* most extreme possible outcomes should constitute the rejection region depends, as always, on what alternatives are to be guarded against.

An example follows:

X	Y
11.6, 12.1, 12.2, 12.6, 13.1	9.5, 10.7, 11.8

We test $\mu_X = \mu_Y$ against the alternative $\mu_X > \mu_Y$.

The arithmetic is made more convenient if from all numbers we subtract 9.5, and then multiply by 10. We now have:

21   26   27   31   36   0   12   23

The average of these eight numbers is 22. If, then, the null hypothesis is true we should expect to find $\Sigma\,Y$ near $(3)\,(22) = 66$. In all there are

$$\binom{5 + 3}{3} = \frac{8 \cdot 7 \cdot 6}{1 \cdot 2 \cdot 3} = 56$$

possible equally likely samples. If we are working at level .05 we shall choose the 2 samples (out of the 56) most likely under the alternative hypothesis $\mu_X > \mu_Y$. These are, obviously

23   26   27   31   36   0   12   21

and

21   26   27   31   36   0   12   23

The second of these is the sample we obtained, and the null hypothesis is rejected. For illustrative purposes the six most extreme (two-sided) samples are listed below:

X					Y			$\Sigma\,Y - 66$
23	26	27	31	36	0,	12,	21	33 − 66 = 33
0	12	21	23	26	27,	31,	36	94 − 66 = 28
21	26	27	31	36	0,	12,	23	35 − 66 = 31
0	12	21	23	27	26,	31,	36	93 − 66 = 27
21	23	27	31	36	0,	12,	26	38 − 66 = 28
0	12	21	26	27	23,	31,	36	90 − 66 = 24

If m and n are large, the carrying out of these computations becomes essentially impossible. But again there exists a convenient approximation to the distribution of the statistic in the randomization distribution of

$$\binom{m + n}{n}$$

possible sample values.
Provided that:

1. $1/4 \le (m/n) \le 4$.
2. $(\mu_4/\mu_2^2) - 3$ (the kurtosis computed for the pooled sample) not large; then the following statistic has approximately the t distribution with $m + n - 2$ degrees of freedom:

$$\frac{\bar{Y} - \bar{X}}{\sqrt{\dfrac{\Sigma (Y - \bar{Y})^2 + \Sigma (X - \bar{X})^2}{m + n - 2} \left(\dfrac{1}{m} + \dfrac{1}{n}\right)}}.$$

It is a curious result; this is the ordinary t statistic. This means that provided conditions 1 and 2 hold (and these can be checked from the sample) the t statistic actually gives a test of the stated significance level *without* the usual assumptions being a part of the inference. It has *not* been assumed that X and Y are normally distributed with a common variance.

If the distributions of X and Y both have finite variance, but different means, the probability that the test will reject the null hypothesis tends to one as both m and n become large. If the distributions are different but have the same mean this is not so.

An alternative to the use of the t statistic to approximate the randomization distribution is to employ the Mann-Whitney U test. There are circumstances under which the U test (though it "throws away" data by reducing the observations to ranks) is the better test. The U test may be regarded as test of the randomization type applied to the *ranks* of the observations.

Confidence Intervals. In both these cases (paired or unpaired observations) confidence intervals can be obtained by adding equal increments to one set of values until a significant positive difference is first reached, and then altering them still further until a significant negative difference is first reached. These two extreme alterations constitute the end points of a confidence interval for the true difference. If the approximations (normal, and t) are to be used, then the conditions for their validity must hold at these extreme points; otherwise the exact procedure has to be used.

Correlation and Tests of Independence.   The problem of correlation can also be attacked by the randomization method.   That is, one can test the hypothesis of zero correlation with samples of small (or large) size without making assumptions about the form of the joint distribution of X and Y.   For a treatment of the problem, see [22].

Tests of independence

When one has a pair of observations (X_i, Y_i) for each member of his sample and desires to test the independence of X and Y there are numerous techniques available.   The rank-order correlation coefficient, or τ, Kendall's rank-order statistic [11], may be used.   The product-moment coefficient can be tested nonparametrically as mentioned in the preceding paragraph.

In addition there is an extraordinarily easily applied method, Olmstead and Tukey's corner test of association [20].   Its efficiency and other properties await a full mathematical investigation, but informed opinion holds that it is likely to be a very good test.

To apply the test one first plots the observations in a scatter diagram.   Then, following simple rules given by Olmstead and Tukey [20] and also by Mood [16], the statistician measures the degree to which the data are concentrated in the "corners" of the scatter diagram. (The instructions referred to essentially define the "corners.")   If a substantial number of observations are concentrated in diagonally opposite corners (which would be expected in the presence of strong association between the variables), then the null hypothesis of independence is rejected.   Although the use of this technique is simple, the explanation of how to construct the corners is rather lengthy and will be omitted here.   The test is entirely distribution-free.   Because of its ease of application it should find frequent use as a preliminary test to determine whether a product-moment correlation coefficient is worth computing in cases where the latter is fully justified.

There also exist nonparametric methods for linear regression, including tests of significance.   They will not be taken up here, but a full treatment of both their mathematical theory and method of application is given by Mood [16, Ch. 16].   In this source there is also a technique for analysing one and two factor experiments; an alternative to the analysis of variance by ranks.   All these methods depend upon the way in which the medians of various subclasses behave.   They are all completely distribution free.   As an attack on the analysis of variance problem they are more flexible than analysis of variance by ranks, but are less efficient, and probably not to be preferred for problems of an uncomplicated design.

Percentiles

If one has a sample of n observations and wishes to estimate the percentiles of the parent distribution he will, of course, employ the percentiles in the sample. Confidence intervals (confidence coefficient $1 - \alpha$) may be obtained as follows. If the sample is arranged in order of increasing size:

$$X_1, X_2, X_3, \ldots, X_n$$

then X_1 is the smallest observation, X_2 the next smallest, etc. Let ξ_p denote the $100\,p$ percentile. Then

$$P(X_r < \xi_p < X_s) = \sum_{i=r}^{s-i} \binom{n}{i} p^i (1 - p)^{n-i}.$$

Using tables of the binomial distribution [19], one then chooses r and s so that the probability (the value of the sum) is at least $1 - \alpha$.

If there are ties in the data then

$$P(X_r < \xi_p < X_s) \geq \sum_{i=r}^{s-1} \binom{n}{i} p^i - (1 - p)^{n-i}.$$

For example, a .90 confidence for the 40th percentile in the population from which this sample comes:

17	21	23	24	24	35	27	30
X_1	X_2	X_3	X_4	X_5	X_6	X_7	X_8

is:

17   to   27,

that is:

X_1 to X_7.

Since:

$$\sum_{i=1}^{6} \binom{8}{i} (.4)^i (.6)^{8-i} = .90,$$

where we have $p = .4$, $n = 8$.

For large samples the binomial sum can be approximated by the normal distribution. The index i is approximately normal (for large n) with mean np and standard deviation $\sqrt{npq}$. So to obtain a 95 percent confidence interval one would count $1.96\sqrt{npq}$ observations to the right and to the left of the $100p$ sample percentile to find the observations whose numerical values constitute a 95 percent confidence interval.

Some other non-parametric methods

Certain important topics in the field of non-parametric methods have been either completely omitted, or merely mentioned in this paper. Among these are:

Rank Correlation Methods. A recent book by Kendall [11] provides the experimenter with a rather generous variety of techniques not elsewhere published. Among other matters of interest considered there are: tied ranks, coefficient of concordance (with significance test) to measure agreement among more than two judges, significance of the difference between two nonzero rank-order correlation coefficients. Work is being done in this field by Kendall and his associates and additional results will be published in the near future.

Kolmogorov-Smirnov Tests. These tests serve as alternatives (preferable for certain reasons) to χ^2 for two classes of problems:

1. To test the hypothesis that a random sample has been drawn from a population with a certain specified distribution.

2. To test that two random samples (of not necessarily equal size) have been drawn from the same population. The methods apply only where the chance variable is continuous. An excellent nonmathematical discussion, with tables and examples, is given by Massey [14]. Some more recent results and tables for the two-sample problem are also given by Massey [15].

Tests for Randomness of a Sequence of Numerical Observations. The Wald and Wolfowitz run test discussed in this paper is one test of this sort, where two groups of observations are involved. Where there is only one sequence of observations, perhaps ordered in time, one may still wish to know whether they may be regarded as a random sequence. An informative nonmathematical discussion of this problem, with several tests, is found in Moore and Wallis [17].

Tolerance Intervals. One can ask the question: "Between what limits can I be nearly sure (say 95 percent, or 99 percent, etc.) that at least 90 percent (or 80 percent, or 98 percent, etc.) of the population values lie?" These limits are called tolerance limits. The problem clearly differs from the confidence interval problem, which is concerned with location of the population mean, or a certain population percentile, etc.

A brief discussion will be found in Dixon and Massey [1]. Some useful charts which eliminate computations are given by Murphy [18], where the relevant literature is also cited.

Literature of non-parametric methods

The textbook literature presents few extended treatments of non-parametric methods. Of those known to the writer, one of the fullest, and surely the least mathematical, is Chapter 17 of Dixon and Massey's text [1]. For the reader with facility in advanced calculus many important methods are explained and derived in Chapter 16 of Mood's text [16]. At a mathematical level intermediate between these two is Chapter 8 of Johnson's text [9] and Chapter 9 of Hoel's text [8]. Finally, the mathematically mature reader will find many of the techniques taken up in this paper (and some others) discussed in somewhat greater detail in Chapter 21, Volume II of Kendall's advanced book [10].

A paper by S. S. Wilks [30] affords a complete but terse review of the whole field up through about 1947. The treatment requires a good knowledge of mathematical statistics. A full bibliography is included.

The following bibliography is not intended to be complete. The reader who wishes to explore any one topic in detail will find little difficulty in uncovering the relevant literature with the aid of the references cited in the papers listed here.

References

1. Dixon, W. J. and F. J. Massey, Jr. *Introduction to statistical analysis.* New York: McGraw-Hill, 1951.

2. Dixon, W. J. and A. M. Mood. The statistical sign test. *J. Amer. statist. Ass.,* 1946, **41,** 557–566.

3. Festinger, L. The significance of difference between means without reference to the frequency distribution function. *Psychometrika,* 1946, **11,** 97–106.

4. Fisher, R. A. *Design of experiments.* London: Oliver and Boyd, 1936.

5. Fisher, R. A. *Statistical methods for research workers*. London: Oliver and Boyd, 1925.

6. Friedman, Milton. Use of ranks to avoid the assumption of normality implicit in the analysis of variance. *J. Amer. statist. Ass.*, 1937, **32**, 675–701.

7. Friedman, Milton. A comparison of alternative tests of significance for the problem of *m* rankings. *Ann. math. Statist.*, 1940, **11**, 86–92.

8. Hoel, P. G. *Introduction to mathematical statistics*. New York: Wiley, 1947.

9. Johnson, P. O. *Statistical methods in research*. New York: Prentice-Hall, 1949.

10. Kendall, M. G. *The advanced theory of statistics*, Vol. II. London: C. Griffin and Co., 1948.

11. Kendall, M. G. *Rank correlation methods*. London: C. Griffin and Co., 1948.

12. Kendall, M. G. and B. B. Smith. The problem of *m* rankings. *Ann. math. statist.*, 1939, **10**, 275–287.

13. Mann, H. B. and D. R. Whitney. On a test of whether one of two random variables is stochastically larger than the other. *Ann. math. Statist.*, 1947, **18**, 50–60.

14. Massey, F. J., Jr. The Kolmogorov-Smirnov test for goodness of fit. *J. Amer. statist. Ass.*, 1951, **46**, 68–78.

15. Massey, F. J., Jr. The distribution of the maximum deviation between two sample cumulative step functions. *Ann. math. Statist.*, 1951, **22**, 125–128.

16. Mood, A. M. *Introduction to the theory of statistics*. New York: McGraw-Hill, 1950.

17. Moore, G. H. and W. A. Wallis. Time series significance tests based on signs of differences. *J. Amer. statist. Ass.*, 1943, **38**, 153–164.

18. Murphy, R. B. Nonparametric tolerance limits. *Ann. math. Statist.*, 1948, **19**, 581–589.

19. National Bureau of Standards. *Tables of the binomial probability distribution*. Washington, D.C.: U.S. Government Printing Office, 1949.

20. Olmstead, P. S. and J. W. Tukey. A corner test for association. *Ann. math. Statist.*, 1947, **18**, 495–513.

21. Pitman, E. J. G. Significance tests which may be applied to samples from any population. *Suppl. J. Royal statist. Soc.*, 1937, **4**, 119.

22. Pitman, E. J. G. Significance tests which may be applied to samples from any population, II. The correlation coefficient test. *Suppl. J. Roy. statist. Soc.*, 1937, **4**, 225.

23. Pitman, E. J. G. Notes on nonparametric statistical inference. (Unpublished.)

24. Swed, F. S. and C. Eisenhart. Tables for testing randomness of grouping in a sequence of alternatives. *Ann. math. Statist.*, 1943, **14,** 66–87.

25. Walsh, J. E. On the power of the sign test for slippage of means. *Ann. math. Statist.*, 1946, **17,** 358–362.

26. Whitney, D. R. *A comparison of the power of nonparametric tests and tests based on the normal distribution under nonnormal alternatives.* Unpublished Ph.D. dissertation at Ohio State University, 1948.

27. Wilcoxon, Frank. Individual comparisons by ranking methods. *Biometrics Bull.*, 1945, **1,** 80–82.

28. Wilcoxon, Frank. Probability tables for individual comparison by ranking methods. *Biometrics*, 1947, **3,** 119–122.

29. Wilcoxon, Frank. *Some rapid approximate statistical procedures.* American Cyanamide Co., 1949.

30. Wilks, S. S. Order statistics. *Bull. Amer. math. Soc.*, 1948, **54,** 6–50.

14

a comparison of the
power of the U and t tests

C. Alan Boneau

In a recent paper (Boneau, 1960), the author summarized the results of a number of theoretical and empirical studies dealing with the effects of violations of assumptions underlying the *t* test. It was concluded that the *t* test is remarkably unaffected by the two common violations: sampling from populations having unequal variances and sampling from nonnormal distributions. One who uses the *t* test can be reasonably sure that the probability of rejecting a true null hypothesis is close to the alpha value he selects for his experiment even though he may have misgivings about the assumptions upon which the *t* test is based. As a result of these considerations, a recommendation was made in the previous paper to the effect that even when the assumptions are not met (except under special conditions) the *t* test and the *F* test on

From: C. A. Boneau, "A comparison of the power of the *U* and *t* test," *Psychological Review* **69,** 1962, 246–256. Copyright © 1962 by the American Psychological Association and reproduced by permission.

This project was supported by NSF Grant G-9592 to the author and by NSF Grant G-6694 to the Duke University Digital Computing Laboratory. The author wishes to express appreciation to Thomas M. Gallie, Director of the Laboratory, for his cooperation and assistance.

means of the analysis of variance be used without those attendant feelings of turpitude which can be attributed to an introjection of the strictures of the proponents of nonparametric methods.

This recommendation was based upon an assumption that the *t* and *F* tests, because they make effective use of the information in the sample and have other desirable properties, should be more powerful techniques than nonparametric competitors. (For readable explanations and discussions of the power of a test see among others Siegel, 1956 or Walker and Lev, 1953.) That is to say, if the null hypothesis is false—if there are true differences between means—the *t* test should signal the detection of small differences by yielding significant results more frequently than should comparable nonparametric methods.

Theoretically, the *t* test is more powerful than any of the usually utilized tests when the assumptions underlying it are met. It is also true, however, that when sampling is from certain nonnormal distributions, other tests may be more powerful than the *t* test. The Wilcoxon-Mann-Whitney *U* test (Wilcoxon, 1945; Mann and Whitney, 1947) for example, in one pathological case, theoretically is infinitely more powerful than the *t* test. Theoretically also, the power of the *U* test is never less than .83 of that of the *t* test (Hodges and Lehman, 1956). In fact even in the case for which the *t* test is designed (normality and equal variances) the *U* test by one measure of the relative power of the two tests is 95% as powerful as the *t* test (Hodges and Lehman, 1956).

Such theoretical statements about relative power of tests are based upon mathematical limiting processes involving conditions which are not representative of most practical situations, for example, infinitely large sample sizes and arbitrarily small differences between population means: (Dixon, 1954; Hodges and Lehman, 1956; and Mood, 1954). Statements as to the relative efficiency in general of various nonparametric competitors of the *t* test are scattered throughout the literature (Dixon, 1954; Hodges and Lehman, 1956; Lehman, 1953; Mood, 1954, to mention only the relatively accessible ones). They seem not, however, to have permeated effectively that hard core of statistical lore which the research psychologist musters in an attempt to wrest truth from chaff.

The present paper is intended to present the facts (culled from the literature as well as manufactured for the purpose) about the power of the *t* test and, in particular, how that power compares with the power of a specific nonparametric competitor in various practical situations. This presentation is meant to temper in part the implications of the previous paper (Boneau, 1960) that the *t* test should be used whenever possible. It would seem that here, as in other areas of human endeavor, a little discretion may pay off.

Attention will be focused upon the U test, a worthy protagonist whose principal strengths vis-à-vis the t test have already been mentioned. The U test, or equivalent versions of procedures based upon ranked scores, has been invented several times in the history of statistics, first by Deuchler (1914), but later by Wilcoxon (1945), Mann and Whitney (1947), among others. (See Kruskal, 1957, for historical discussion.) As used in the present context, the statistic U is computed by determining the number of scores in the second sample which are exceeded by each score in the first sample. The sum of all such counts summed over the scores in the first sample is called U, tables for which have been developed by Mann and Whitney (1947), extended by Auble (1953), and made readily accessible by Siegel (1956). Wilcoxon's T test (1945), although limited to equal-size samples, gives exactly equivalent results even though it is computed in a different fashion.

The null distribution of U may be derived from the assumption that ranks are assigned to the two samples on a random basis such that every combination of ranks among samples is equally likely. For example, given that n_1, the first sample size, is 2 and n_2 is 3, the possible values of the two ranks in the first sample (assuming no ties) are 1 and 2, 1 and 3, 1 and 4, 1 and 5, 2 and 3, 2 and 4, 2 and 5, 3 and 4, 3 and 5, and finally, 4 and 5. By the definition above, these lead to U values of 6, 5, 4, 3, 4, 3, 2, 2, 1, and 0, respectively. If all of these combinations are equally likely—the two samples came from the same distribution for example—the probability of getting values as extreme as 6 or 0 by chance is the sum of the individual probabilities:

$$\tfrac{1}{10} + \tfrac{1}{10} = \tfrac{1}{5}.$$

By the logic of statistical decisions, however, one attributes extreme values of U not to these accidents of random sampling which occur with known probability if the null hypothesis is true, but to actual differences between the distributions. In actuality, differences in distribution usually lead to non-equally-likely combinations of ranks. Ranks 1 and 2 occur together with relatively greater frequency as the difference between the means of the populations increases and as a result more frequent extreme U values occur. For this reason U is generally considered to be a test of displacement or shift of distributions, the main focus being on differences in central tendency. Note also that discrepancies of variance tend also to produce non-equally-like combinations of ranks. If two populations have the same mean, the values 1 and 5 tend more to occur together as the size of the variance of the first increases relative to the size of that of the second. However, these combinations give rise to middling values of U and hence are ignored, in effect, by the U test. We shall see, however, that there are cases for which differences in distribution other than central tendency affect the value of U.

One further statement might be made about the sensitivity of the U test in specific cases. Since essentially it is based only upon ranks, first and last scores get rank 1 and n whether they are close to the mean or several standard deviations away. Thus the occasional score which is apparently not in the distribution but which furnishes no real justification for exclusion is treated as a member of the ingroup by the U test but as the pariah it may well be by the t.

The method of the present paper is quite similar to the approach followed by the author in the previous paper dealing with the probability of rejecting the null hypothesis if it is true. In that study populations having specified characteristics were constructed and the values of t arising from the differences between means of random samples drawn from them were computed. The empirical probability of rejecting the null hypothesis was obtained by determining the proportion of sample t values falling outside the ordinary tabled values for the appropriate number of degrees of freedom (i.e., falling in the region of rejection). Since the null hypothesis was indeed true, these empirical probabilities or proportions could be compared with the nominal values to determine the effects of modifying the specified characteristics of the populations in such a way as to violate the assumptions underlying the t test. In the present study, the concern is with the proportion of obtained t's and U's falling in the region of rejection (or critical region) when the null hypothesis is false—when there is a built-in, specified difference between means. To generate this information, the only required addition to the previous t test program is a provision for changing the mean of the first sample to any value desired.

The program using the IBM 650 Electronic Data Process System for generating t's from random deviates was discussed in detail in the previous paper (Boneau, 1960). To summarize briefly, 10-digit random numbers were generated by a multiplication process. These were converted into random deviates from a specified population by a table-look-up procedure; the random deviates were injected into the computing formula for the t test for the difference between means of two independent samples; and the resulting t value was sorted and tallied on an internally contained table within the computer.

The program designed for the present study for the U test utilized the existing random number and random deviate generating procedures. The value of U was computed by the simple expedient of subtracting every score in the first sample from every score in the second sample and counting the number of minus signs which resulted. This number is U by definition. The possibility for a tie was ignored since the expected rate of ties was approximately one per thousand U's, a rate which, while significant, would seem to have little effect on the observed results. As in the t program, the obtained U values were sorted and tallied on an internally contained table which was punched out in card from when the desired number of U's from the specified populations was reached.

Results

Since the results of the study will be expressed in terms of empirical power functions, the investment of a small amount of space to elaborate on the method of their determination may be in order at this point.

For any given set of conditions, i.e., combination of means, variances, and distributions, the result of the computer procedure is a set of t's or U's which may be arranged in a frequency distribution. Figure 1 shows two such distributions. The distributions are of t's obtained on the basis of sample sizes of 15 from normal populations having a variance of 1.0. One of the distributions shown, that centered around the t value of zero, arose when the means of the two samples were both equal to zero. For the other distribution, that centered around 2.8 and shaded, the difference between the means of the two

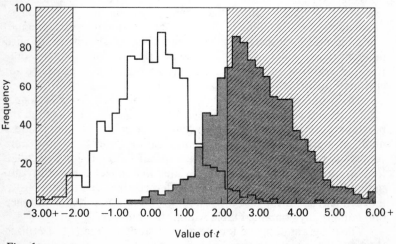

Fig. 1
Empirical t *distribution for mean difference of* (a) 0.00 (*unshaded area*) *and* (b) 1.00 (*shaded area*) *for sample sizes of* 15. (*The hatched area is the region of rejection for the .05 level of significance.*)

samples was equal to 1.0, that is, equal to one standard deviation. The vertical lines divide the range of possible t values into two regions. The unhatched region marks off those values of t which result in a decision to *accept* (or fail to reject) the null hypothesis at the .05 level. The hatched regions, those values of t which result in a decision to *reject* the null hypothesis at that level. As can be seen, when the null hypothesis is true most of the obtained t's fall in the region of acceptance. The proportion which fall in the region of rejection, in this case .049, we have called the empirical alpha level.

Sometimes a decision is made to accept a false null hypothesis, the so-called beta error. In Figure 1, such an error would be made in the case of those values of t from the shaded distribution which fall in the region of acceptance. On the other hand, decisions to reject the null hypothesis when it is indeed false occur for that proportion of the t's from the shaded distribution which fall in the region of rejection, in this case .737. It is this proportion which we call the empirical power of the test under the given conditions. It should be noted that both the empirical alpha and the empirical power are estimates of the exact theoretical values which obtain for these conditions.

The data of the present study are empirical power values considered as functions of the actual difference between population means. We shall consider separately, the functions for the one- and two-tailed tests and for the .05 and .01 values of alpha. The figures which will be presented will, for a given set of conditions, depict such functions for both that t and U tests so that visual comparisons may be made.

One further thing should be said about nomenclature before results are presented. As in the previous paper, the conditions of sampling will be symbolically represented. For example, $N(2, 1)5$-$N(0, 1)15$ indicates that the first sample is from a normal population N with a mean of 2 and a variance of 1, the sample size being 5. In this instance, the second sample is from a normal distribution having a mean of 0, a variance of 1, and the sample size is 15. In the text and figures, we will use the variable "x" for the value of the first mean to indicate that it takes on the several values necessary for the $\mu_1 - \mu_2$ values on the abscissa. In all cases the value of the mean of the second distribution is zero. One thousand U's and t's were obtained for each condition.

Normal distribution:
homogeneous variances

First to be considered are the cases in which the sizes of both samples are the same. Figure 2 depicts the various empirical power functions obtained when the condition of sampling is $N(x, 1)5$-$N(0, 1)5$. Because

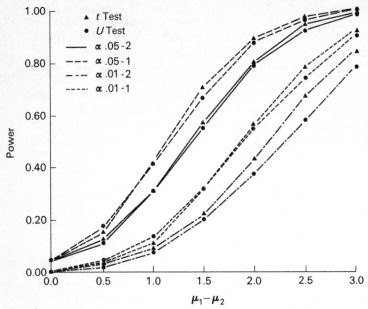

Fig. 2
Empirical power functions for U and t tests with sampling scheme
N(x, 1)5-N(0, 1)5.

of the discrete nature of the *U* distribution, exact alpha values of .05 and .01 are not possible. When both samples sizes are 5, the following alpha values obtained from tables are used: .056 for the two-tailed test and .048 for the one-tailed test in place of .05, and .008 for both the one- and two-tailed test in place of .01.

A number of interesting facts can be observed in Figure 2. First is the expected superiority of the one-tailed test to the two-tailed test. Of prime importance for the present paper is the remarkable lack of difference in power of the *t* and *U* tests over the range of values presented. Only in the case of the two-tailed at the .008 level does the *t* test seem to exhibit a definite superiority and here only for gross difference between the means. In most of the other cases, the differences between the obtained points are well within the margin of sampling error (i.e., not significantly different). This would indicate that although the *t* test is theoretically a uniformly (over all mean differences) most powerful test, the margin over the *U* test is not very much. Because of this power property of the *t* test under these conditions, the points at which the *U* test shows a superiority must be attributed to sampling error.

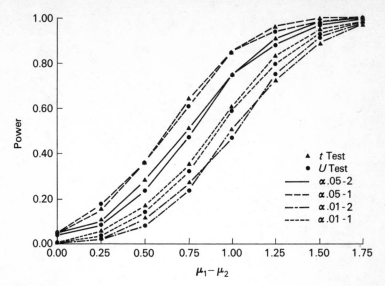

Fig. 3
Empirical power functions for U and t tests for sampling scheme N(x, 1)15-N(0, 1)15.

It is also clear that the alpha values ($\mu_1 - \mu_2 = 0$) are virtually identical and are approximately the theoretical values expected.

Increasing both sample sizes from 5 to 15 tends, as shown in Fig. 3, to increase the power of the test, but to leave virtually unaffected the things which we have said about the smaller sizes. For example, at the .05 level for a one-tailed test, the power of both tests for a difference between means of 1.0 is around .42 for sample sizes of 5, and .85 for samples of size 15.

Still maintaining the condition of sampling from a normal distribution with equal variances of the parent populations, we may allow the sample sizes to be different, 5 as opposed to 15, and generate another series of curves, Figure 4. The results are similar to those preceding, with the power for the one-tailed test at the .05 level and a mean difference of 1.0 being in this case about .60. This, too, is to be expected since the power of the test among other things is an increasing function of the difference between the means but a decreasing function of the expected standard error of the difference between means where

$$\sigma_{\bar{x}_1 - \bar{x}_2} = \sqrt{\sigma_1^2/n_1 + \sigma_2^2/n_2}.$$

Figure 4 shows more clearly than any of the preceding graphs the

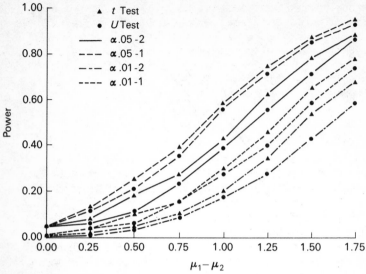

Fig. 4
Empirical power functions for U and t tests for sampling scheme
N(x, 1)5-N(0, 1)15.

superiority of the *t* test to the *U* test, but the largest obtained difference is only .12, and being the largest probably overestimates the true difference.

The results we have observed thus far are for conditions in which the assumptions underlying the *t* test are satisfied. Under these conditions we know that theoretically the *t* test is the most powerful test of the difference between two means. The power functions and relations between the powers of the two tests obtained in this study are comparable with those found in several sources (Dixon, 1954; Dixon and Massey, 1957; Ferris, Grubbs, and Weaver, 1946, to name a few). Thus they contribute only a confirmation of the general method and at the same time furnish a graphical demonstration of the fact that, while less powerful than the *t* test, the *U* test performs quite well in those situations for which the *t* test is expressly suited.

When the assumptions of the *t* test are not fulfilled, it is not necessarily a most powerful test. Moreover, as stated earlier, there are theoretical conditions for which the *t* test is considerably less powerful than other tests including the *U* test. The remainder of this paper will compare power functions for the *U* and *t* tests for those violations of assumptions which arise from various combinations of the three distributions, the two variances, and the two sample sizes which have been selected for the study. We will determine whether the power functions for the *t* test show any drastic deviations from those power functions we have already seen, and we shall discover those cases, if any, for which the *U* test performs better than does the *t* test. This, of course, must be within the limitations imposed by the selection of conditions.

Normal distributions:
heterogeneous variances

Initially, we shall proceed by examining the effect of violating the assumption of homogeneity of variances with normal distribution. In the previous study, it was determined that inequality of variances up to at least a ratio of 1 to 4 produced a very little effect in alpha provided the sizes of the two samples are the same. If the sample sizes are different, gross disturbances in alpha occur.

Figure 5, depicting the equal-sample-size case ($n = 5$), reveals that for *t* the alpha is relatively undisturbed and power also seems little affected. It should be noted that the relatively low power for Figure 5 (and for some following figures) for a given mean difference is to be attributed to a change in the standard error of the difference between

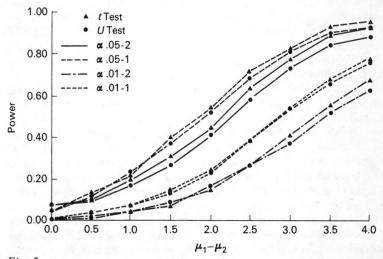

Fig. 5
Empirical power functions for U and t tests for sampling scheme
N(x, 1)5-N(0, 4)5.

means occasioned by the change in σ_2 from 1 to 4. For a given mean difference in standard error units, the power remains essentially the same. For example, the true standard error of the difference between means for the case $N(x, 1)5$-$N(0, 4)5$ is .63, while for the case $(x, 1)5$-$N(0, 4)5$ it is 1.0. A mean difference of 2.0 (2 standard errors) in Figure 5 shows the power of the two-tailed t test at the .056 level to be approximately .45. On Figure 2, a mean difference of 1.26 (2 standard errors) shows the comparable power to be approximately .44. In terms of the true standard error of the difference between sample means, then, the power of the t test seems relatively unaffected by violating the homogeneity of variances assumption.

Likewise, the power of the U test is maintained, but at a level again slightly less powerful than the t test. Similar results (not shown) obtain when both sample sizes are changed to 15.

Introducing heterogeneity of sample size as well as heterogeneity of variance produces discrepancies which might be predicted from what is already known about the effect of this condition on the alpha level. Figures 6 and 7 portray these effects for the two possible combinations of variance and sample size considered, $N(x, 1)5$-$N(0, 4)15$ and $N(x, 4)5$-$N(0, 1)15$ respectively. The first thing to observe in these figures is that effect on the alpha level (the power for a mean difference of zero). In Figure 6 the alpha is for all curves less than the nominal values of .05 and .01, although the magnitude of the difference for the U curves is less than those for t. The actual values observed are as follows: (one-tailed test-.05 level) $t = .010$; $U = .029$; (two-tailed test-.05 level) $t = .009$; $U = .027$; (one-tailed test-.01 level) $t = .002$; $U = .005$; (two-tailed test-.01 level) $t = .001$; $U = .004$. The power functions reflect the fact that while nominally at a .05 level, the tests are actually operating at a reduced alpha value. At the reference value, a mean difference equal to two standard errors, the power of the two-tailed .05-level t test is approximately .24, while the power for the comparable U test is about .28. Both of these values are much less than the values of about .45 which obtained under the other conditions. We may conclude that the conditions of heterogeneity of variances and sample sizes which produced Figure 6 have affected the alpha level of both U and t, U to a lesser extent, however, than t. Since the alpha level for the U test under these conditions is greater than that for the t test, the resulting power functions should and do reflect a superiority of U to t. What we are observing is the power curve for t for an alpha level of about .01 and for U of about .03 when we consider, for example, the curves which were constructed on the basis of the normal boundaries of the region of rejection for the .05 level of alpha.

We may make exactly the same comparisons for the results

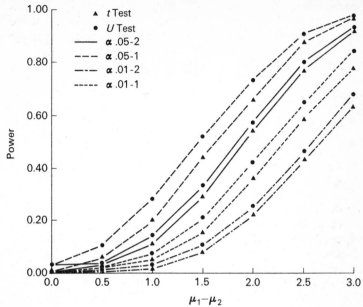

Fig. 6
Empirical power functions for U and t tests for sampling scheme
$N(x, 1)5$-$N(0, 4)15$.

depicted in Figure 7, but note that the effects are in the opposite direction to those found in Figure 6. For example, the alpha values obtained are all greater than the nominal values, and again the distortion to the *t* values is greater than those for *U*. For this case—$N(x, 4)5$-$N(0, 1)15$—the actual alpha values observed are: (one-tailed test-.05 level) $t = .115$; $U = .081$; (two-tailed test-.05 level) $t = .145$; $U = .064$; (one-tailed test-.01 level) $t = .048$; $U = .020$; (two-tailed test-.01 level) $t = .058$; $U = .021$. Considering the reference point used earlier, the empirical power of the two-tailed test with alpha equal to .05 for a difference between means equal to two standard errors of the difference between means, we find these values to be .75 for *t* and .52 for *U*. And as before, the power curves behave as if they were the power curves for the observed value of alpha, the curves for *t* being considerably above those for *U* at all points.

We may conclude that violating the assumption of homogeneity of variance if the underlying distributions are normal has little effect on either the alpha level or the power of the *t* or the *U* test as long as sample sizes are the same. The violation of this assumption coupled

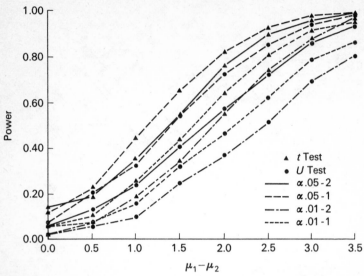

Fig. 7
Empirical power functions for U and t tests for sampling scheme
N(x, 4)5-N(0, 1)15.

with heterogeneous sample sizes changes the alpha level of both the *t*
and the *U* tests and produces power functions which seemingly are
roughly appropriate for the true alpha level rather than the nominal
one. The *U* test seems much less disturbed by this particular violation
than does the *t* test, but it is by no means true that the *U* test is completely unaffected as would seem to be implied by the term "non-
parametric." Rather it seems to behave much as does the *t* test, but
somewhat less sensitively to the violation of the assumption of
homogeneity.

Nonnormal distributions

At this point we will examine the empirical power functions for the *t*
and the *U* tests when sampling for at least one sample is from nonnormal
distributions. In this way we will observe the effects, if any, on the
functions if one or both of the parent populations is exponential, or
if one or both of the parent populations is rectangular. From an
examination of the empirical alpha for the *t* test, we already know
what the effects of sampling from a rectangular distribution are minimal
on alpha. When the exponential distribution is involved, however,

some perturbations in alpha may occur because of differences in skewness of the two distributions. The magnitude of these disturbances as seen in the earlier study was progressively lessened as sample size increased. At sample sizes of 25, the effect was virtually unnoticeable.

These earlier observations are confirmed in this study. Figure 8, for example, depicts the results of sampling from two rectangular distributions—$R(x, 1)5$-$R(0, 1)5$. Alpha is approximately the correct value for both levels for both tests. In this figure, it appears that the power of t is quite generally greater than that for U, but never by much except for the .01 level. Indeed, it would seem that for small differences between means, say, 0.5, U may be superior to t. Similar results (not shown) were obtained when both sample sizes were increased to 15.

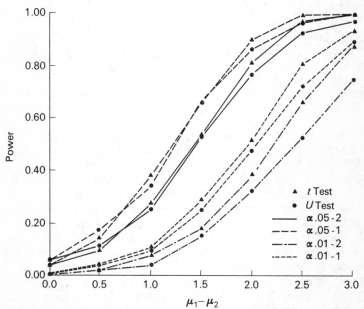

Fig. 8
Empirical power functions for U and t tests for sampling scheme R(x, 1)5-R(0, 1)5.

The next distribution to be examined occurs when both samples are taken from exponential distributions as in Figure 9—$E(x, 1)5$-$E(0, 1)5$. The empirical alpha values are in the appropriate ranges. Here again, for small differences between the means, the U test seems consistently more powerful than the t test, but this advantage disappears

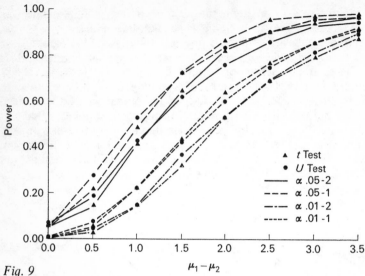

Fig. 9

$\mu_1 - \mu_2$

Empirical power functions for U and t tests for sampling scheme E(x, 1)5-E(0, 1)5.

with greater mean differences. All in all one may conjecture that when both distributions have the same shape, even though not normal, the power functions of the *t* and *U* tests have a relatively constant relationship. In most instances, the *t* test is slightly more powerful than the *U* test, as we have observed in most of our examples.

All of the foregoing power functions have come from combinations of distributions which produce essentially symmetric distribution of *t* and *U* when the null hypothesis is true (zero difference between means). We might expect more severe disturbances in power functions in those cases which, because of basic asymmetries in the observed *t* distributions, exhibited discordant obtained alpha values in the previous study. As may be recalled, the asymmetric distributions arose when the two parent populations differed in skew, one normal, the other exponential, for example. It was true, however, that increasing the sample size greatly diminished the asymmetries since the underlying probability mechanisms tend to normalize the distribution of *t* as sample size increases.

It is such conditions, probably not too uncommon in the experience (or at least the imagination) of the research worker, which motivate a desire to seek statistical tools which exhibit fewer allergic reactions to violations of assumptions.

Because of these considerations, it is interesting to compare the power functions of the t and the U test under such conditions of sampling. Figure 10 makes the comparisons for the case of exponential and normal distributions with samples of size 5—$E(x, 1)5$-$N(0, 1)5$. First to be noted are the discrepancies in the obtained alpha values for the one-tailed tests due to the asymmetrical distribution of t and, surprisingly enough, for U. The .048-one-tailed values are .022 for U, .014 for t. Likewise, the .008-one-tailed values are .002 for U, .001 for t. This is to be contrasted with the two-tailed values which are relatively close to the nominal values—the .056-two-tailed value for U is .049, for t it is .068; and the .008-two-tailed value for U is .014, for t, .011. These results for t are comparable to those found in the previous study. Thus we find that when considering alpha, t and U both are affected by sampling from populations which differ in skew, although it is possible that the effect on U is less than that on t.

A further examination of Figure 10 reveals that the empirical power functions for U are, with one or two exceptions, higher than the power functions for t, but the advantage is slight.

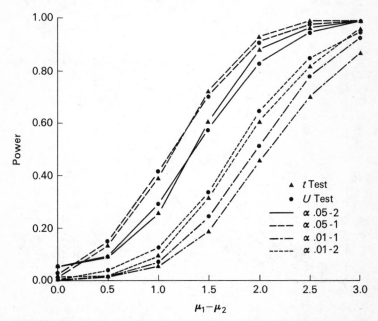

Fig. 10
Empirical power functions for U and t tests for sampling scheme $E(x, 1)5$-$N(0, 1)5$.

As mentioned previously, increasing the sample size tends to normalize the distribution of *t* in the null case, the effect being to lessen the discrepancy of nominal and obtained values for the one-tailed test. Figure 11 presents the curves for the increased sample size case— $E(x, 1)15-N(0, 1)15$. As before, our attention is first directed to the zero-mean-difference points, and as expected, the values for *t* have become closer to the nominal values—one-tailed test, .037 for .05 level, and .006 for .01 level; two-tailed test, .044 for .05 level and .012 for .01 level. Increasing the sample size to 15, however, does not seem to improve the performance of the *U* test. For the one-tailed *U* test, the obtained alpha values are .016 for the .05 level, and .000 for the .01 level. For the two-tailed test, the obtained alpha values again seem to be higher than the nominal values—.068 for the .05 level, and .019 for the .01 level. In Figure 11, we note that the power functions for the *U* test are almost invariably below those for the *t* test.

A notable phenomenon occurs for the .05-level, two-tailed *U* test. This particular curve shows a decrease in power from 0 mean difference to 0.25 before starting up again. While sampling error may well account

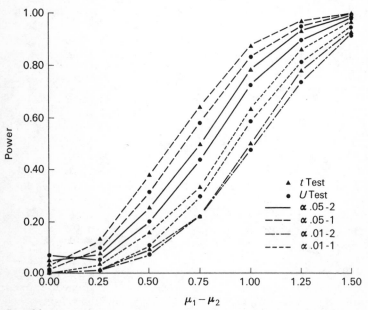

Fig. 11
Empirical power functions for U and t tests for sampling scheme
$E(x, 1)15-N(0, 1)15.$

for the dip, it is certainly possible for a test to be "biased," the technical term for such an occurrence. In fact there is no reason to believe that the U test as a test for mean differences should not be biased. The U test is only fortuitously a test for mean differences, being fundamentally a test for differences between distributions. As we have seen it is less sensitive to some kinds of differences between distributions than others, being perhaps maximally sensitive to differences in central tendency of two distributions. But there are many measures of central tendency, the mean and the median, for example. We know that the mean and median are different in skewed distributions. In the combination of distributions with which Figure 11 is concerned, namely, exponential and normal, it is possible for medians to be the same for the two distributions which necessitates that the means be different and vice versa. For the t test which explicitly evaluates differences in sample means this seems to present no problem. The U test, however, may well be more sensitive to median differences and thus show the bias when used as a test for differences between means.

Other combinations of distributions which were explored in no way change the general picture which we have continually observed. We may summarize that picture as follows: In general the t test is more powerful than the U test, but never by much. Based on the evidence we have seen, one might conjecture that over a long series of experiments involving distributions of the kind we have used, a consistent use of the t test might result in, say, 5% more rejections of a false null hypothesis than would a consistent application of the U test. There are many other kinds of distributions arising in research, however, for which this statement need not apply. Depending upon one's inclinations, such a conclusion could be interpreted as ample grounds for habitual use of either of the two tests. There are, as we have seen, other considerations. As a general rule we might say that the t test seems to provide the appropriate power curve for the actual alpha level involved, whereas, the U test shows more variability in its power functions. That is to say that if the actual (not the nominal) alpha is .05, the power curve for the t test in most cases is probably very similar to the power function for the theoretical case for the .05 level; it is also to say that the statement is not nearly so true of the U test. This property of the t test is useless, however, unless we know what the actual alpha is. In cases when assumptions are violated we will not. It is true that the violations of the assumptions underlying the t test can produce large discrepancies between nominal and actual alpha when the sample sizes are other than nearly equal. This in itself contraindicates the use of the t test in these instances. A further somewhat surprising consideration is that the U test is not truly distribution free. It is always sensitive to differences in distributions, and sometimes seems more affected by differences (other than mean differences) than is the *t* test.

If one final word is to be said it might be that one should not avoid using the *t* test (provided relevant considerations have been made) solely on the grounds that it is subject to error when assumptions are violated and that the *U* test is not subject to error under the same conditions. Both of the statements are unreasonable in view of the data. One should not, however, refrain from using the *U* test in place of the *t* test on the grounds that it is considerably less powerful than the *t* test. This is simply not true.

References

Auble, D. Extended tables for the Mann-Whitney statistic. *Bull. Inst. Educ. Res., Ind. U.*, 1953, **1** (2).

Boneau, C. A. The effects of violations of assumptions underlying the *t* test. *Psychol. Bull.*, 1960. **57,** 49–64.

Deuchler, G. Über die Methoden der Korrelationsrechnung in der Pädagogik und Psychologie. *Z. Pädag. Psychol.*, 1914, **15,** 114–131, 145–159, and 229–242.

Dixon, W. J. Power under normality of several nonparametric tests. *Ann. math. Statist.*, 1954, **25,** 610–614.

Dixon, W. J. and F. J. Massey. *Introduction to statistical analysis.* (2nd ed.) New York: McGraw-Hill, 1957.

Ferris, C. D., F. E. Grubbs, and C. L. Weaver. Operating characteristics for the common statistical tests of significance. *Ann. math. Statist.*, 1946, **17,** 178–197.

Hodges, J. L. and E. L. Lehman. The efficiency of some nonparametric competitors of the *t*-test. *Ann. math. Statist.*, 1956, **27,** 324–335.

Kruskal, W. H. Historical notes on the Wilcoxon unpaired two-sample test. *J. Amer. Statist. Ass.*, 1957, **52,** 356–360.

Lehman, E. L. The power of rank tests. *Ann. math. Statist.*, 1953, **24,** 23–43.

Mann, H. B. and D. R. Whitney. On a test of whether one of two random variables is stochastically larger than the other. *Ann. math. Statist.*, 1947, **18,** 50–60.

Mood, A. M. On the asymptotic efficiency of certain nonparametric two-sample tests. *Ann. math. Statist.*, 1954, **25,** 514–522.

Siegel, S. *Nonparametric statistics: For the behavioral sciences.* New York: McGraw-Hill, 1956.

Walker, H. M. and J. Lev. *Statistical inference.* New York: Holt, 1953.

Wilcoxon, F. Individual comparisons by ranking methods. *Biometrics*, 1945, **1,** 80–83.

15

a *general equation and
technique for the exact
partitioning of chi-square
contingency tables*

Jean L. Bresnahan
Martin M. Shapiro

Brief references to the partitioning of chi-square contingency tables have appeared in the statistical literature for many years (e.g., Fisher, 1932), but few detailed discussions of the topic exist. Essentially, until this time there has been a formula (Irwin, 1949) for partitioning into 2×2 tables, its computational equivalent (Kimball, 1954), and an equation (Kastenbaum, 1960) for applications in which one dimension has been reduced and the remaining table has more than one degree of freedom. In a source more readily available to psychologists, Castellan (1965) has recently reviewed some of these procedures.

This paper will present additional, more complex patterns of partitioning, supplemented by a general equation not heretofore formulated. Furthermore, it can be shown that this general equation is applicable for any mode or degree of reduction of a contingency table

From: Jean L. Bresnahan and M. M. Shapiro, "A general equation and technique for the exact partitioning of chi-square contingency tables," *Psychological Bulletin* **66**, 1966, 252–262. Copyright © 1966 by the American Psychological Association, and reproduced by permission.

This research was supported in part by grants HD-00927 and HD-01333 from the National Institutes of Health, United States Public Health Service.

and that the technique provides a most suitable solution to the problem of nonexhaustive categories or expected frequencies which are too small.

Purpose of partitioning

When a chi-square test of independence is calculated for a contingency table of more than one degree of freedom by the usual formula

$$\chi^2_{(r-1)(c-1)} = \sum \frac{(f_{oij} - f_{eij})^2}{f_{eij}} \tag{1}$$

where r = number of rows, c = number of columns, f_{oij} = observed frequency in cell ij $(i = 1, \ldots, r; j = 1, \ldots, c)$, f_{eij} = expected frequency in cell ij $(i = 1, \ldots, r; j = 1, \ldots, c)$, statistical interpretation of the outcome is difficult. A significant value of chi-square indicates nonindependence of the variables, but provides no information regarding whether nonindependence occurs throughout the whole table, or in any specific part of the table. A nonsignificant value indicates that for the table considered as a whole there is independence, but provides no information regarding the possibility of nonindependence within specific parts of the table.

By partitioning the total chi-square it is possible to make additional comparisons of cells within the whole table. It has been shown (Irwin, 1949; Kimball, 1954; Lancaster, 1949, 1950; Maxwell, 1961) that an $r \times c$ contingency table with $(r-1)(c-1)$ degrees of freedom can be subdivided into $(r-1)(c-1)$ 2×2 tables, each with one degree of freedom. The chi-squares of the individual partitions are classified as additive components, their sum being equal to the chi-square calculated for the whole table. Castellan (1965) has provided a detailed summary exposition of these procedures and those for partitioning $2 \times N$ tables into components of more than one degree of freedom.

For computing chi-square on partitioned tables of one or more degrees of freedom, Kastenbaum (1960) has provided a formula which is applicable to situations where only one dimension has been reduced, that is, either rows or columns, but not both:

$$\chi^2_{(r-1)(m-1)} = N \sum_{i=1}^{r} \frac{1}{n_{i.}} \left[\sum_{j=1}^{m} \frac{n_{ij}^2}{n_{.j}} - \frac{(\sum_{j=1}^{m} n_{ij})^2}{\sum_{j=1}^{m} n_{.j}} \right] \tag{2}$$

where r = number of rows; c = number of columns in the whole table; m = number of columns in the partitioned table, $m < c$; n_{ij} = observed frequency in cell ij;

$$n_{.j} = \sum_{i=1}^{r} n_{ij}$$

$$n_{i.} = \sum_{j=1}^{c} n_{ij}$$

$$N = \sum_{i=1}^{r} \sum_{j=1}^{c} n_{ij} = \sum_{j=1}^{c} n_{.j} = \sum_{i=1}^{r} n_{i.}$$

This procedure has greater generality than those reviewed by Castellan (1965) because it is not restricted to partitions of one degree of freedom from $r \times c$ tables or to partitions of more than one degree of freedom from $2 \times N$ tables. The equation may be used to determine the contribution of a portion of the table to the overall chi-square, but with the requirement that only the number of rows or only the number of columns has been reduced.

Determination of permissible partitions

Irwin (1949), Kimball (1954), Lancaster (1949, 1950), and Maxwell (1961) have discussed a procedure for determining the permissible 2×2 partitions. The scheme entails beginning in one corner of the table and systematically isolating and eliminating the single element appearing in that corner. For every row and column, this procedure results in comparisons between the first cell and all succeeding cells pooled, between the second cell and all succeeding cells pooled, and so on, until the final comparison between the second-last and last cells. An example of partitions of this kind for a 4×4 table is shown in Figure 1.

It is easy to demonstrate that other schemes for partitioning exist, and Kastenbaum (1960) has given an example; but if the conventional plan is analyzed, three general rules are apparent:

a) Each element appears by itself once and only once.

b) The same combination of elements does not appear more than once.

c) The dividing lines of the partitions are invariant in that once used, no elements may be combined across them in future partitions.

By following these three rules it is possible to create new partitioning schemes, thus further increasing the number of possible sets of partitions and comparisons for any given table. An example of such a different kind of scheme is illustrated in Figure 2 for a 4×4 table.

Fig. 1
Example of partitioning in a 4 × 4 table using the conventional method of successively eliminating one column and one row.

$$
\begin{array}{|c|c|c|c|c}
\hline
n_{11} & n_{12} & n_{13} & n_{14} & n_{1.} \\
\hline
n_{21} & n_{22} & n_{23} & n_{24} & n_{2.} \\
\hline
n_{31} & n_{32} & n_{33} & n_{34} & n_{3.} \\
\hline
n_{41} & n_{42} & n_{43} & n_{44} & n_{4.} \\
\hline
n_{.1} & n_{.2} & n_{.3} & n_{.4} & N \\
\end{array}
$$

$$\chi^2_9$$

$$= \quad
\begin{array}{|c|c|c|c|c}
\hline
n_{11} & n_{12} & n_{13} & n_{14} & n_{1.} \\
\hline
n_{21} & n_{22} & n_{23} & n_{24} & n_{2.} \\
n_{31} & n_{32} & n_{33} & n_{34} & n_{3.} \\
n_{41} & n_{42} & n_{43} & n_{44} & n_{4.} \\
\hline
n_{.1} & n_{.2} & n_{.3} & n_{.4} & N \\
\end{array}
\quad + \quad
\begin{array}{|c|c|c|c}
\hline
n_{12} & n_{13} & n_{14} & n_{1.'} \\
\hline
n_{22} & n_{23} & n_{24} & n_{2.'} \\
n_{32} & n_{33} & n_{34} & n_{3.'} \\
n_{42} & n_{43} & n_{44} & n_{4.'} \\
\hline
n_{.2} & n_{.3} & n_{.4} & N_{c'} \\
\end{array}
$$

$$\chi^2_1 \qquad\qquad\qquad \chi^2_1$$

$$+ \quad
\begin{array}{|c|c|c}
\hline
n_{13} & n_{14} & n_{1.''} \\
\hline
n_{23} & n_{24} & n_{2.''} \\
n_{33} & n_{34} & n_{3.''} \\
n_{43} & n_{44} & n_{4.''} \\
\hline
n_{.3} & n_{.4} & N_{C''} \\
\end{array}
\quad + \quad
\begin{array}{|c|c|c|c}
\hline
n_{21} & n_{22} & n_{23} & n_{24} & n_{2.} \\
\hline
n_{31} & n_{32} & n_{33} & n_{34} & n_{3.} \\
n_{41} & n_{42} & n_{43} & n_{44} & n_{4.} \\
\hline
n_{.1'} & n_{.2'} & n_{.3'} & n_{.4'} & N_{R'} \\
\end{array}
$$

$$\chi^2_1 \qquad\qquad\qquad \chi^2_1$$

$$+ \quad
\begin{array}{|c|c|c|c}
\hline
n_{31} & n_{32} & n_{33} & n_{34} & n_{3.} \\
\hline
n_{41} & n_{42} & n_{43} & n_{44} & n_{4.} \\
\hline
n_{.1''} & n_{.2''} & n_{.3''} & n_{.4''} & N_{R''} \\
\end{array}
\quad + \quad
\begin{array}{|c|c|c}
\hline
n_{22} & n_{23} & n_{24} & n_{2.'} \\
\hline
n_{32} & n_{33} & n_{34} & n_{3.'} \\
n_{42} & n_{43} & n_{44} & n_{4.'} \\
\hline
n_{.2'} & n_{.3'} & n_{.4'} & N_{R'C'} \\
\end{array}
$$

$$\chi^2_1 \qquad\qquad\qquad \chi^2_1$$

$$+ \quad
\begin{array}{|c|c|c}
\hline
n_{23} & n_{24} & n_{2.''} \\
\hline
n_{33} & n_{34} & n_{3.''} \\
n_{43} & n_{44} & n_{4.''} \\
\hline
n_{.3'} & n_{.4'} & N_{R'C''} \\
\end{array}
\quad + \quad
\begin{array}{|c|c}
\hline
n_{32} & n_{33} & n_{34} & n_{3.'} \\
\hline
n_{42} & n_{43} & n_{44} & n_{4.'} \\
\hline
n_{.2''} & n_{.2''} & n_{.4''} & n_{R''C'} \\
\end{array}
\quad + \quad
\begin{array}{|c|c}
\hline
n_{33} & n_{34} & n_{3.''} \\
\hline
n_{43} & n_{44} & n_{4.''} \\
\hline
n_{.3''} & n_{.4''} & N_{R''C''} \\
\end{array}
$$

$$\chi^2_1 \qquad\qquad \chi^2_1 \qquad\qquad \chi^2_1$$

194

Fig. 2
Example of a partitioned 4×4 table using a variant of the conventional method of partitioning.

n_{11}	n_{12}	n_{13}	n_{14}	$n_{1.}$
n_{21}	n_{22}	n_{23}	n_{24}	$n_{2.}$
n_{31}	n_{32}	n_{33}	n_{34}	$n_{3.}$
n_{41}	n_{42}	n_{43}	n_{44}	$n_{4.}$
$n_{.1}$	$n_{.2}$	$n_{.3}$	$n_{.4}$	N

$$\chi^2_9$$

$=$

n_{11}	n_{12}	n_{13}	n_{14}	$n_{1.}$
n_{21}	n_{22}	n_{23}	n_{24}	$n_{2.}$
n_{31}	n_{32}	n_{33}	n_{34}	$n_{3.}$
n_{41}	n_{42}	n_{43}	n_{44}	$n_{4.}$
$n_{.1}$	$n_{.2}$	$n_{.3}$	$n_{.4}$	N

$$\chi^2_1$$

$+$

n_{11}	n_{12}	$n_{1.''}$
n_{21}	n_{22}	$n_{2.''}$
n_{31}	n_{32}	$n_{3.''}$
$\dot{n}_{41}$	n_{42}	$n_{4.''}$
$n_{.1}$	$n_{.2}$	Nc_n

$$\chi^2_1$$

$+$

n_{11}	n_{12}	n_{13}	n_{14}	$n_{1.}$
n_{21}	n_{22}	n_{23}	n_{24}	$n_{2.}$
$n_{.1''}$	$n_{.2''}$	$n_{.3''}$	$n_{.4''}$	N_{Rn}

$$\chi^2_1$$

$+$

n_{31}	n_{32}	n_{33}	n_{34}	$n_{3.}$
n_{41}	n_{42}	n_{43}	n_{44}	$n_{4.}$
$m_{.1''}$	$m_{.2''}$	$m_{.3''}$	$m_{.4''}$	N_{Rm}

$$\chi^2_1$$

$+$

n_{13}	n_{14}	$m_{1.''}$
n_{23}	n_{24}	$m_{2.''}$
n_{33}	n_{34}	$n_{3.''}$
n_{43}	n_{44}	$m_{4.''}$
$n_{.3}$	$n_{.4}$	N_{Cm}

$$\chi^2_1$$

$+$

n_{11}	n_{12}	$n_{1.''}$
n_{21}	n_{22}	$n_{2.''}$
$n_{.1''}$	$n_{.2''}$	N_{RnCn}

$$\chi^2_1$$

$+$

n_{31}	n_{32}	$n_{3.''}$
n_{41}	n_{42}	$n_{4.''}$
$m_{.1''}$	$m_{.2''}$	N_{RmCn}

$$\chi^2_1$$

$+$

n_{13}	n_{14}	$m_{1.''}$
n_{23}	n_{24}	$m_{2.''}$
$n_{.3''}$	$n_{.4''}$	N_{RnCm}

$$\chi^2_1$$

$+$

n_{33}	n_{34}	$m_{3.''}$
n_{43}	n_{44}	$m_{4.''}$
$m_{.3''}$	$m_{.4''}$	N_{RmCm}

$$\chi^2_1$$

**Calculation of chi-square
for partitions**

Irwin (1949) has presented a general formula for the $(r - 1)(c - 1)$ independent 2×2 tables partitioned from the whole table:

$$\chi_1^2 = \frac{E}{e_{1.}e_{.1}e_{2.}e_{.2}}(a_{11}e_{22} + a_{22}e_{11} - a_{12}e_{21} - a_{21}e_{12})^2 \tag{3}$$

where a_{ij} = observed frequency in cell ij of the 2×2 table $(i, j = 1, 2)$; $e_{i.}$ = the sum of the expected frequencies calculated from the margins of the original table for cells $i1$ plus $i2$ $(i = 1, 2)$; $e_{.j}$ = the sum of the expected frequencies calculated from the margins of the original table for cells $1j$ plus $2j$ $(j = 1, 2)$; and

$$E = \sum_{i=1,2} e_{i.} = \sum_{j=1,2} e_{.j}$$

This formula reduces to the usual expression for a 2×2 table if the expected frequencies are calculated from the margins of the 2×2 table itself; and not, as here, from the margins of the original table.

To illustrate the use of this formula, the 4×4 table discussed previously (Figures 1 and 2) is now presented with actual numbers and chi-square values calculated for each of the partitions (Figure 3). For both methods of partitioning, the sum of the χ_1^2 is equal to the total χ_9^2.

Snedecor (1956) has shown that the formula

$$\chi_{(N-1)}^2 = \frac{(\Sigma_{x_jp_j}) - (\hat{p}T_x)}{\hat{p}\hat{q}}, \tag{4}$$

where n_j = margin frequency in category j; $j = 1, \ldots, N$; $n_j = x_j + x'_j$; x_j = observed frequency in one cell of category j; and

$$p_j = \frac{x_j}{n_j}$$

$$T = \sum_{j=1}^{N} x_j + \sum_{j=1}^{N} x'_j = \sum_{j=1}^{N} n_j$$

$$T_x = \sum_{j=1}^{N} x_j$$

$$\hat{p} = T_x/T$$

$$\hat{q} = 1 - \hat{p}$$

can be used for the total chi-square of a $2 \times N$ contingency table. An equivalent formula for a $2 \times N$ table using frequencies can be found in Walker and Lev (1953). Cochran (1954) further noted that when the denominator is kept constant, the formula is equal to χ_1^2 for a 2×2 partition from a $2 \times N$ table. If this new expression is converted from proportions to frequencies, the following formula results:

$$\chi^2 = \sum \frac{(f_o - f_e)^2}{F_e} \tag{5}$$

where

f_o = observed frequency of partitioned table;

f_e = expected frequency of partitioned table calculated from marginal totals of partitioned table; and

F_e = expected frequency of partitioned table calculated from marginal totals of original table.

It can be demonstrated that this formula is applicable to 2×2 partitions, not only from a $2 \times N$ table, but from any $r \times c$ table, the sole restriction being that only one dimension has been reduced. That is, chi-square calculated by this formula equals chi-square calculated by Irwin's formula if one or more rows (or columns) have been sliced off, provided that all columns (or rows) remain. The first five partitions for the 4×4 table meet the criterion of either complete rows or columns, and the chi-square values for these partitions can be obtained by either formula.

Equation (5) is also equivalent to Eq. (2) (the proof requires only algebraic manipulations) since for any partition which includes all the categories of one dimension, the sum of the expected frequencies as determined by the original marginal totals is equal to the sum of the observed frequencies. An alternative statement is that the sum of the expectations is equal to the expectation of the sum; and, an even stronger statement is that the sum of the original expectations is equal to the sum of the observed in either each row or each column (but not both). This relationship does not exist when both dimensions have been reduced. Nevertheless, it should be apparent that reducing only the rows or only the columns may not provide sufficient information. It shall now be shown that these reductions are only first steps in a complete analysis.

6	7	9	8
10	5	6	2
4	5	8	2
6	15	4	3

$$\chi_9^2$$

16.563214

$$=$$

6	7	9	8
10	5	6	2
4	5	8	2
6	15	4	3

$$\chi_1^2$$

0.801901

$$+$$

7	9	8
5	6	2
5	8	2
15	4	3

$$\chi_1^2$$

2.992469

$$+$$

9	8
6	2
8	2
4	3

$$\chi_1^2$$

1.836734

$$+$$

10	5	6	2
4	5	8	2
6	15	4	3

$$\chi_1^2$$

3.956341

$$+$$

4	5	8	2
6	15	4	3

$$\chi_1^2$$

0.000831

$$+$$

5	6	2
5	8	2
15	4	3

$$\chi_1^2$$

1.069129

$$+$$

6	2
8	2
4	3

$$\chi_1^2$$

0.033535

$$+$$

5	8	2
15	4	3

$$\chi_1^2$$

4.685159

$$+$$

8	2
4	3

$$\chi_1^2$$

1.187114

Fig. 3
Examples of partitioning with chi-square values calculated.

a) *Table from Figure 1, with numbers substituted for symbols.*

6	7	9	8
10	5	6	2
4	5	8	2
6	15	4	3

$$\chi_9^2$$

16.563214

$$=
\begin{array}{|cccc|}
\hline
6 & 7 & 9 & 8 \\
10 & 5 & 6 & 2 \\
\hline
4 & 5 & 8 & 2 \\
6 & 15 & 4 & 3 \\
\hline
\end{array}
\quad + \quad
\begin{array}{|cc|}
\hline
6 & 7 \\
10 & 5 \\
\hline
4 & 5 \\
6 & 15 \\
\hline
\end{array}
\quad + \quad
\begin{array}{|cc cc|}
\hline
6 & 7 & 9 & 8 \\
\hline
10 & 5 & 6 & 2 \\
\hline
\end{array}
$$

$$\chi_1^2 \qquad\qquad\qquad \chi_1^2 \qquad\qquad\qquad \chi_1^2$$

1.237229   3.327629   2.559479

$$+ \quad
\begin{array}{|cccc|}
\hline
4 & 5 & 8 & 2 \\
\hline
6 & 15 & 4 & 3 \\
\hline
\end{array}
\quad + \quad
\begin{array}{|cc|}
\hline
9 & 8 \\
6 & 2 \\
\hline
8 & 2 \\
4 & 3 \\
\hline
\end{array}
\quad + \quad
\begin{array}{|cc|}
\hline
6 & 7 \\
\hline
10 & 5 \\
\hline
\end{array}
$$

$$\chi_1^2 \qquad\qquad\qquad \chi_1^2 \qquad\qquad\qquad \chi_1^2$$

3.547708   0.477911   1.695502

$$+ \quad
\begin{array}{|cc|}
\hline
4 & 5 \\
\hline
6 & 15 \\
\hline
\end{array}
\quad + \quad
\begin{array}{|cc|}
\hline
9 & 8 \\
\hline
6 & 2 \\
\hline
\end{array}
\quad + \quad
\begin{array}{|cc|}
\hline
8 & 2 \\
\hline
4 & 3 \\
\hline
\end{array}
$$

$$\chi_1^2 \qquad\qquad\qquad \chi_1^2 \qquad\qquad\qquad \chi_1^2$$

1.138282   1.392359   1.187114

Fig. 3
Examples of partitioning with chi-square values calculated.

b)   *Table from Figure 2, with numbers substituted for symbols.*

**Additional applications and
advantages of the
alternative equation**

The expression

$$\sum \frac{(f_o - f_e)^2}{F_e}$$

is easier to calculate than Irwin's equivalent formula because in a
2×2 table all the squared deviations are equal. Apart from convenience, however, this formula has the important advantage of not being
restricted to 2×2 tables. This fact enables it to have an application
not directly available by Irwin's formula. If a researcher's interest lies
in a particular configuration consisting of all the rows (or columns)
of the original table, with one or more of the columns (or rows)
eliminated, then for this partition considered as a whole, that is, not
merely as a 2×2 partition, chi-square can be calculated by this
formula. Using Irwin's formula, the chi-square would have to be
found by calculating all the 2×2 partitions which contain in single
form elements not included in the partition of interest, and subtracting
the sum of the values from the chi-square of the whole table.

As an illustration of this principle the first row has been removed
from the 4×4 table of Figure 1, and the χ_1^2 calculated for Partitions 1,
2, and 3, and χ_6^2 calculated for Partition 4. Similarly, the first two rows
have been removed and the χ_1^2 calculated for Partitions 1, 2, 3, 4, 6,
and 7, and χ_3^2 calculated for Partition 5. The results are shown in
Figure 4a and 4b, respectively.

Equation (5) has no apparent advantage over Kastenbaum's
Eq. (2), other than ease of interpretation and conceptualization;
however, if the notation is changed and the terms rearranged, a
general equation for any partition of any mode or degree can be
derived.

Let l = number of rows in partitioned table; m = number of
columns in partitioned table; r = number of rows in whole table;
c = number of columns in whole table; n_{ij} = observed frequency in
cell ij ($i = 1$ to l to $r, j = 1$ to m to c);

$$n_{i.} = \sum_{j=1}^{m} n_{ij}$$

$$n_{.j} = \sum_{i=1}^{l} n_{ij}$$

$$\chi_1^2 = 0.801901$$
$$\chi_1^2 = 2.992469$$
$$\chi_1^2 = 1.836734$$
$$\chi_6^2 = 10.932109$$

10	5	6	2
4	5	8	2
6	15	4	3

$$\chi_9^2 = 16.563213$$

a)   *Table for six degrees of freedom remaining after the first row has been removed from the 4 × 4 table of Figure 3, and the chi-square values for each of the partitions.*

$$\chi_1^2 = 0.801901$$
$$\chi_1^2 = 2.992469$$
$$\chi_1^2 = 1.836734$$
$$\chi_1^2 = 3.956341$$
$$\chi_1^2 = 1.069129$$
$$\chi_1^2 = 0.033535$$
$$\chi_3^2 = 5.873104$$

4	5	8	2
6	15	4	3

$$\chi_9^2 = 16.563213$$

b)   *Table for three degrees of freedom remaining after the first two rows have been removed from the 4 × 4 table from Figure 3, and the chi-square values for each of the partitions.*

Fig. 4
Examples of partitioning in which some of the components have more than one degree of freedom.

e_{ij} = expected frequency for cell ij calculated from the margins of the original table

$$e_{i.} = \sum_{j=1}^{m} e_{ij}$$

$$e_{.j} = \sum_{i=1}^{l} e_{ij}$$

Then Eq. (5), when only the number of rows has been reduced, may be written as

$$\chi^2_{(l-1)(c-1)} = \sum_{i=1}^{l} \sum_{j=1}^{c} \frac{[n_{ij} - (\Sigma_{i=1}^{l} n_{ij}/\Sigma_{i=1}^{l} n_{i.})]^2}{e_{ij}}$$

and by algebra

$$\chi^2_{(l-1)(c-1)} = \sum_{i=1}^{l} \sum_{j=1}^{c} \frac{n_{ij}^2}{e_{ij}} - \sum_{j=1}^{c} \frac{(\Sigma_{i=1}^{l} n_{ij})^2}{e_{.j}} \qquad (6)$$

for the partitioned table. Similarly, if only the number of columns has been reduced, Eq. (5) may be written as

$$\chi^2_{(r-1)(m-1)} = \sum_{i=1}^{r} \sum_{j=1}^{m} \frac{n_{ij}^2}{e_{ij}} - \sum_{i=1}^{r} \frac{(\Sigma_{j=1}^{m} n_{ij})^2}{e_{i.}} \qquad (7)$$

for the partitioned table. Consider now that chi-square for the whole table can be written in the commonly used form

$$\chi^2_{(r-1)(c-1)} = \sum_{i=1}^{r} \sum_{j=1}^{c} \frac{n_{ij}^2}{e_{ij}} - N \qquad (8)$$

Therefore, the only differences between Eqs. (6), (7), and (8) are the last terms. Equation (8) has N, Eq. (6) has the square of the observed value of each attenuated column divided by its original expectation, and Eq. (7) has the square of the observed value of each attenuated row divided by its original expectation. That is, Eqs. (6) and (7) take into account the deviations from proportionality, respectively, by considering the expected and observed values of the remaining portions of the columns and rows.

Now, consider the possibility of obtaining an equation for chi-square when both the number of rows and the number of columns have been reduced, that is, both columns and rows have been attenuated. It can be shown by the most elementary algebra, although laboriously lengthy, that

$$\chi^2_{(l-1)(m-1)} = \sum_{i=1}^{l} \sum_{j=1}^{m} \frac{n_{ij}^2}{e_{ij}} - \sum_{i=1}^{l} \frac{(\Sigma_{j=1}^{m} n_{ij})^2}{e_{i.}}$$
$$- \sum_{j=1}^{m} \frac{(\Sigma_{i=1}^{l} n_{ij})^2}{e_{.j}} + \frac{(\Sigma_{i=1}^{l} \Sigma_{j=1}^{m} n_{ij})^2}{\Sigma_{i=1}^{l} \Sigma_{j=1}^{m} e_{ij}} \tag{9}$$

Let $o_{i.}$ and $o_{.j}$ be the observed margin totals in the partitioned table, and O be the total observed frequency in the partitioned table for which E is the total expected frequency; then Eq. (9) becomes

$$\chi^2_{(l-1)(m-1)} = \sum_{i=1}^{l} \sum_{j=1}^{m} \frac{n_{ij}^2}{e_{ij}} - \sum_{i=1}^{l} \frac{o_{i.}^2}{e_{i.}} - \sum_{j=1}^{m} \frac{o_{.j}^2}{e_{.j}} + \frac{O^2}{E}, \tag{10}$$

where

$$o_{i.} = \sum_{j=1}^{m} n_{ij}, \qquad o_{.j} = \sum_{i=1}^{l} n_{ij}$$
$$O = \sum_{i=1}^{l} \sum_{j=1}^{m} n_{ij}, \qquad E = \sum_{i=1}^{l} \sum_{j=1}^{m} e_{ij}$$

All previous equations for chi-square are special cases of this general equation. Even the standard Eq. (1) is the special case of exhaustive categories. It is easily shown that Eq. (10) reduces to the other equations when the appropriate special conditions are met. This equation may also be written in the following form, which has interesting properties, conceptually,

$$\chi^2_{(l-1)(m-1)} = \sum_{i=1}^{l} \sum_{j=1}^{m} \frac{(n_{ij} - e_{ij})^2}{e_{ij}} - \sum_{i=1}^{l} \frac{(o_{i.} - e_{i.})^2}{e_{i.}}$$
$$- \sum_{j=1}^{m} \frac{(o_{.j} - e_{.j})^2}{e_{.j}} + \frac{(O - E)^2}{E}. \tag{11}$$

Equation (10) may, therefore, be considered as a test of independence involving (a) the squared deviations of observation from expectation divided by expectation, for each cell; (b) a correction or subtraction out of the squared deviations of observation from expectation divided by expectation, for each margin total; and (c) a further correction for having counted the total observed deviation from expectation twice. That is, it is a test of independence corrected for lack of goodness-of-fit in the margins.

Implications of the general equation

An additional application of the equation derived in this paper,

$$\chi^2_{(l-1)(m-1)} = \sum_{i=1}^{l} \sum_{j=1}^{m} \frac{n_{ij}^2}{e_{ij}} - \sum_{i=1}^{l} \frac{o_{i.}^2}{e_{i.}} - \sum_{j=1}^{m} \frac{o_{.j}^2}{e_{.j}} + \frac{O^2}{E}, \tag{10}$$

arises in situations where two assumptions of the chi-square test of independence have not been satisfied. These common violations involve the pooling of data to obtain desired minimum expectations, and the failure to meet the requirement of exhaustive categories. Lancaster (1950) had previously noted the relationship between partitioning and pooling; the relationships among partitioning, pooling, and non-exhaustiveness can now be explicitly determined with the above equation.

Various investigators have consistently cautioned against the use of small cell entries, some setting the desired minimum expectation at 5 (e.g., Cochran, 1954), or more conservatively at 10 (e.g., Lewis and Burke, 1949). In order to follow this advice, a researcher must often resort to the alternatives of either discarding the categories which do not have minimum expectations, or pooling these categories with adjacent categories. Both of these alternatives are inadequate since they provide a way of achieving desired minimum expectations at the expense of introducing other, and perhaps equally serious, errors.

When data are pooled, error is usually introduced, since only in trivial cases are the relationships of the marginal totals not altered. Moreover, for chi-square, the categories often do not have any natural ordering, so that choosing the categories with which the small cell frequencies will be combined becomes an arbitrary decision, accompanied by a spurious lowering or raising of the chi-square value. There are certain situations where the categories do follow a natural ordering, and pooling may be a legitimate operation, as in goodness-of-fit tests. There are also numerous occasions when an ordering seems apparent but is, in fact, imposed by the researcher and not the natural events.

The alternative procedure of discarding categories is patently an inefficient procedure since all data should be utilized. More important, the discarding of categories fails to satisfy the requirement of exhaustiveness.

The errors caused by either the pooling of data or the use of nonexhaustive categories can be eliminated by the technique suggested in this paper. That is, if one or more rows and/or columns consist of cells which do not have desired minimum expectations, instead of discarding these rows and/or columns, or pooling them with adjacent entries, a chi-square value should be calculated for the table remaining by Eq. (10). This value can be regarded as the contribution of the table remaining to the chi-square of the original table. The degrees of freedom for this table are the same as they would be if the small expectations were pooled or discarded completely, but the value of the statistic is now exact.[1]

It is interesting to note that although the requirement of exhaustiveness has been repeatedly mentioned in the literature, it has not been elaborated upon and appears to have been treated more as a theoretical ideal than one to be sought in practice. Perhaps this cursory treatment of the problem in the past indicated the lack of a satisfactory solution.

An example

It is perhaps useful to present a real-life example to demonstrate the utility of these techniques and the manner in which the general equation for chi-square facilitates the computation. The example to be used is Table 35 from Hollingshead and Redlich (1958, p. 288). It shall be assumed that the sample of 1,442 constituted a random sample from the population of psychotic patients. Each subject was categorized according to the diagnostic groups affective psychoses (Af), alcoholic psychoses (Al), organic psychoses (Or), schizophrenic psychoses (Sc), senile psychoses (Se); and treatments psychotherapy (Ps), organic therapy (OT), custodial care (CC). The analysis is done using Eq. (10). The term

$$\frac{(\text{observed})^2}{(\text{expected})}$$

is given for each cell and each margin in the tables below, even when the terms are redundant or corresponding terms sum to zero. To further facilitate the readers' following the computations, the individual terms are shown to only one decimal place, although the chi-square values are computed to six decimal places.

Table 1 shows Hollingshead and Redlich's percentage data converted to frequencies. Table 2 shows that the original table yields a chi-square for eight degrees of freedom equal to 254.254660. (The

---

1. It should be noted that in some sense no computed value of chi-square is exact since the computational formulas yield values which are only approximately distributed as chi-square. That is, chi-square is approached as the number of frequency entries approaches infinity. In this sense, the components add up exactly to an approximation.

Table 1

	Ps	OT	CC
Af	30	102	28
Al	48	23	20
Or	19	80	75
Sc	121	344	382
Se	18	11	141

chi-square value in the original text obviously contains an inconsequential computational error.) Table 3 shows the chi-square calculation for the diagnostic groups Or and Sc versus Al, Af, and Se. It can be seen that these two sets of diagnostic groups and the treatment categories are not independent. Table 4 shows, however, that diagnostic categories Or and Sc and the treatment categories must be considered independent. Table 5 shows that the diagnostic categories Af, Al, and Se are not independent of the treatment categories CC versus Ps plus OT combined. Table 6 shows that Af versus Al plus Se combined are not independent of Ps and OT. Table 7 shows that Al and Se are not independent of Ps and OT.

Table 2

	Ps	OT	CC	
Af	34.4	167.4	10.9	160.0
Al	154.7	15.0	9.8	91.0
Or	12.7	94.7	72.2	174.0
Sc	105.6	359.8	384.6	847.0
Se	11.6	1.8	261.0	170.0
	236.0	560.0	646.0	1442.0

$$\chi^2 = 254.254660, p < .001$$

Table 3

	Ps	OT	CC	
Or + Sc	117.3	453.4	456.6	1021.0
Af + Al + Se	133.8	113.1	189.4	421.0
	236.0	560.0	646.0	1442.0

$$\chi_2^2 = 21.583895, p < .001$$

Table 4

	Ps	OT	CC	
Or	12.7	94.7	72.2	174.0
Sc	105.6	359.8	384.6	847.0
	117.3	453.4	456.6	1021.0

$$\chi_2^2 = 2.196957, p \cong .33$$

Table 5

	Ps + OT	CC	
Af	90.0	10.9	160.0
Al	100.3	9.8	91.0
Se	9.0	261.0	170.0
	231.6	189.4	421.0

$$\chi_2^2 = 60.116576, p < .001$$

Table 6

	Ps	OT	
Af	34.4	167.4	90.0
Al + Se	102.0	11.4	69.4
	133.8	113.1	231.6

$$\chi_1^2 = 140.513219, p < .001$$

Table 7

	Ps	OT	
Al	154.7	15.0	100.3
Se	11.6	1.8	9.0
	102.0	11.4	69.4

$$\chi_1^2 = 29.844013, p < .001$$

Although the overall chi-square for eight degrees of freedom is a very large number, it may be concluded that the diagnostic categories of organic psychoses and schizophrenic psychoses do not significantly differ from each other in terms of the proportion of patients given psychotherapy, organic therapy, or custodial care. The organic and schizophrenic psychoses groups differ from the three other diagnostic categories in the proportion of patients given the three types of treatment, but the organic and schizophrenic groups do not differ from each other. All other tests of independence are significant.

Although this example involves neither the problem of small expected frequencies or originally nonexhaustive categories, it is an interesting illustration. The overall analysis yields what looks to be an exceedingly "strong" relationship; but on a more detailed analysis, the relationship fails to exist where one might logically expect to find it.

References

Castellan, N. J., Jr. On the partitioning of contingency tables. *Psychological Bulletin*, 1965, **64,** 330–338.

Cochran, W. G. Some methods for strengthening the common χ^2 tests. *Biometrics*, 1954, **10,** 417–451.

Fisher, R. W. *Statistical methods for research workers* (4th ed.). Edinburgh: Oliver & Boyd, 1932.

Hollingshead, A. B. and F. C. Redlich. *Social class and mental illness: A community study.* New York: Wiley, 1958.

Irwin, J. O. A note on the subdivision of χ^2 into components. *Biometrika*, 1949, **36,** 130–134.

Kastenbaum, M. A. A note on the additive partitioning of chi-square in contingency tables. *Biometrics*, 1960, **16,** 416–422.

Kimball, A. W. Short-cut formulas for the exact partition of χ^2 in contingency tables. *Biometrics*, 1954, **10,** 452–458.

Lancaster, H. O. The derivation and partition of χ^2 in certain discrete distributions. *Biometrika*, 1949, **36**, 117–129.

Lancaster, H. O. The exact partition of χ^2 and its application to the problem of the pooling of small expectations. *Biometrika*, 1950, **37**, 267–270.

Lewis, D. and C. J. Burke. The use and misuse of the chi-square test. *Psychological Bulletin*, 1949, **46**, 433–489.

Maxwell, A. E. *Analysing qualitative data.* London: Methuen, 1961.

Snedecor, G. W. *Statistical methods.* (5th ed.). Ames, Iowa: Iowa State College Press, 1956.

Walker, H. M. and J. Lev. *Statistical inference.* New York: Holt, 1953.

16

note on the sampling error of the difference between correlated proportions or percentages

Quinn McNemar

It is well known that the sampling variance of the difference between two proportions, p_1 and p_2, based on independent samples is given by

$$\sigma_d^2 = \sigma_{p_1}^2 + \sigma_{p_2}^2 = \frac{p_1 q_1}{N_1} + \frac{p_2 q_2}{N_2}, \tag{1}$$

or by

$$\sigma_d^2 = \frac{pq}{N_1} + \frac{pq}{N_2}, \tag{2}$$

in which p_1 and p_2 as separate estimates of the unknown population parameters are replaced by

$$p = \frac{p_1 N_1 + p_2 N_2}{N_1 + N_2}$$

as a better estimate which is consistent with the to be tested null

Reprinted from *Psychometrika* **12**, 153–157 (1947) by permission of Q. McNemar and The Psychometric Corporation. Copyright © 1947 by The Psychometric Corporation.

hypothesis, and therefore to be preferred. It is also known that when σ_d^2 is calculated by (2) the value of d^2/σ_d^2 equals χ^2 with one degree of freedom.

There are many situations in which the sampling variance of the difference between two proportions (or percentages) must take into account the fact that the two proportions are not based on independent samples. For example, p_1 may represent the proportion of individuals who give a particular response prior to a provided experience and p_2 the proportion of the *same* individuals giving the response after the interpolated experience; or p_1 might be the proportion passing one test item and p_2 the proportion of the same group passing a second item, and we wonder whether items differ significantly as to difficulty; or we may wish to test the significance of the difference between the responses of a group to two opinion questions; or we may need to evaluate the difference between two proportions based on paired or matched individuals.

For such situations as the foregoing, neither Formula (1) nor (2) is applicable. To be applicable, a subtractive correlational term should be included. The needed correlation is that between the sampling variations of the two proportions. Since it can readily be shown that proportions are means, and since it is known that the correlation between sample means equals that between variates, it follows that the needed correlation is that between first and second responses, or between performances on the two items being compared for difficulty, or between responses to two opinion questions, or between the responses of matched cases. The correlation "scatter plot" for these situations involves a two-by-two table, for which one may apparently choose either the contingency coefficient or tetrachoric r or the four-fold point r as the measure of correlation. Which type of coefficient do we need for the sampling variance of the difference between correlated proportions?

If the answer to this question is to be found in the statistical literature, the writer has failed to locate it. If the answer were obvious, one would not expect the near universal failure of researchers to include the needed correlational term in those situations where it must certainly be taken into account in testing significance. We have found only one text* which considers the correlational term, and the authors of this text, after saying that "it is seldom that we know the correlation factor when dealing with proportions," go on to state

---

* Peters, C. C. and W. R. Van Voorhis. *Statistical procedures and their mathematical bases.* New York: McGraw-Hill, 1940, p. 183.

without proof that "it would need to be computed by the tetrachoric method." We shall presently see that this idea is incorrect.

The desired sampling variance formula would be of the form

$$\sigma_d^2 = \sigma_{p_1}^2 + \sigma_{p_2}^2 - 2r_{p_1 p_2} \sigma_{p_1} \sigma_{p_2}, \tag{3}$$

in which r is not as yet specified. Suppose a fourfold table of frequencies, and the corresponding table of proportions, for a first (I) and a second (II) set of responses from the same individuals (see Table 1). The difference between the two marginal values, $p_2 - p_1$, is the difference for which we seek a standard error. For the sake of exposition, let us assume that this difference represents a change in responses. Then the B and C individuals are those who have not changed, while A represents those who moved from yes to no, and D those who changed from no to yes. The lower-case letters represent the corresponding proportions. Let us score those who changed to yes as $+1$, those who changed to no as -1, and those who changed not at all as 0. This leads to the frequency distributions for changes shown in Table 2, which includes easily derived expressions for the mean and variance of the distributions of changes.

Obviously, the mean change equals

$$(D - A)/N = (d - a) = p_2 - p_1,$$

or the mean of the changes (or differences) equals the difference between the two proportions. The sampling error of $p_2 - p_1$ must be the same as that for M, its equivalent, and the sampling variance of M is easily obtained by dividing the distribution variance by N. Thus, in terms of proportional frequencies, we have

$$\sigma_M^2 = \sigma_{p_2 - p_1}^2 = (1/N)[(d + a) - (d - a)^2]. \tag{4}$$

Now by easy, but somewhat cumbersome algebra which need not be reproduced here, it can be shown that (4) reduces to (3) *providing*

Table 1
Fourfold table of original and proportional frequencies

		(II)						(II)		
		No	Yes					No	Yes	
	Yes	A	B	$A + B$			Yes	a	b	p_1
(I)						(I)				
	No	C	D	$C + D$			No	c	d	q_1
		$A + C$	$B + D$	N				q_2	p_2	1.00

Table 2
Distributions for changes in terms of original
and proportional frequencies

Original		Proportional	
X	f	X	f
+1	D	+1	d
0	B + C	0	b + c
−1	A	−1	a
	N		1.00

Mean $= (D - A)/N = d - a = p_2 - p_1$

$$\text{S.D.}^2 = \frac{1}{N^2}[N(D + A) - (D - A)^2] = (d + a) - (d - a)^2$$

the r of (3) is the fourfold point correlation coefficient. It will be noted that (4) requires less computation than (3) even when r has been calculated for its own sake.

It will be seen that (3), hence by implication that (4), involves the use of two separate estimates of the unknown population proportions, and therefore both are analogous to (1). If we wish a formula analogous to the preferred (2), that is, one involving an estimate based on the combined sets of responses or a p based on the total as a better estimate, we note that such a p would, as in the case of (2), imply that the population values for the two proportions are equal. This would be consistent with the null hypothesis that $p_2 - p_1 = 0$ except for random sampling fluctuations. The proper p to replace p_2 and p_1 in (3) becomes the simple average of p_2 and p_1 since for the given situation $N_2 = N_1 = N$. Now the null hypothesis that $p_2 = p_1$ also implies that the equivalent, $d - a$, must equal zero except for sampling errors; hence formula (4) becomes

$$\sigma^2_{p_2 - p_1} = (1/N)(d + a), \tag{5}$$

which is algebraically identical to (3) with p_2 and p_1 replaced by p. Since (2) is associated exactly with χ^2, it is of interest to point out the connection of (5) with χ^2. Table 3 contains the setup for χ^2 for the original observed (O) frequency distribution of Table 2. Since the net change (or difference) between the two sets of responses depends upon the D and A individuals, the expected frequencies (E) are written on the assumption that the $D + A$ cases would be divided evenly, on the

Table 3
Schema for χ^2 test of changes

X	0	E	$(0 - E)^2/E$
+1	D	$(D + A)/2$	$\dfrac{(D - A)^2}{4} \cdot \dfrac{2}{D + A} = \dfrac{1}{2}\dfrac{(D - A)^2}{D + A}$
0	$B + C$		
−1	A	$(D + A)/2$	$\dfrac{(A - D)^2}{4} \cdot \dfrac{2}{D + A} = \dfrac{1}{2}\dfrac{(D - A)^2}{D + A}$

basis of the null hypothesis, between plus and minus changes. The value of χ^2 becomes the sum of the right-hand terms, or

$$\chi^2 = \frac{(D - A)^2}{D + A}. \tag{6}$$

When we write the square of the critical ratio with (5) as the sampling variance, we have

$$(CR)^2 = \frac{(d - a)^2}{(d + a)/N}.$$

Replacing proportions by frequencies, this becomes

$$\frac{[(D/N) - (A/N)]^2}{\dfrac{(D/N) + (A/N)}{N}} = \frac{(D - A)^2}{D + A}.$$

Thus $(CR)^2$, using Formula (5), is identical to the χ^2 of (6). Obviously, $CR = (D - A)/\sqrt{D + A}$, and therefore the significance of the difference between p_2 and p_1 can readily be computed from the fourfold table of frequencies or from the fourfold table of proportions.

The use of either (5) or (6) is to be preferred over (3) or (4) just as, and for the same reason that, Formula (2) is preferable to (1).

Although the foregoing development was in terms of changes in responses, the resulting formulas are applicable to the other three situations mentioned at the beginning of this note. The limitation on chi square regarding size of expected frequencies suggests that Formulas (5) and (6) should not be used unless $A + D$ is 10 or greater.

17

note on the "correction for continuity" in testing the significance of the difference between correlated proportions

Allen L. Edwards

McNemar [1] developed several formulas for testing the significance of the difference between two correlated proportions. His formulas should prove extremely valuable, but their usefulness and accuracy may be increased if it is shown how corrections for continuity may be applied in using them. We are dealing with discrete frequencies and if the data are to be evaluated in terms of continuous distributions, either the normal distribution or the chi square distribution, a correction is in order [2]. The methods of making the correction are relatively simple and can best be illustrated with a numerical example.

Let us take the hypothetical data of Table 1. We are interested in the significance of the difference between the two proportions, .60 and .50. If the evaluation is to be made by means of the chi square distribution, then the correction for continuity is made by adding .5 to the smaller of the two frequencies corresponding to cells A and D of Table 1, and subtracting .5 from the larger of the two frequencies. This correction will have the obvious result of reducing the absolute

Table 1
Fourfold table of original and proportional frequencies

		(I)					(I)		
		No	Yes				No	Yes	
(II)	Yes	A	B	$A + B$	(II)	Yes	20	80	100
	No	C	D	$C + D$		No	60	40	100
		$A + C$	$B + D$	N			80	120	200

		(I)					(I)		
		No	Yes				Yes	No	
(II)	Yes	a	b	p_2	(II)	Yes	.10	.40	.50
	No	c	d	q_2		No	.30	.20	.50
		q_1	p_1	1.00			.40	.60	1.00

value of the difference, $D - A$, by unity. Then McNemar's formula (6), corrected for continuity, may be written

$$\chi^2 = \frac{(|D - A| - 1)^2}{D + A}. \tag{1}$$

Substituting in (1), above, we obtain

$$\frac{(|40 - 20| - 1)^2}{40 + 20} = \frac{361}{60} = 6.0167.$$

If the evaluation is to be made by means of the normal distribution, the correction for continuity is made by adding .5 to the frequency corresponding to the smaller value of p of Table 1 and subtracting .5 from the frequency corresponding to the larger value of p. Thus the corrected values are

$$p_2 = \frac{100.0 + .5}{200} = .5025 \quad \text{and} \quad p_1 = \frac{120.0 - .5}{200} = .5975.$$

The difference between these two values, .095, will, when divided by the standard error of the difference arrived at by means of McNemar's formula (5), be equal to the t ratio corrected for continuity. The correction may be most easily made by taking

$$p_1 - p_2 = \frac{|(B + D) - (A + B)| - 1}{N} = \frac{|D - A| - 1}{N}. \tag{2}$$

Using the difference obtained by means of (2) above and applying McNemar's formula (5), we obtain

$$t^2 = \frac{(p_1 - p_2)^2}{\sigma^2_{p_1 - p_2}} = \frac{(p_1 - p_2)^2}{(d + a)/N} = \frac{(.095)^2}{.0015} = 6.0167,$$

which is identical, as it should be, with χ^2 corrected for continuity.

It may be noted that if we were working consistently at the 1 percent *level* of significance, the probability value attaching to χ^2 or t, through failure to apply the correction for continuity, would, for the example cited, result in the rejection of the hypothesis tested. Correcting for continuity, however, the obtained value of χ^2 or t would be consistent with the hypothesis tested. It is apparent that the correction may be of some importance in critical cases. This will be particularly true when any theoretical cell frequency is small for, in this instance, the probability arrived at by the ordinary χ^2 test or t test will considerably overestimate the significance. The correction for continuity will increase the accuracy and usefulness of McNemar's formulas (5) and (6) under these conditions and its application should be made a matter of routine procedure.

References

1. McNemar, Q. Note on the sampling error of the difference between correlated proportions. *Psychometrika*, 1947, **12**, 153–157.

2. Yates, F. Contingency tables involving small numbers and the χ^2 test. *Suppl. J. Roy. Stat. Soc.*, 1934, **1**, 217–235.

18

non-parametric methods in psychological research

John Gaito

In recent years statistical techniques have been developed which do not rely on parameters of a known distribution in making statistical inferences. These have been called non-parametric or distribution-free methods. The main presentations of this subject matter with which psychologists are familiar are probably those by Edwards [8], Moses [22], Mosteller and Bush [23], and Siegel [27]. However, there are numerous other treatises in this area [e.g., 14, 21, 31]. These techniques have been developed mainly to avoid the need for making numerous assumptions as is the case with parametric techniques, thus providing certain advantages. However, in light of recent research it appears that at least with one parametric technique some of the assumed advantages of non-parametric analyses cited have been premature inasmuch as the assumptions of this parametric technique are not as restrictive as once supposed. The purpose of this paper is to consider effects of failure to meet assumptions of the analysis of variance technique on subsequent tests of significance and to suggest that in this area non-parametric techniques be given very limited use in psychological research.

Reprinted with permission of author and publisher: Gaito, J. Nonparametric methods in psychological research. *Psychological Reports*, 1959, **5**, 115–125.

**Assumptions for use of
parametric techniques**

Before one can use a parametric technique he must make certain assumptions. For this discussion we will concentrate on the analysis of variance technique which is a general model for tests of homogeneity of means (the common problem which seems to confront psychologists). The *t* test is a special case of the analysis of variance model when the between groups degrees of freedom equal one. *It must be emphasized that the following statements are relevant only to an analysis of variance type situation.*

The assumptions required for the use of this technique are as follows.

a. The errors must be independent. In the one variable design each observation must be independent, i.e., the selection of any one case must not affect the chances of any other case for inclusion in the sample. In multivariable designs independence refers to the portions of the effect which is to be used as the error estimate.

b. The variables included within the experiment must be additive, i.e., the means of these variables or effects must be linear combinations.

c. The variance of the different portions of the appropriate error term is the same for each treatment population.

d. The distribution of the observations which are used as the appropriate error term must be normal in the treatment population.

e. The variables involved must be mensurable by an interval scale [29] for valid use of the technique.

Some individuals include all of the above requirements [e.g., 27]; others list fewer assumptions [9, 18]. However, all individuals include Assumptions *a*, *c*, and *d*.

Let us look carefully at each one of the assumptions to determine how restrictive each is, as compared with non-parametric methods. We can immediately cast aside Assumption *a*, that of independence. This assumption must apply also to non-parametric techniques inasmuch as they are based on probability distributions which assume chance distribution of errors.

Assumption *b* is not considered a necessary condition by some individuals [18]. Furthermore, there has been much confusion concerning the interpretation of this assumption. Some individuals define additivity as an absence of interaction between treatment and experimental units [9, 16] while others define additivity as linear combinations of the experimental effects [27] and do not consider interactions in the definition of additivity. However, the presence or absence of interactions has a definite effect on the procedure and inferences involved.

One can write the linear equation for the analysis of variance model and include interactions [2]. However, if the interaction does not include a random effect, the test of the main effects may not be appropriate. For example, if the interaction involves fixed effects and is of a "reversal" type, i.e., one treatment may be more effective at one level of a second variable while another treatment is more effective at other levels, then a test of the main effect is misleading because generalizations are not meaningful. One would be interested in looking at the "simple" effects [18]. However, if the interaction is a "continuous spread" one, i.e., one treatment is more effective at all levels of the second variable but the difference between the treatments varies at different levels, then a test of the main effect is meaningful and generalizations are appropriate. These two types of interactions are indicated most readily by a graphical procedure. In any event the investigator can determine the type of interaction present and take the appropriate measures in his analysis and interpretation of the results.

It appears that Assumptions *c* and *d* have been studied more than any of the others. Furthermore, it seems that these assumptions are the main ones that have prompted the development of some non-parametric methods. However, the mathematical and empirical data indicate that tests of homogeneity of means by analysis of variance (and two-tailed *t* tests) are relatively insensitive to both deviations from normality and from homogeneity of variance.

For example, the most important empirical investigation in this area was that by Norton (cited by Lindquist [18]). In one phase of this study Norton chose numerous samples from each of four different populations: a J-shaped distribution, a markedly skewed one, a moderately skewed one, and a normal distribution. Accompanying this extreme deviation from normality was extreme heterogeneity of variance, one variance being almost 45 times that of another. This situation probably represents more of a discrepancy than is found in most experimental situations. However, even with this violent departure from the theoretical assumptions, the *F* distribution still represented a fairly good fit. The effect was to approximately double the probability level. However, Lindquist asserts that if the investigator allows for this effect, he may still use the normal theory test to great advantage, e.g., set .025 rather than .05 or .005 rather than .01 for probability levels. The data of the Norton study provide tables which might be used as a guide when deviations from assumptions are suspected.

In an earlier study with different schools in which heterogeneity of variance was being investigated, Lindquist [17] noted that more significant *F*'s occurred than expected when Methods was tested against either the Methods × Schools interaction or the Within Classes effect. However, the discrepancy between the expected and theoretical frequencies for various probability levels was greater for the latter test. Yet Lindquist maintained that the divergence of observed from theoretical frequencies was not large enough to render the *F* test inadequate.

Numerous other individuals have investigated the effects of nonnormality or heterogeneity of variance on the *F* or *t* tests of significance. Pearson [24] and Rider [25] found little effect of nonnormality on the *F* and two-tailed *t* tests, respectively. Box and Anderson, after reviewing studies by Box, Gayen, Geary, and others concerning the analysis of variance and two-tailed *t* tests, maintain that, "From the foregoing tables it can be seen that a large variety of tests for comparing means are highly robust to both nonnormality and inequality of variances. *Therefore the practical experimenter may use these tests of significance with relatively little worry concerning the failure of these assumptions to hold exactly in experimental situations.* The rather striking exception to this rule is the sensitivity of the analysis of variance heterogeneity when the groups are of unequal size" [4, p. 60, italics mine]. The latter statement is occasioned because, when the number of observations within groups differed greatly, the probability level became two or three times as great as was expected.

Likewise, Cochran in a review of studies by Hey, Bartlett, and others concerning nonnormality stated, "The consensus from these investigations is that no serious error is introduced by nonnormality in the significance levels of the *F*-test or of the two-tailed *t*-test. While it is difficult to generalize about the range of populations that were investigated, this appears to cover most cases encountered in practice. If a guess may be made about the limits of error, the true probability corresponding to the tabular 5 percent significance level may be between 4 and 7 percent. For the 1 percent level, the limits might be taken as $\frac{1}{2}$ percent and 2 percent" [5, p. 24]. Cochran maintains that heterogeneity of errors has an unpredictable effect on the data. If extreme heterogeneity occurs he recommends subdividing error variance, omitting part of the experiment, or the use of a transformation.

From the above, it appears that in the great majority of cases little distortion of significance levels will be effected with nonnormality and heterogeneity of variance present. However, if the numbers within the groups differ greatly (which is usually not the case) deviations from normality and homogeneity of errors will have a greater effect.

In the event that extreme deviations from these two theoretical

assumptions occur, the investigator has available various transformations by which the deviations may be reduced. The most common
ones are the arc sine or angular transformation for distributions of
binomial nature, the square root transformation for Poisson distributions, and the logarithmic transformation when it appears that the
mean will be proportional to the standard deviation [3, 28, 30].
Fortunately, if a suitable transformation is chosen, both nonnormality
and heterogeneity may be reduced inasmuch as these tend to vary
together [3].

Assumption *e* would appear to be the most serious obstacle to the
use of parametric techniques inasmuch as most psychological research
deals with subinterval type data, i.e., with ordinal or nominal scales.
However, the important point in this connection is that it is possible
to relate the scale to the normal curve. If the scores may be regarded
as following a normal distribution in the population being sampled,
then parametric statistical tests should be appropriate (provided other
assumptions are approximated) no matter what the formal scale
properties of the scores. Thus Assumption *e* appears to reduce, in the
final analysis, to Assumption *d*. Considered in this light the restrictive-
ness of this assumption appears to diminish. As has been pointed out
above the parametric test seems to be relatively insensitive to moderate
departures from normality and to be affected slightly by extreme
departures.

In connection with Assumption *e* it appears that even some ranked
(ordinal) data are amenable to treatment by analysis of variance. The
distances between the various rankings by an *S* may not be equal or
not of such interval size as to be related to the normal distribution.
However, when the rankings of each of a number of *S*'s are averaged,
these average ranks would appear to more closely approximate the
normal curve. Furthermore, each individual's ranked data could be
transformed to normal scores by a procedure recommended by Fisher
and Yates [10] so as to improve the validity of the analysis of variance.

Guilford [12] maintains that there are various approaches to
achieving an interval scale, *viz.*, observational techniques, transformations, and scaling procedures. However, even without these modifica-
tions he states that experimental data often approach the conditions
of an interval scale sufficiently well to justify using these statistics.
Concerning ordinal data involved in the Method of Rank Order, he
specifies that, "Stimuli that have been ranked by a number of observers
can be placed in a 'pooled' rank order. More than that, scale values
that refer to an interval scale can be assigned to the stimuli" [12, p. 178].
For ordinal data he recommends the use of a normalizing rank transformation or the comparative judgment approach, preferably the

normalized rank process because it is simpler, more direct, and does not require a large N.

However, even when the population distribution is not known, it is reasonable to make the assumption that this distribution would be normal or near normal inasmuch as in practice many distributions seem to be of this nature. Concerning this matter Guilford states that, "If the objects are living things or the product of living things, there is a good possibility that they come from a normally distributed population. Even in a small sample, the distances between neighboring objects are probably smaller as we go toward their central tendency and larger at the extremes" [12, p. 181].

Advantages of non-parametric techniques

Now that we have considered the assumptions required for the use of parametric tests and the consequences when these assumptions are not attained, let us consider the advantages and disadvantages of the use of non-parametric and parametric techniques. We shall look at the ones reported by Siegel [27] which are essentially the same as those reported by Moses [22] and by Mosteller and Bush [23].

1. Probability statements are exact when obtained from most non-parametric tests regardless of the shape of the population distribution from which the sample was drawn.

This is certainly true. However, this situation is similar to the one between Chebyshev's Inequality and the Central Limit Theorem. In the former case a gross probability statement can be made while in the latter instance a more refined probability can be reported. Thus this advantage reduces to a question as to whether the *exact gross* probability statement is the most appropriate one in light of the above arguments concerning the normality assumption.

2. For samples with as few as six cases, there is no alternative to using a non-parametric test unless the nature of the distribution is known exactly.

This statement is not justified if we consider the empirical results. Many distributions tend to follow the normal one. Furthermore, the statements by Box and Anderson [4], and others cited above, indicate that as long as the distribution does not deviate too greatly from normality, an investigator may use a parametric technique no matter what the size of the sample. Having only 6 S's is no different than having 10 S's (or slightly more) inasmuch as small sample data rarely approach the normal form thus providing clues as to the distribution form in the parent population. The unreliability of small samples is considered in the tabular values required for significance. Furthermore, Norton's study indicates that the investigator may use the analysis of variance even when he is certain that the distributions may be markedly skewed if he makes adjustments in the probability level required for significance.

3. There are suitable non-parametric statistical tests for treating samples made up of observations from several different populations whereas no parametric techniques are available for this purpose without requiring unrealistic assumptions.

The important point here is what effect the failure of these assumptions would have on the data. It is possible that little distortion would be introduced but, as there is no empirical evidence on this point, it is best to admit that this is a definite advantage of the non-parametric tests.

4. Non-parametric tests can treat ranked data whereas precarious and unrealistic assumptions about the distribution forms are required if one uses parametric tests.

This statement is, likewise, too conservative in light of the above review of studies pertinent to normality. Furthermore, the transformations of Fisher and Yates or of Guilford may be employed so as to use parametric techniques for some ranked data.

5. Non-parametric tests can treat data which are of classificatory (frequency) nature whereas no parametric techniques apply to this problem area.

This statement is certainly correct. Classificatory data can be handled only by non-parametric techniques.

6. Non-parametric techniques are computationally more simple and easier to learn.

This is one of the greatest advantages of non-parametric methods. However, the computational simplicity should be given a low priority.

Disadvantages of non-parametric techniques (relative to parametric methods)

The following disadvantages are usually cited.

1. If the assumptions of a parametric technique are met or approximated but non-parametric techniques are used, the latter are less powerful. Siegel considers this aspect as power-efficiency. For example,

if a non-parametric test has a power-efficiency of 90%, a parametric technique would be just as effective with a 10% smaller sample, if the assumptions of the parametric test are met.

2. There are few non-parametric tests for interaction effects. Mood [21] and Wilcoxon [31] have reported interaction tests; however, these are crude or computationally laborious. Wilson [32] has recently presented a simple χ^2 non-parametric test which allows a partitioning of the total sum of squares into sums of squares for main and interaction effects. However, this test is suitable only for the Fixed Variate Model wherein all effects are fixed ones. This is certainly a defect of this test as well as of other non-parametric measures. Furthermore, McNemar [19] has criticized the Wilson test because of the above mentioned inflexibility and its low power. McNemar used both the analysis of variance and the Wilson test for six sets of data reported in the literature and a seventh which he provided. Each set of data involved a two way classification; thus each set allowed for three tests, i.e., of column, row, and interaction effects. He found that for all effects the non-parametric technique was less discriminative. For example, of the 11 p's reaching the .01 level of the F-test, six failed to do so by the Wilson test. Furthermore, five of these six failed by a wide margin. Results were similar for the .05 level comparisons. Because of the above defects and because of the relative insensitivity of the analysis of variance to deviations from normality and homogeneity of variance, McNemar suggests that the parametric test be used in analysis of experimental data. In a later article, McNemar [20] has pointed out further inadequacies of the Wilson technique.

To these two disadvantages we would like to add four more.

1. The non-parametric technique may involve much computation in reporting differences between various groups after the overall null hypothesis has been rejected if numerous groups are included in the experiment. The analysis has to be repeated with pairs of two unless only two groups are involved; therefore, there are $n(n - 1)/2$ analyses to be conducted. However, this problem can be easily handled for the case when the analysis of variance F test is significant by partitioning the n degrees of freedom for treatments into n orthogonal components (each with 1 df), or by various multiple comparisons tests, e.g., Duncan [6, 7], Tukey,[1] Scheffe [26], which require a minimal amount of computation.

---

1. Tukey, J. W. The problem of multiple comparisons. Unpublished dittoed notes, Princeton Univer., 1953.

2. With the analysis of variance technique, estimates of parameters can be obtained whereas this is impossible with the non-parametric techniques. Usually in psychological work the investigator stops with tests of significance; however, if estimates are required these may be obtained by the analysis of variance technique [9, 18, 28, and Greenwood[2]].

3. Another advantage of the analysis of variance procedure has been indicated previously by the author, that of determining a coefficient of utility to indicate the practical significance of the parameters [11]. One determines what components of variance are included in each mean square, estimates each parameter from the sample data, and compares the magnitude of each parameter with the sum of all parameters included in the analysis. This allows one to specify the proportion of total variance contributed by each parameter.

4. Another important aspect which favors the analysis of variance technique over the non-parametric tests is that with the former an estimate of the reliability of the experiment can be obtained. The analysis of variance has been used to estimate test reliability [12, 15] and the reliability of experiments when repeated trials on the same S are available [1]. However, it would appear to be of valuable use in almost every experiment. Reliability (the proportion of reliable variance in an experiment) is obtained by dividing reliable variance by the sum of reliable and unreliable variance. However, this estimate is an underestimation in experiments which involve independent groups inasmuch as unreliable variance (errors of measurements and other uncontrollable sources of variance) is confounded with variance due to subjects, which is reliable variance. On the other hand, if a Treatments × Subjects experimental design is used, this confounding is prevented.

The formula for estimating reliability is of the following nature:

$$(A\sigma_a^2 + B\sigma_b^2 + \cdots + N\sigma_n^2)/(A\sigma_a^2 + B\sigma_b^2 + \cdots + N\sigma_n^2 + \sigma_e^2),$$

where $\sigma_a^2, \sigma_b^2, \sigma_n^2$, represents reliable variance; σ_e^2 is unreliable variance; and $A, B, \ldots, N$ represent the coefficients for the variances. Reliability would be approximated by a ratio of various mean squares. (For the technique of obtaining estimates of each parameter and coefficients for these parameters see Greenwood[2] or Lindquist [16].)

However, usually the only reliable variance that is included in the

---

2.   Greenwood, J. A. Analysis of variance and components of variance-factorial experiments. Unpublished paper, Bureau of Aeronautics, 1956 (rev.).

estimation is subjects variance. In such case the estimation is by the following [12]:

$$\frac{\text{Subjects Mean Square} - \text{Experimental Error Mean Square}}{\text{Subjects Mean Square}}.$$

In terms of expected value of mean square this reduces to

$$S\sigma_s^2/(S\sigma_s^2 + \sigma_e^2)$$

where σ_s^2 and σ_e^2 refer to subjects and error variance, respectively, and S is the coefficient for subjects variance.

Recently, Haggard [13] has proposed that the reliability of each effect be obtained by means of intraclass correlation from the analysis of variance technique and cogently criticizes the use of the product-moment correlation technique in reliability studies. He maintains that the latter technique is appropriate for bivariate distributions while the intraclass correlation technique is more suitable for univariate distributions which are involved in reliability studies.

The estimates involved in 2, 3, and 4 above must be viewed as approximate unless there is good reason to believe that the theoretical assumptions are met. These estimates may be modified more than the probability levels of the F tests of homogeneity of means. There appear to be no data available to indicate any definite effect. However, these approximations would provide, in many cases, valuable additional information.

From the above arguments, it appears that the parametric analysis of variance technique has such great flexibility that an investigator would want to use this design unless there is definite information to indicate great deviations from the required assumptions.

In light of these statements, what is to be the role of non-parametric methods in analysis of variance type situations? There are two functions which these techniques would appear to serve.

First, even if a parametric technique is applicable it would appear to be efficient in time and effort to use a suitable non-parametric technique as a screening device. For example, if eight S's are run under two different treatments, the investigator could use elementary probability (in this case the same as the binomial expansion or the sign test) as a preliminary test. If all eight S's did better in Treatment 1 than Treatment 2 the analysis would be complete, for the probability of such an event (two-tailed test) would be .008. Therefore, inasmuch as non-parametric methods are usually less powerful, the investigator could be relatively certain that a parametric test also would indicate significant differences. Likewise, if the probability level is much greater than .05 (e.g., .50), the analysis would be complete. However, within some interval (with .05 as the lower limit) the investigator would be interested in using a parametric test for a more definitive result. The author has found that .25 will serve as a reasonable approximation for the upper limit of this interval of uncertainty until empirical research has clarified this problem. In summary, if either a parametric or non-parametric technique appears suitable, the investigator may use a non-parametric test and the analysis is considered complete if the probability level is .05 or lower, or greater than .25. However, if p falls between .05 and .25 further analysis with the suitable parametric technique is suggested.

Second, in some cases it will be obvious from previous research or other *a priori* information that the use of a parametric technique will be incorrect because of extremely gross deviations from assumptions. In this case the investigator is justified in using a non-parametric technique unless a suitable transformation is available to correct the deviations.

Summary

Much has been written concerning the advantages of non-parametric techniques when the assumptions of parametric methods are not satisfied. However, a review of studies, concerned with investigating the effects on tests of significance of failure to satisfy the assumptions of the analysis of variance and the two-tailed t test, indicates little distortion even when marked deviations from assumptions occur. In some cases the distortion is so small as to be disregarded; in other cases where the deviations are more marked, the investigator may set a lower probability level for significance, e.g., .025 instead of .05, .005 instead of .01, or use a suitable transformation for correcting the deviations. Under some situations even ordinal data can be analyzed by parametric techniques; under other conditions this type of data can be transformed for interval scale analysis.

The use of the above suggested procedures involves more effort and risk than the use of non-parametric techniques. However, the data (especially the Box and Anderson review and the Norton study) appear to justify the procedure. Furthermore, the added effort is warranted when we consider the greater flexibility of the analysis of variance technique, i.e., greater power; the ability to handle the Fixed, Mixed, and Random Variates Models; multiple comparisons completed easily after analysis; making tests of significance of interactions; obtaining estimates of the parameters; providing coefficients of utility; and, most important of all, the ability to obtain an estimate of the reliability of the experimental procedure. The last three estimates should be used cautiously, however. The non-parametric techniques do serve a useful function under some circumstances, *viz.*, as "screeners" to determine if the analysis should be considered as complete or if further analysis by a suitable parametric test should be effected; and when deviations from theoretical assumptions are too extreme and no suitable transformation will rectify the deviations.

References

1. Alexander, H. W. The estimation of reliability when several trials are available. *Psychometrika*, 1947, **12,** 79–99.

2. Anderson, R. L. and T. A. Bancroft. *Statistical theory in research.* New York: McGraw-Hill, 1952.

3. Bartlett, M. S. The use of transformations. *Biometrics*, 1947, **3,** 39–52.

4. Box, G. E. P. and S. L. Anderson. Robust tests for variances and effect of nonnormality and variance heterogeneity on standard tests. *Tech. Rep. No.* 7, Ordinance Project No. TB 2–0001 (832), Dept. of Army Project No. 599–01–004.

5. Cochran, W. G. Some consequences when the assumptions for the analysis of variance are not satisfied. *Biometrics*, 1947, **3,** 22–38.

6. Duncan, D. B. On the properties of the multiple comparisons test. *Va. J. Sci.*, 1952, **3,** 49–67.

7. Duncan, D. B. Multiple range and multiple F tests. *Biometrics*, 1955, **11,** 1–42.

8. Edwards, A. L. *Statistical methods for the behavioral sciences.* New York: Rinehart, 1954.

9. Eisenhart, C. The assumptions underlying the analysis of variance. *Biometrics*, 1947, **3,** 1–21.

10. Fisher, R. A. and F. Yates. *Statistical tables for biological, agricultural and medical research.* New York: Hafner, 1953.

11. Gaito, J. The Bolles-Messick coefficient of utility. *Psychol. Rep.*, 1958, **4,** 595–598.

12. Guilford, J. P. *Psychometric methods.* New York: McGraw-Hill, 1954.

13. Haggard, E. A. *Intraclass correlation and the analysis of variance.* New York: Dryden, 1958.

14. Hoel, P. G. *Introduction to mathematical statistics.* New York: Wiley, 1954.

15. Hoyt, C. Test reliability estimated by analysis of variance. *Psychometrika*, 1941, **6,** 153–160.

16. Kempthorne, O. The randomization theory of experimental inference. *J. Amer. Statist. Ass.*, 1955, **50**, 946–967.

17. Lindquist, E. F. *Statistical analysis in educational research.* New York: Houghton Mifflin, 1940.

18. Lindquist, E. F. *Design and analysis of experiments in psychology and education.* New York: Houghton Mifflin, 1953.

19. McNemar, Q. On Wilson's distribution-free test of analysis of variance hypotheses. *Psychol. Bull.*, 1957, **54**, 361–362.

20. McNemar, Q. More on the Wilson test. *Psychol. Bull.*, 1958, **55**, 334–335.

21. Mood, A. M. *Introduction to the theory of statistics.* New York: McGraw-Hill, 1950.

22. Moses, L. E. Nonparametric statistics for psychological research. *Psychol. Bull.*, 1952, **49**, 122–143.

23. Mosteller, F. and R. R. Bush. Selected quantitative techniques. In G. Lindzey (Ed.), *Handbook of social psychology.* Vol. 1. *Theory and method.* Cambridge, Mass.: Addison-Wesley, 1954.

24. Pearson, E. S. The analysis of variance in cases of nonnormal variation. *Biometrika*, 1931, **23**, 114–133.

25. Rider, P. R. On the distribution of the ratio of mean to standard deviation in small samples from nonnormal populations. *Biometrika*, 1929, **21**, 124–143.

26. Scheffe, H. A method for judging all contrasts in the analysis of variance. *Biometrika*, 1953, **40**, 87–104.

27. Siegel, S. *Non-parametric statistics for the behavioral sciences.* New York: McGraw-Hill, 1956.

28. Snedecor, G. W. *Statistical methods.* Ames, Iowa: Iowa State College Press, 1946.

29. Stevens, S. S. Mathematics, measurement, and psychophysics. In S. S. Stevens (Ed.), *Handbook of experimental psychology.* New York: Wiley, 1951. Pp. 1–49.

30. Villars, D. S. *Statistical design and analysis of experiments for development research.* Dubuque, Ia.: Brown, 1951.

31. Wilcoxon, F. *Some rapid approximate statistical procedures.* Stamford, Conn.: American Cyanamid Co., 1949.

32. Wilson, K. V. A distribution-free test of analysis of variance hypotheses. *Psychol. Bull.*, 1956, **53**, 96–101.

19

the effects of violations of assumptions underlying the t test

C. Alan Boneau

As psychologists who perform in a research capacity are well aware, psychological data too frequently have an exasperating tendency to manifest themselves in a form which violates one or more of the assumptions underlying the usual statistical tests of significance. Faced with the problem of analyzing such data, the researcher usually attempts to transform them in such a way that the assumptions are tenable, or he may look elsewhere for a statistical test. The latter alternative has become popular because of the proliferation of the so-called non-parametric or distribution-free methods. These techniques quite generally, however, couple their freedom from restricting assumptions with a disdain for much of the information contained within the data.

From: C. A. Boneau, "The effects of violations of assumptions underlying the t test," Psychological Bulletin **57**, 1960, 49–64. Copyright © 1960 by the American Psychological Association and reproduced by permission.

This project was undertaken while the author was a Public Health Service Research Fellow of the National Institute of Mental Health at Duke University. The computations involved in this study were performed in the Duke University Digital Computing Laboratory which is supported in part by National Science Foundation Grant G-6694. The author wishes to express his appreciation to Thomas M. Gallie, Director of the Laboratory, for his cooperation and assistance.

For example, by classifying scores into groups above and below the median one ignores the fact that there are intracategory differences between the individual scores. As a result, tests which make no assumptions about the distribution from which one is sampling will tend not to reject the null hypothesis when it is actually false as often as will those tests which do make assumptions. This lack of power of the non-parametric tests is a decided handicap when, as is frequently the case in psychological research, a modicum of reinforcement in the form of an occasional significant result is required to maintain the research response.

Confronted with this discouraging prospect and a perhaps equally discouraging one of laboriously transforming data, performing related tests, and then perhaps having difficulty in interpreting results, the researcher is often tempted simply to ignore such considerations and go ahead and run a *t* test or analysis of variance. In most cases, he is deterred by the feeling that such a procedure will not solve the problem. If a significant result is forthcoming, is it due to differences between means, or is it due to the violation of assumptions? The latter possibility is usually sufficient to preclude the use of the *t* or *F* test.

It might be suspected that one could finesse the whole problem of untenable assumptions by better planning of the experiment or by a more judicious choice of variables, but this may not always be the case. Let us examine the assumptions more closely. It will be recalled that both the *t* test and the closely related *F* test of analysis of variance are predicated on sampling from a normal distribution. A second assumption required by the derivations is that the variances of the distributions from which the samples have been taken is the same (assumption of homogeneity of variance). Thirdly, it is necessary that scores used in the test exhibit independent errors. The third assumption is usually not restrictive since the researcher can readily conduct most psychological research so that this requirement is satisfied. The first two assumptions depend for their reasonableness in part upon the vagaries inherent in empirical data and the chance shape of the sampling distribution. Certain situations also arise frequently which tend to produce results having intrinsic nonnormality or heterogeneity of variance. For example, early in a paired-associate learning task, before much learning has taken place, the modal number of responses for a group will be close to zero and any deviations will be in an upward direction. The distribution of responses will be skewed and will have a small variance. With a medium number of trials, scores will tend to be spread over the whole possible range with a mode at the center, a more nearly normal distribution than before, but with greater variance. When the task has been learned by most of the group, the distribution will be skewed downward and with smaller variance. In this particular case, one would probably more closely approximate normality and homogeneity in the data by using some other measure, perhaps number of trials for mastery. In many situations this option may not be present.

There is, however, evidence that the ordinary *t* and *F* tests are nearly immune to violation of assumptions or can easily be made so if precautions are taken (Pearson, 1931; Bartlett, 1935; Welch, 1937; Daniels, 1938; Quensel, 1947; Gayen, 1950a, 1950b; David and Johnson, 1951; Horsnell, 1953; Box, 1954a, 1954b; Box and Anderson, 1955). Journeyman psychologists have been apprised of this possibility by Lindquist (1953) who summarizes the results of a study by Norton (1951). Norton's technique was to obtain samples of *F*'s by means of a random sampling procedure from distributions having the same mean but which violated the assumptions of normality and homogeneity of variance in predetermined fashions. As a measure of the effect of the violations, Norton determined the obtained percentage of sample *F*'s which exceeded the theoretical 5% and 1% values from the *F* tables for various conditions. If the null hypothesis is true, and if the assumptions are met, the theoretical values are *F* values which would be exceeded by chance exactly 5% or 1% of the time. The discrepancy between these expected percentages and the obtained percentages is one useful measure of the effects of the violations.

Norton's results may be summarized briefly as follows:

a. When the samples all came from the same population, the shape of the distribution had very little effect on the percentage of *F* ratios exceeding the theoretical limits. For example, for the 5% level, the percentages exceeding the theoretical limits were 7.83% for a leptokurtic population as one extreme discrepancy and 4.76% for an extremely skewed distribution as another.

b. For sampling from populations having the same shape but different variances, or having different shapes but the same variance, there was little effect on the empirical percentage exceeding theoretical limits, the average being between 6.5% and 7.0%.

c. For sampling from populations with different shapes and heterogeneous variances, a serious discrepancy between theoretical and obtained percentages occurred in some instances.

On the basis of these results, Lindquist (1953, p. 86) concluded that "unless the heterogeneity of either form or variance is so extreme as to be readily apparent upon inspection of the data, the effect upon the *F* distribution will probably be negligible."

This conclusion has apparently had surprisingly little effect upon the statistical habits of research workers (or perhaps editors) as is evident from the increasing reliance upon the less powerful non-parametric techniques in published reports. The purpose of this paper is to expound further the invulnerability of the *t* test and its next of kin the *F* test to ordinary onslaughts stemming from violation of the assumptions of normality and homogeneity. In part, this will be done by reporting results of a study conducted by the author dealing with the effect on the *t* test of violation of assumptions. In addition, supporting evidence from a mathematical framework will be used to bolster the argument.

To temper any imputed dogmatism in the foregoing, it should be emphasized that there are certain restrictions which preclude an automatic utilization of the *t* and *F* tests without regard for assumptions even when these tests are otherwise applicable. It is apparent, for example, that the violation of the homogeneity of variance assumption is drastically disturbing to the distribution of *t*'s and *F*'s if the sample sizes are not the same for all groups, a possibility which was not considered in the Norton study. It also seems clear that in cases of extreme violations, one must have a sample size large enough to allow the statistical effects of averaging to come into play. The need for such considerations will be made apparent in the ensuing discussion. There is abundant evidence, however, that both the *t* and the *F* tests are much less affected by extreme violations of the assumptions than has been generally realized.

A sampling experiment

At this point we will concern ourselves with the statement of the results of a random sampling study. The procedure is one of computing a large number of *t* values, each based upon samples drawn at random from distributions having specified characteristics, and constructing a frequency distribution of the obtained *t*'s. The present study was performed on the IBM 650 Electronic Computer programmed to perform the necessary operations which can be summarized as follows: (a) the generation of a random number, (b) the transformation of the random number into a random deviate from the appropriate distribution, (c) the successive accumulation of the sums and sums of squares of the random deviates until the appropriate sample size is reached, (d) the computation of a *t* based upon the sums and sums of squares of the two samples, (e) the sorting of the *t*'s on the basis of size and sign and the construction of a frequency distribution based upon the sorting operation. The complete sequence of operations was performed internally, the end result, the frequency distribution of 1,000 t's, being punched out on IBM cards.

Comments on many of the above operations are relevant and will be made according to their order above.

a.   The random numbers consisted of 10 digits, the middle 10 digits of the product of the previously generated random number and of one of a sequence of 10 permutations of the 10 digits (0, 1, 2, . . . , 9) placed as multipliers in the machine. To start the process it was necessary to place in the machine a 10 digit random number selected from a table of random numbers. The randomness of numbers generated in such a fashion was checked by sorting 5,000 of them into 50 categories on the basis of the first 2 digits. A χ^2 was computed to determine the fit of the obtained distribution to a theoretical one consisting of 100 scores in each of the 50 categories. The obtained χ^2 of 47.83 is extremely close to the 49.332 value, which is the theoretical median of the χ^2 distribution with 50 degrees of freedom.

b.   In order to obtain the random deviates (the individual random scores from the appropriate population), the random numbers obtained in the above fashion were considered to be numbers between 0 and 1 and interpreted as the cumulative probability for a particular score from the prescribed population. From a table entered in the machine, a random deviate having that probability was selected. This is identical with the procedure one uses in entering the ordinary z table to determine the score below which, say, 97.5 % of the scores in the distribution lie. The obtained value, 1.96, is the deviate corresponding to that cumulative percentage. The distribution of such deviates from a normal population obtained by using a large random sample of probabilities is normally distributed. Similar tables can be constructed for other populations. The populations selected for this study were the normal, the exponential (**J**-shaped with a skew to the right) having a density function of $y = e^{-x}$, and the rectangular or uniform distribution. These distributions represent extremes of skewness and flatness to compare with the normal. The tables of deviates corresponding to each of the selected distributions were contained internally in the computer and were so arranged that the mean of each distribution was 0 and the variance 1. To verify these values, population means and variances based on samples of 5,000 deviates from each of the three populations were estimated by the usual formulas. The results were for the normal distribution a sample mean of .0024 and a variance of 1.0118, for the exponential a mean of .0128 and a variance of 1.0475, and for the rectangular a mean of −.0115 and a variance of .9812. All of these results could quite easily have arisen from random sampling from distributions having the assumed characteristics. To change the size of the variance of the population, all deviates were multiplied when necessary by a constant, in this case, the number 2. The resulting distribution has a mean of 0 and variance of 4. The only variances used in this study were 1 and 4.

c.   The sample sizes selected were 5 and 15.

d.   The formula used for the computation of t was the following:

$$t = \frac{M_1 - M_2}{\sqrt{\dfrac{\Sigma X_1^2 - N_1 M_1^2 + \Sigma X_2^2 - N_2 M_2^2}{N_1 + N_2 - 2}\left(\dfrac{1}{N_1} + \dfrac{1}{N_2}\right)}}$$

where M_1 and M_2 are the means of the first and second samples and N_1 and N_2 are the respective sample sizes. This expression, or an equivalent statement of it, is found in any statistics book and is undoubtedly employed in a preponderance of the research in which a t test involving nonrelated means is used. As pointed out in most statistic texts, this test is not appropriate when variances are different. Tests are available which are more or less legitimate under these conditions, but a certain amount of approximation is involved in them. It was felt, however, that the ordinary t test might under some conditions be as good an approximation as the more complex forms of t tests and that a verification of this notion was desirable. In addition, the above formula makes use of a pooled estimate of variance for the error term and in this respect is similar to the F test of analysis of variance. Because of this fact, certain results can be generalized from the t to the F test.

To summarize, random samples were drawn from populations which were either normal, rectangular, or exponential with means equal to 0 and variances of 1 to 4. For several combinations of forms and variances, t tests of the significance of the difference between sample means were computed using combinations of the sample sizes 5 and 15. For each of these combinations, frequency distributions of sample t's were obtained on the IBM 650 Electronic Computer.

Results

The results of the sampling study will be presented in part as a series of frequency distributions in the form of bar graphs of the obtained distribution of t's for a particular condition. Upon these have been superimposed the theoretical t distribution curve for the appropriate degrees of freedom. This furnishes a rapid comparison of the extent to which the empirical distribution conforms to the theoretical.

First we shall consider those combinations possible when both of the samples are from normal distributions but variances and sample sizes may vary. Next will be considered the results of sampling from nonnormal distributions, but both samples are from the same type of distribution. Finally we deal with the results of sampling from two different kinds of populations, for example, one sample from the normal distribution, and another from the exponential.

Potentially, a very large number of such combinations are possible. Limitations of the time available on the computer necessitated a paring down to a reasonable number. Although the computer is relatively fast when optimally programmed, it nevertheless required almost an hour, on the average, to complete a frequency distribution of 1,000 t's. The combinations presented here are those which seemed most important at the time the study was made.

As a measure of the effect of violation of assumptions, the percentage of obtained t's which exceed the theoretical values delineating the middle 95% of the t distribution is used. For 8, 18, and 28 df which arise in the present study, the corresponding values are respectively ± 2.262, ± 2.101, and ± 2.048. If the assumptions are met, and if the null hypothesis of equality of means is true, 5% of the obtained t's should fall outside these limits. The difference between this nominal value and the actual value obtained by sampling should be a useful measure of the degree to which violation of assumptions changes the distribution of t scores. There is, of course, a random quality to the obtained percentage of t's falling outside the theoretical limits. Hence, the obtained value should be looked upon as an approximation to the true value which should lie nearby.

In the figures and in the text, the various combinations of population, variance, and sample size will be represented symbolically in the following form: $E(0, 1)5$-$N(0, 4)15$. Here the letters E, N, and R refer to the population from which the sample was drawn, E for exponential-N for normal, and R for rectangular. The first number in the parenthesis is the mean of the population distribution, in all cases zero, while the second number is the variance. The number following the parenthesis is the sample size for that particular sample. In the example above, the first sample is of Size 5 from an exponential distribution having a variance of 1. The second sample is from a normal distribution with variance of 4 and the sample size is 15.

Sampling from normal distributions

In order to justify the random sampling approach utilized in this study, and partly to confirm the faith placed in the tabled values of

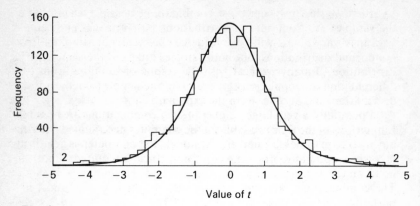

Fig. 1
Empirical distribution of t's from N(0, 1)5-N(0, 1)5 and theoretical distribution with 8 df.

the mathematical statisticians, the initial comparisons are between the theoretical distributions and the obtained distributions with assumptions inviolate. Figures 1 and 2 exhibit the empirical distributions of *t*'s when both samples are taken from the same normal distribution with zero mean and unit variance—designated *N*(0, 1). In Figure 1 both samples are of Size 5, while both are 15 in Figure 2. The theoretical curves, one for 8 *df*, the other for 28, represent quite well the obtained distributions. Ordinates approximately two units from the mean of

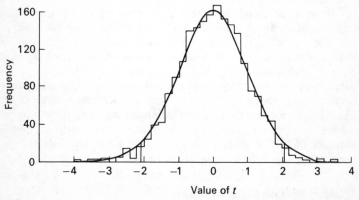

Fig. 2
Empirical distribution of t's from N(0, 1)15-N(0, 1(15 and theoretical distribution with 28 df.

the theoretical distributions mark off the respective 5% limits for rejecting the null hypothesis. In Figure 1,[1] 5.3% of the obtained t's fall outside these bounds, while in Figure 2 only 4.0% of the sample t's are in excess. Since in both cases the expected value is exactly 5%, we must attribute the discrepancy to random sampling fluctuations. The size of these discrepancies should be useful measures in evaluating the discrepancies which will be encountered under other conditions of sampling. For examples of 2,000 t's a discrepancy as large as 1% from the nominal 5% value evidently occurs frequently, and for this reason should not be considered as evidence to reject the theoretical distribution as an approximation to the empirical one.

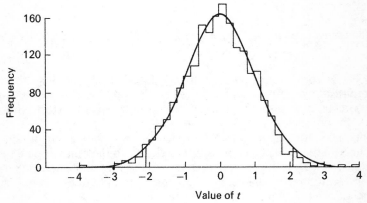

Fig. 3
Empirical distribution of t's from $N(0, 1)5$-$N(0, 1)15$ and theoretical distribution with 18 df.

As an initial departure from the simplest cases just presented, Figure 3 compares theoretical and empirical distributions when samples are taken from the same $N(0, 1)$ population, but the first sample size is 5, the second is 15—that is, $N(0, 1)5$-$N(0, 1)15$. While this in no sense is a violation of the assumptions of the t test, it is interesting to note that again sampling fluctuations have produced an empirical distribution with 4.0% of the t's falling outside the nominal 5% limits.

The violation of the assumption of homogeneity of variance has effects as depicted in Figure 4. Here the obtained distribution is based upon two samples of Size 5, one from $N(0, 1)$ and the other from

---

1. The numbers in the tails of some of the figures report the number of obtained t's falling outside the boundaries.

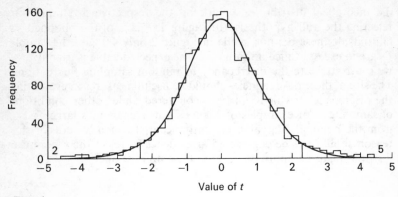

Fig. 4
Empirical distribution of t's from N(0, 1)5-N(0, 4)5 and theoretical distribution with 8 df.

$N(0, 4)$. The fit is again seen to be close between theoretical and empirical distributions, and 6.4 % of the obtained t's exceed the theoretical 5 % limits. By increasing the sample size to 15, a distribution results (not shown here) for which only 4.9 % of the t's fall outside the nominal limits. It would seem that increasing the sample size produces a distribution which conforms rather closely to the t distribution. As will be seen later, this is a quite general result based upon mathematical considerations, the implications of which are important to the argument. For the moment it is evident that differences in variance at least in the ratio of 1 to 4 do not seriously affect the accuracy of probability statements made on the basis of the t test.

This last conclusion is true only so long as the size of both samples is the same. If the variances are different, with the present set of conditions there are two combinations of variance and sample size possible. In one case the first sample may be of Size 5 and drawn from the population with the smaller variance, while the second sample of Size 15 is drawn from the population having the larger variance—$N(0, 1)5-N(0, 4)15$. In the second case the small sample size is coupled with the larger variance, the larger sample size with the smaller variance—$N(0, 4)5-N(0, 1)15$. The respective results of such sampling are presented in Figures 5 and 6. The empirical distributions are clearly not approximated by the t distribution. For the distribution of Figure 5, only 1 % of the obtained t's exceed the nominal 5 % values, while in Figure 6, 16 % of the t's fall outside those limits.

There are good mathematical reasons why a difference in sample size should produce such decided discrepancies when the variances are

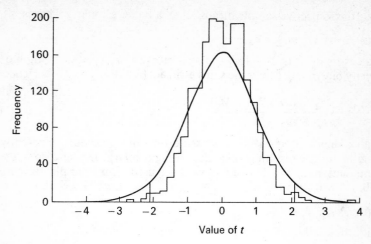

Fig. 5
Empirical distribution of t's from N(0, 1)5-N(0, 4)15 and theoretical distribution with 18 df.

unequal. Recall that $\Sigma (X - M)^2/(N - 1)$ is an estimate of the variance of the population from which the sample is drawn. Hence, $\Sigma (X - M)^2$ will in the long run be equal to $(N - 1)\sigma^2$. The formula used in this study for computing t makes use of this fact and, in addition, under the assumption that the variances of the populations from which the two samples are drawn are equal, pools the sum of the squared deviations

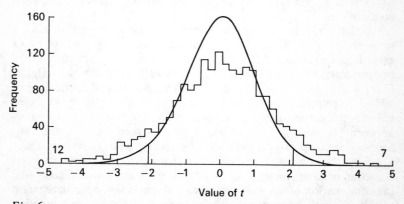

Fig. 6
Empirical distribution of t's from N(0, 4)5-N(0, 1)15 and theoretical distribution with 18 df.

from the respective sample means to get a better estimate. That is

$$\sum (X_1 - M_1)^2 + \sum (X_2 - M_2)^2$$

is an estimate of $(N_1 - 1)\sigma_1^2 + (N_2 - 1)\sigma_2^2$. If $\sigma_1^2 = \sigma_2^2 = \sigma^2$ (homogeneity of variance), then the sums estimate $(N_1 + N_2 - 2)\sigma^2$. Hence,

$$\frac{\Sigma (X_1 - M_1)^2 + \Sigma (X_2 - M_2)^2}{N_1 + N_2 - 2} \tag{1}$$

is an estimate of σ^2. If $\sigma_1^2 \neq \sigma_2^2$ the estimating procedure is patently illegitimate, the resulting value depending in a large measure upon the combination of sample size and variance used. For example, the case $N(0, 1)5$-$N(0, 4)15$ has $N_1 = 5$, $N_2 = 15$, $\sigma_1^2 = 1$, $\sigma_2^2 = 4$, and

$$N_1 + N_2 - 2 = 18.$$

With these values, Formula 1 has an expected value of

$$[(4 \cdot 1) + (14 \cdot 4)]/18 = 3.33.$$

Using the appropriate values for the other situation, $N(0, 4)5$-$N(0, 1)15$, the result of Formula 1 is $[(4 \cdot 4) + (14 \cdot 1)]/18 = 1.67$. This means that on the average, the denominator for the t test will be larger for the first case than for the second. If the sample differences between means were of the same magnitude for the two cases, obviously more "significant" t's would emerge when the denominator is smaller. It so happens that when this latter condition exists, the variance of the numerator also tends to be greater than in the other condition, a fact which accentuates the differences between the two empirical distributions.

Welch (1937) has shown mathematically that in the case of sample sizes of 5 and 15, a state which prevails here, the percentage of t's exceeding the nominal 5% value varies as a function of the ratio of the two population variances and can be as low as 0% and as high as 31.3%. If $N_1 = N_2$ there is never much bias, except perhaps in the case in which the sample sizes are both 2. For $N_1 = N_2 = 10$, the expected value of the percentage of t's exceeding the nominal 5% limits varies between 5% and 6.5% regardless of the difference between the variances. For larger sample sizes, the discrepancy tends to be even less.

Since the pooling procedure for estimating the population variance is used in ordinary analysis of variance techniques, it would seem that the combination of unequal variances and unequal sample sizes might play havoc with F test probability statements. That is, a combination of large variance and large sample size should tend to make the F test more conservative than the nominal value would lead one to expect, and, as with the t test, small variance and large sample size should produce a higher percentage of "significant" F's than expected. These conclusions are based upon a very simple extension to more than two samples of the explanation for the behavior of the t test probabilities with unequal sample sizes.

A more sophisticated mathematical handling of the problem by Box (1954a) reaches much the same conclusions for the simple-random-ized analysis of variance. In a table in his article are given exact (i.e., mathematically determined) probabilities of exceeding the 5% point when variances are unequal. In this case, sampling is assumed to be from normal distributions. If the sample sizes are the same, the probability given for equal sample sizes range from 5.55% to 7.42%, for several combinations of variances, and numbers of samples. If, when variances are different, the samples are of different sizes, large discrepancies from the nominal values result. Combining large sample and large variance lessens the probability of obtaining a "significant" result to much less than 5%, just as we have seen for the t test. In a subsequent article, Box (1954b) presents some results from two-way analysis of variance. Since these designs generally have equal cell frequencies the results are not too far from expected. His figures all run within 2% of the 5% value expected if all assumptions were met.

It would seem then that both empirically and mathematically there can be demonstrated only a minor effect on the validity of probability statements caused by heterogeneity of variance, provided the sizes of the samples are the same. This applies to the F as well as the t test. If however, the sample sizes are different, major errors in interpretation may result if normal curve thinking is used.

Sampling from identical nonnormal distributions: (equal variances)

Let us now proceed to violate the other main assumption, that of normality of distribution from which sampling takes place. At this time we will consider the t distributions arising when both samples are taken from the same non-normal distribution. The distributions shown here, and all subsequent ones, are based upon only 1,000 t's, and hence will exhibit somewhat more column to column fluctuation than the preceding distributions.

Figure 7 compares the theoretical t distribution and the empirical distribution obtained from two samples of Size 5 from the exponential distribution—$E(0, 1)5$-$E(0, 1)5$. The fit is fairly close, but the proportion of cases in the tails seems less for the empirical distribution than for the

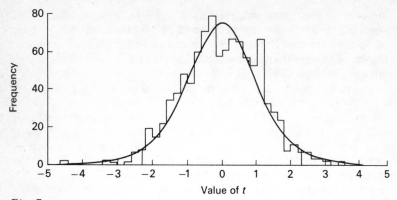

Fig. 7
Empirical distribution of t's from E(0, 1)5-E(0, 1)5 and theoretical distribution with 8 df.

theoretical. By count, 3.1 % of the obtained t's exceed the nominal 5 % values—that is, the test in this case seems slightly conservative. If both sample sizes are raised to 15 (distribution not shown here), the corresponding percentage of obtained t's is 4.0 %. While this is probably not an appreciably better fit than for samples of Size 5, we shall see later that there are theoretical reasons to suspect that increasing the sample size should better the approximation of the empirical curve by the theoretical no matter what the parent population may be.

If both samples are of Size 5 from the same rectangular distribution—R(0, 1)5-R(0, 1)5—the result is as depicted in Figure 8. The fit

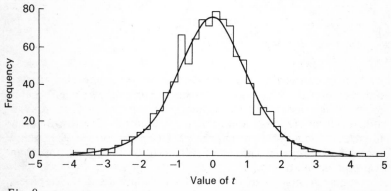

Fig. 8
Empirical distribution of t's from R(0, 1)5-R(0, 1)5 and theoretical distribution with 8 df.

of theoretical curve to empirical data here is as good as any thus far observed. The percentage of obtained t's exceeding the 5% values is 5.1% in this particular case. For the case in which the sample sizes are both 15 (not shown here), the fit is equally good, with 5.0% of the cases falling outside of the nominal 5% bounds.

Sampling from nonnormal distributions: (unequal variances)

We may assume that if the variances are unequal, and at the same time the sample sizes are different, the resulting distributions from non-normal populations will be affected in the same way as the distributions derived from normal populations, and for the same reasons. These cases will not be considered.

If sampling is in sizes of 5 from two exponential distributions, one with a variance of 1, and the other of 4, a skewed distribution of obtained t's emerges (not shown here). We shall discover that a skewed distribution of t's generally arises when the sampling is from distributions which are different in degree of skewness or asymmetry. (For an explanation, see discussion of $E(0, 1)5$-$N(0, 1)5$ below.) Apparently, the effect of increasing the variance of the exponential distribution as in the present case—$E(0, 1)5$-$E(0, 4)5$—is to make the negative sample means arising from the distribution with larger variance even more negative than those from the distribution with smaller variance. In terms of percentage exceeding the nominal 5% limits for this case, the value is 8.3%, of which 7.6% comes from the skewed tail. This combination of variances and distribution was not tested with larger samples, but we shall see when comparing exponential and normal distributions that an increase in the sample size decreases the skew of the obtained t distribution there. Theoretically, this decrease should occur in almost all cases, including the present one.

The result is much less complicated if, while variances are different, the sampling is from symmetrical rectangular distributions—$R(0, 1)$-$R(0, 4)5$. For this small sample situation, (not illustrated), there occurs a distribution of obtained t's having 7.1% of the values exceeding the nominal 5% points. This is roughly the same magnitude as the corresponding discrepancy from normal distributions. For the normal, it will be recalled that an increase of the sample sizes to 15 decreased the obtained percentage to 4.9%. There is no reason to believe that increasing the size of the rectangular samples would not have the same effect. However, time did not permit the determination of this distribution.

Sampling from two
different distributions

By drawing the first sample from a distribution having one shape, and by drawing the second from a distribution having another shape (other than shape differences arising from heterogeneity of variance), yet another way has been found to do violence to the integrity of the assumptions underlying the *t* test. Perhaps the least violent of these happenings is that in which at least one of the populations is normal.

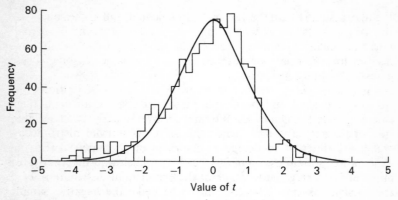

Fig. 9
Empirical distribution of t's from E(0, 1)5-N(0, 1)5 and theoretical distri-
bution with 8 df.

When one sample is from the exponential distribution and the other from the normal, the interesting result shown in Figure 9 occurs. This is the small sample case—*E*(0, 1)5-*N*(0, 1)5. It will be recalled that for skewed distributions the mean and median are at different points. In the exponential distributions, for example, the mean is at the 63rd centile. If samples from the exponential distribution are small, there will be a tendency for the sample mean to be less than the population mean, obviously since nearly two thirds of the scores are below that mean. Since the population mean of the present distributions is 0, the result will be a preponderance of negative sample means for small samples. If the other sample is taken from a symmetrical distribution, which would tend to produce as many positive as negative sample means, the resulting distribution of obtained *t*'s would not balance about its zero point, an imbalance exacerbated by small samples. In Figure 9, 7.1 % of the obtained cases fall outside the 5 % limits, with most, 5.6 %, lying in the skewed tail. The effect of increasing the sample

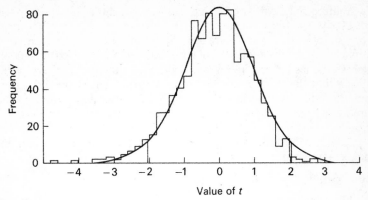

Fig. 10
Empirical distribution of t's from E(0, 1)15-N(0, 1)15 and theoretical distribution with 28 df.

size to 15 is to normalize the distribution considerably; the resulting curve, Figure 10, is fairly well approximated by the t distribution. One of the tails, however, does contain a disproportionate share of the cases, 4.2% to 0.9% for the other tail, or a total of 5.1% falling outside the nominal 5% limits. Nevertheless, the degree to which the theoretical and empirical distributions coincide under these conditions is striking. It seems likely that if both samples were each of Size 25, the resulting sample distribution of t's would be virtually indistinguishable from the t distribution for 48 df, or the next best thing, the normal curve itself. To test this hypothesis, an additional empirical t distribution based on sample sizes of 25 from these same exponential and normal populations was obtained (not shown here). The results nicely confirm the presumption. Comparison with the usual 5% values reveals 4.6% of the empirical t's surpassing them. Whereas with the smaller samples the ratio of t's in the skewed tail to those in the other tail is roughly 80:20, the corresponding ratio for the larger sample case is 59:41. Clearly, the increase in sample sizes has tended to normalize the distribution of t's.

For these conditions, involving rather drastic violation of the mathematical assumptions of the test, the t test has been observed to fare well with an adequate sample size. Such a state of affairs is to be expected theoretically. By invoking a few theorems of mathematical statistics it can be shown that if one samples from any two populations for which the Central Limit Theorem holds, (almost any population that a psychologist might be confronted with), no matter what the variances may be, the use of equal sample sizes insures that the resulting distribution of *t*'s will approach normality as a limit. It would appear from the present results that the approach to normality is rather rapid, since samples of sizes of 15 are generally sufficient to undo most of the damage inflicted by violation of assumptions. Only in extreme cases, such as the last which involves distributions differing in skew, would it seem that slightly larger sizes are prescribed. Thus it would appear that the *t* test is functionally a distribution-free test, providing the sample sizes are sufficiently large (say, 30, for extreme violations) and equal.

The distributions arising when sampling is from the normal and the rectangular distributions,

$$N(0, 1)5\text{-}R(0, 1)5 \qquad \text{and} \qquad N(0, 1)15\text{-}R(0, 1)15,$$

would further tend to substantiate this claim. The respective percentages exceeding the 5% nominal values are 5.6% and 4.6% from the empirical distributions for these cases, the distributions of *t*'s being symmetrical and close to the theoretical (not shown).

The only other combination examined in the sampling study is the uninteresting case of exponential and rectangular distributions. This distribution (not shown) is again skewed with the effect of increase of sample size from 5 to 15 to cut down the skew and to decrease the percentage of cases falling outside the theoretical 5% values from 6.4% to 5.6%. For those cases falling outside the nominal 5% values, the ratio is 79:21 for the smaller samples. This is changed to 69:31 for the sample size of 15. Here again it would seem that larger sample sizes would be required to insure the validity of probability statements utilizing the *t* distribution as a model.

The results of the total study are summarized in Table 1 which gives for each combination of population, variance, and sample size (a) the percentage of obtained *t*'s falling outside the nominal 5% probability limits of the ordinary *t* distribution, and (b) the percentage of obtained *t*'s falling outside the 1% limits. The combinations are represented symbolically as before. The table is divided into two parts, the first part presenting information on the empirical distributions which are intrinsically symmetrical. The second part is based upon the intrinsically nonsymmetrical distributions, additional information in this section of the table being the percentage of obtained *t*'s falling in the larger of the tails. The percentage for the smaller tail may be obtained by subtraction of the percentage in the larger tail from the total.

Certain implications of the table should be discussed. In the Norton study, more severe distortions sometimes occurred with significance levels of 1% and .1% than appeared with the 5% level. The inclusion in Table 1 of the percentages of obtained *t*'s falling outside the nominal

Table 1
Obtained percentages of cases falling outside the appropriate
values for the 5% and 1% level of significance

Symmetric Distributions	Obtained Percentage at	
	5% Level	1% Level
N(0, 1)5-N(0, 1)5	5.3	0.9
N(0, 1)15-N(0, 1)15	4.0	0.8
N(0, 1)5-N(0, 1)15	4.0	0.6
N(0, 1)5-N(0, 4)5	6.4	1.8
N(0, 1)15-N(0, 4)15	4.9	1.1
N(0, 1)5-N(0, 4)15	1.0	0.1
N(0, 4)5-N(0, 1)15	16.0	6.0
E(0, 1)5-E(0, 1)5	3.1	0.3
E(0, 1)15-E(0, 1)15	4.0	0.4
R(0, 1)5-R(0, 1)5	5.1	1.0
R(0, 1)15-R(0, 1)15	5.0	1.5
R(0, 1)5-R(0, 4)5	7.1	1.9
N(0, 1)5-R(0, 1)5	5.6	1.0
N(0, 1)15-R(0, 1)15	5.6	1.1

Asymmetric Distributions	Obtained Percentage at			
	5% Level		1% Level	
	Total	Larger Tail	Total	Larger Tail
E(0, 1)5-N(0, 1)5	7.1	5.6	1.9	1.9
E(0, 1)15-N(0, 1)15	5.1	4.2	1.4	1.2
E(0, 1)25-N(0, 1)25	4.6	2.7	1.3	1.1
E(0, 1)5-R(0, 1)5	6.4	5.0	3.3	2.5
E(0, 1)15-R(0, 1)15	5.6	3.9	1.6	1.2
E(0, 1)5-E(0, 4)5	8.3	7.6	1.7	1.7

1% values makes possible the comparison of the 1% and 5% results. The 1% values seem to be approximately what would be expected considering that sampling fluctuations are occurring. It was not felt feasible to determine the results for the .1% level since with only 1,000 or 2,000 cases the number of obtained t's falling outside the prescribed limits was negligible in most cases. It is possible, however, that the distortions in the apparent level of significance are more drastic for the smaller α values.

All the results and discussion have been limited thus far to the two-tailed *t* test. With notable exceptions, the conclusions we have reached can be applied directly to the one-tailed *t* test as well. The exceptions involve those distributions which are intrinsically *asymmetric* (see Table 1). In these distributions a preponderance of the obtained *t*'s fall in one tail. Depending upon the particular tail involved in the one-tailed test the use of *t* should produce too many or too few significant results when sampling is from a combination of populations from which an asymmetric *t* distribution is expected. It seems impossible to make any simple statements about the behavior of the tails in the general case of asymmetric *t* distribution except to say that such distributions are expected whenever the skew of the two parent populations is different. The experimenter must determine for each particular instance the direction of skew of the expected distribution and act accordingly. Table 1 gives for the intrinsically asymmetric distributions the total percentage of obtained *t*'s falling outside the theoretical 5% and 1% limits and the percentage in the larger tail. From these values can be assessed the approximate magnitude of the bias incurred when a one-tailed test is used in specific situations.

Discussion and conclusions

Having violated a number of assumptions underlying the *t* test, and finding that, by and large, such violations produce a minimal effect on the distribution of *t*'s, we must conclude that the *t* test is a remarkably *robust* test in the technical sense of the word. This term was introduced by Box (1953) to characterize statistical tests which are only inconsequentially affected by a violation of the underlying assumptions. Every statistical test is in part a test of the assumptions upon which it is based. For example, the null hypothesis of a particular test may be concerned with sample means. If, however, the assumptions underlying the test are not met, the result may be "significant" even though the population means are the same. If the statistical test is relatively insensitive to violations of the assumptions other than the null hypothesis, and, hence, if probability statements refer primarily to the null hypotheses, it is said to be robust. The *t* and *F* tests apparently possess this quality to a high degree.

In this particular context, an important example of a test lacking robustness is Bartlett's test for homogeneity of variance (Bartlett, 1937). Box (1953) has shown that this test is extremely sensitive to nonnormality and will under some conditions be prone to yield "significant" results even if variances are equal. For example, Box tables a number of exact probabilities of exceeding the 5% normal theory significance level in the Bartlett test for various levels of λ_2, the kurtosis parameter, for different quantities of variances being compared. As an extreme case, if $\lambda_2 = 2$ (i.e., a peaked distribution) with 30 variances being tested, the probability of rejecting the hypothesis at the nominal .05 level is actually .849. If $\lambda_2 = -1$ (i.e., a flat distribution), the probability is .00001. Note that in both these cases, all variances are actually equal. Box, realizing that in the case of equal sample sizes the analysis of variance is affected surprisingly little by heterogeneous variance and nonnormality, concludes that the use of the nonrobust Bartlett test to "make the preliminary test on variances is rather like putting out to sea in a rowing boat to find out whether conditions are sufficiently calm for an ocean liner to leave port!" Apparently, as reported in this same article, other commonly used tests for evaluating homogeneity are subject to the same weakness.

We may conclude that for a large number of different situations confronting the researcher, the use of the ordinary t test and its associated table will result in probability statements which are accurate to a high degree, even though the assumptions of homogeneity of variance and normality of the underlying distributions are untenable. This large number of situations has the following general characteristics: (a) the two sample sizes are equal or nearly so, (b) the assumed underlying population distributions are of the same shape or nearly so. (If the distributions are skewed they should have nearly the same variance.) If these conditions are met, then no matter what the variance differences may be, samples of as small as five will produce results for which the true probability of rejecting the null hypothesis at the .05 level will more than likely be within .03 of that level. If the sample size is as large as 15, the true probabilities are quite likely within .01 of the nominal value. That is to say, the percentage of times the null hypothesis will be rejected when it is actually true will tend to be between 4% and 6% when the nominal value is 5%.

If the sample sizes are unequal, one is in no difficulty provided the variances are compensatingly equal. A combination of unequal sample sizes and unequal variances, however, automatically produces inaccurate probability statements which can be quite different from the nominal values. One must in this case resort to different testing procedures, such as those by Cochran and Cox (1950), Satterthwaite (1946), and Welch (1947). The Welch procedure is interesting since it has been extended by Welch (1951) to cover the simple randomized analysis of variance which suffers the same defect as the t test when confronted with both unequal variance and unequal sample sizes.

The Fisher-Behrens procedure suggested by many psychologically oriented statistical textbooks has had its validity questioned (Bartlett, 1936) and, hence, is ignored by some statisticians (e.g., Anderson and Bancroft, 1952, p. 82).

If the two underlying populations are not the same shape, there seems to be little difficulty if the distributions are both symmetrical. If they differ in skew, however, the distribution of obtained t's has a tendency itself to be skewed, having a greater percentage of obtained t's falling outside of one limit than the other. This may tend to bias probability statements. Increasing the sample size has the effect of removing the skew, and, due to the Central Limit Theorem and others, the normal distribution is approached by this maneuver. By the time the sample sizes reach 25 or 30, the approach should be close enough that one can, in effect, ignore the effects of violations of assumptions except for extremes. Since this is so, the t test is seen to be functionally nonparametric or distribution-free. It also retains its power in some situations (David and Johnson, 1951). There is, unfortunately, no guarantee that the t and F tests are uniformly most powerful tests. It is possible, even probable, that certain of the distribution-free methods are more powerful than the t and F tests when sampling is from some unspecified distributions or combination of distributions. At present, little can be said to clarify the situation. Much more research in this area needs to be done.

Since the t and F tests of analysis of variance are intimately related, it can be shown that many of the statements referring to the t test can be generalized quite readily to the F test. In particular, the necessity for equal sample sizes, if variances are unequal, is important for the same reasons in the F test of analysis of variance as in the t test. A number of the cited articles have demonstrated both mathematically and by means of sampling studies that most of the statements we have made do apply to the F test. It is suggested that psychological researchers feel free to utilize these powerful techniques where applicable in a wider variety of situations, the present emphasis on the nonparametric methods notwithstanding.

References

Anderson, R. L. and T. A. Bancroft. *Statistical theory in research.* New York: McGraw-Hill, 1952.

Bartlett, M. S. The effect of nonnormality on the t-distribution. *Proc. Camb. Phil. Soc.*, 1935, **31**, 223–231.

Bartlett, M. S. The information available in small samples. *Proc. Camb. Phil. Soc.*, 1936, **32**, 560–566.

Bartlett, M. S. Properties of sufficiency and statistical tests. *Proc. Roy. Soc. (London)*, 1937, **160**, 268–282.

Box, G. E. P. Nonnormality and tests on variances. *Biometrika*, 1953, **40**, 318–335.

Box, G. E. P. Some theorems on quadratic forms applied in the study of analysis of variance problems, I. Effect of inequality of variance in the one-way classification. *Ann. of math. Statist.*, 1954a, **25**, 290–302.

Box, G. E. P. Some theorems on quadratic forms applied in the study of analysis of variance problems, II. Effects of inequality of variance and of correlation between errors in the two-way classification. *Ann of math. Statist.*, 1954b, **25**, 484–498.

Box, G. E. P. and S. L. Andersen. Permutation theory in the derivation of robust criteria and the study of departures from assumption. *J. Roy. Statist. Soc. (Series B)*, 1955, **17**, 1–34.

Cochran, W. G. and G. M. Cox. *Experimental designs.* New York: Wiley, 1950.

Daniels, H. E. The effect of departures from ideal conditions other than nonnormality on the *t* and *z* tests of significance. *Proc. Camb. Phil. Soc.*, 1938, **34**, 321–328.

David, F. N. and N. L. Johnson. The effect of nonnormality on the power function of the *F*-test in the analysis of variance. *Biometrika*, 1951, **38**, 43–57.

Gayen, A. K. The distribution of the variance ratio in random samples of any size drawn from nonnormal universes. *Biometrika*, 1950a, **37**, 236–255.

Gayen, A. K. Significance of difference between the means of two nonnormal samples. *Biometrika*, 1950b, **37**, 399–408.

Horsnell, G. The effect of unequal group variances on the *F*-test for the homogeneity of group means. *Biometrika*, 1953, **40**, 128–136.

Lindquist, E. F. *Design and analysis of experiments in psychology and education.* Boston: Houghton Mifflin, 1953.

Norton, D. W. An empirical investigation of some effects of nonnormality and heterogeneity on the *F*-distribution. Unpublished doctoral dissertation, State Univer. of Iowa, 1952.

Pearson, E. S. The analysis of variance in the case of nonnormal variation. *Biometrika*, 1931, **23**, 114–133.

Quensel, C. E. The validity of the *Z*-criterion when the variates are taken from different normal populations. *Skand. Aktuarietids*, 1947, **30**, 44–55.

Satterthwaite, F. E. An approximate distribution of estimates of variance components. *Biomet. Bull.*, 1946, **2**, 110–114.

Welch, B. L. The significance of the difference between two means when the population variances are unequal. *Biometrika,* 1937, **29,** 350–362.

Welch, B. L. The generalization of Student's problem when several different population variances are involved. *Biometrika,* 1947, **34,** 28–35.

Welch, B. L. On the comparison of several mean values: An alternative approach. *Biometrika,* 1951, **38,** 330–336.